Morphogenesis

AN ESSAY ON DEVELOPMENT

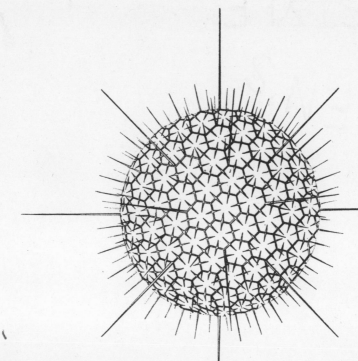

Morphogenesis

AN ESSAY ON DEVELOPMENT

By JOHN TYLER BONNER

PRINCETON UNIVERSITY PRESS

1952 · PRINCETON, NEW JERSEY

Preface

THE germ of this book started in 1946-47 when after leaving the Army I returned to Harvard University to complete my graduate studies. There William P. Jacobs, Edmund R. Brill and myself, all interested in problems of morphogenesis, formed a seminar in which we attempted to relate problems of development in as wide a variety of different organisms as possible; Brill concentrating on the animals, Jacobs on the plants, and I on the "lower forms." These discussions with good friends have left pleasant memories and they taught us the great advantage of comparing widely divergent groups of organisms. In 1948-49 I was fortunate enough to have the chance at Princeton University to teach a course on development, on "Growth and Form," and this course was and is in many respects an outgrowth of the original seminar. This book is now the next stage for it comes quite directly from the course. Other than the original idea of grouping different organisms together and comparing their development, the ideas are not from the seminar but are largely new, so should the reader object strongly to any point made here, I must be the one to take the blame.

Recently, I have read some remarks of Douglas Bush in the beginning of his little volume on "Science and English Poetry" that so exactly express my prefatory feelings that I must quote him here. "These headings [the principal themes of his book] are large subjects in themselves, and many large books have been written on one or another of their multitudinous aspects. I can only acknowledge a congenital weakness for biting off more than I can chew; I have always had a fellow feeling for a graduate student I once heard of, who proposed doing a thesis on the influence of the eighteenth century on the nineteenth. As we proceed, therefore, I shall doubtless be leaping like a circus rider from horse to horse, or rather, perhaps, be imitating the hero who mounted his horse and rode off in all directions."

[v]

PREFACE

I should like to acknowledge and thank those people who have read and criticized some or all of the manuscript: E. G. Butler, A. M. Chase, K. W. Cooper, J. R. Gregg, W. P. Jacobs, P. Oppenheim, and various members of my undergraduate class. Also I am indebted to the Eugene Higgins Fund of Princeton University for financial assistance in the preparation of the book.

I wish to take this opportunity to record that I shall forever be grateful to Professor William H. Weston at Harvard, for it was he who (among many other things) showed me and interested me in the many merits of lower forms (most especially the lower plants) as objects of study in biology. I owe my introduction to problems of development to the encouragement of Professor Leigh Hoadley. It is through the generosity of the Society of Fellows at Harvard University that the beginning of this book was made possible, and the completion through the opportunities afforded by Princeton University. The writing of the bulk of the book took place at the Marine Biological Laboratory at Woods Hole, Massachusetts, where Professor Edwin Grant Conklin was kind enough to let me use a corner of his laboratory room, a privilege and pleasure to be long remembered.

JOHN TYLER BONNER

Woods Hole, Massachusetts
August, 1951

Contents

Morphogenesis

AN ESSAY ON DEVELOPMENT

1. Introduction

T. H. MORGAN, who has achieved such fame for his contributions towards the theory of the gene, is supposed to have said, in a lighter moment, that since he had been unable to solve the problem of regeneration (to which much of his early work was devoted) he had decided to try something easier such as the problem of heredity. This sentiment, concerning the difficulty of the problem of regeneration and of development as a whole, is still as alive today as it was then. The array of facts about development has become increasingly vast and as time goes on the generalizations which would keep these facts together and within bounds have lagged behind. So there is a feeling (and one which stimulated me strongly to write this book) that these facts should be classified and sorted and that they should be controlled with more system and order. Some would do this by attempting to include all the facts and write a great encyclopedia, but my method will be shorter. I will attempt to sort out what seem to me the most important aspects of development and then illustrate them with only a few selected examples. But a very special effort will be made to use examples from the greatest variety of living forms possible, so that this book will concern the development of living organisms in general.

There is little doubt that ultimately the only way of finding a solution to the riddle of development will be to discover new and penetrating facts. Biologists are empirical, experimental scientists, and this course is unquestionably the right one. But empirical work is a little bit like prospecting for gold; we may become, by a combination of hard work and a few other gifts, able prospectors, but gold is hard to find. There is, however, some value in taking a general glance at the whole subject, if for no other reason than to guide the tenor of future experiments.

One of the prime concerns of a science, and our concern here, is what constitutes an explanation. When we say, for instance, that problems of development are unsolved we mean that they are unexplained. Exactly what explanations consist of is a profound problem considered in great detail by many philosophers[1] and here I shall mention only a few points. It is obvious that an explanation involves the relating of facts, or generalizations from facts. One may know, as Mendeleev did, that the elements have certain properties that recur periodically. This generalization is in no way explanatory. But when later it was discovered that the electrons surrounded the nucleus in shells, and that the number of electrons in the outer shell correlated with the periodic properties, then the periodic table was felt to be explained. Here then two generalizations were related; the number of electrons in the outer shell of an element and its periodic properties. Not all related generalizations give satisfactory explanations, for if one has a correlation and no understanding of the relation, then the phenomena are still unexplained. This situation arises only too frequently in biology where we have statistical correlations, but no understanding of why such correlations should exist.

Hempel and Oppenheim (1948, p. 147) make an important point about the type of explanation that apparently is especially satisfactory to the human mind. They say that the most appealing type "consists of explaining a class of phenomena by means of a theory concerning their micro-structure." And later they say, "It is often felt that only the discovery of a micro-theory affords real scientific understanding of any type of phenomenon, because only it gives us insight into the inner mechanism of the phenomenon, so to speak." The example of the periodic table which I have just given is an excellent illustration of this point, for we have more satisfactorily explained the periodic properties when they are expressed in terms of the micro-structure of the elements. And when T. H. Morgan left regeneration we might say he did so because he was unable to devise a micro-theory, and just

[1] J. H. Woodger (1929) does this specifically for biological problems.

this is what he did so successfully in the gene theory of heredity.

For a biologist, a micro-theory would ultimately bring him to physics and chemistry, and back to the old question of whether or not we are to explain biological phenomena in terms of physics and chemistry. The frequently proposed reply is that this is so, but that we must not expect the answer necessarily to be found in the physics and chemistry of today, in that those fields may have to be enlarged to encompass all theories involving living organisms. It is perhaps easier to say, with Hempel and Oppenheim, that our explanation will be especially satisfactory if it is expressed in terms of a micro-structure theory. Moreover, it is quite possible, and often the case, that a biological explanation is not reduced all the way to physics and chemistry, but that some intermediate micro-theory is quite satisfactory. After all, "micro" is used here in a relative sense, and provided the explanation involves units smaller than the phenomenon which is explained, we will have a micro-theory. In the gene theory, as conceived by Morgan and others, the genes were merely some sort of unspecified units, and numerous attempts including recent ones have been made to identify the physico-chemical nature of these units.

So to abstract what has been said into a thimble, we see that biology is an empirical science, in which we are almost totally dependent on the discovery by experiment of new facts for the development of our generalizations and of our theories. We can periodically, as shall be done now, stand off as far as possible to get the best perspective of these facts and generalizations that is obtainable. From this we may see ways to the future, but it is just as likely that all we shall see is the rubble of our present knowledge.

Perhaps the easiest way to discuss development, since we know so much of physics and chemistry, is to start backwards and first discuss some of what is known of the physics and chemistry of development. This, as I shall attempt to show, will not lead us very far into our problem, but it will serve to give some picture of the distant, ultimate goal. It will also point up the fact that there are a number of very general classes of phenomena which are noteworthy because they have been especially refractory to any physico-chemical interpretation. The biologist usually does not state the matter in quite this way, but instead refers to them as the "strictly biological aspects." There is sort of a chauvinist pride among biologists, and we like to think that there are some aspects of living organisms that are strictly ours, and they are far too subtle for the crude physicist and chemist to appreciate. I make fun of this here, but it is true that there are problems in biology that can best be encompassed and understood if one momentarily ignores the preconceptions imposed on one by the physics and chemistry of today.

The bulk of this book will be devoted to the biological generalizations of development. But, if an elaborate process such as development is subdivided into component parts, it is inevitable that while some of its aspects will be better understood upon such subdivision, the very broad general properties will suffer. Specifically I mean that development as a whole seems, to a biologist, to have a coordinated wholeness to it and he hesitatingly attempts to signify this by such terms as "organization." There is an unabashed aroma of awe and wonder which surrounds such a word and its grand notions, for who would deny that there is a marvelous design to nature as we see a bud turn into a flower or an egg turn into a chick. And it is clear that the wonder comes in part because we know so extremely little about development. If we attempt to dissect this whole and analyze the parts, as will be done in this book, it will seem to some that I have quite missed the main point and become lost in the details. I will be put in the same category as an art historian who analyzes the perspective of a Flemish master and is accused of failing to see that the pictures themselves are great and beautiful. But the chances are excellent that the art historian will first have been motivated by the beauty, and I suspect that those who study nature, even if only subconsciously, were also first motivated by noble emotions. I do not contest the notion of "organization" in development, but because it is an expression of our ignorance it is not a useful notion to us here. In fact, unless the term be given a more specific meaning it would seem to foster confusion, and to me its main value is as a name for those undoubtedly extremely important areas of knowledge that we do not understand. When all is known, "organization" will be an altered word, rich with specific meaning for development, or perhaps new words will replace it with the new ideas.

To subdivide development into parts can only be done in an artificial abstract way. It is impossible to obtain any kind of all-inclusive list of parts, or be entirely sure of their classification and interrelations. What has been done here is to adopt a reasonable but arbitrary list and follow it in an arbitrary sequence.

Development is first separated into two broad categories which we will call the "constructive" processes and the "limiting" processes. The former are all those which tend to build up, which are progressive, and the latter those which check, guide, and channel the constructive processes. This introduces the idea that development is a result of the interaction of two somewhat opposed processes, one building up, the other checking. It might be compared to the old Scottish game of curling, where the stone is first propelled across the glare ice and its progression is guided and cajoled by the player who frantically roughs the ice in front of the stone with his broom so as to give it just the right speed and direction.

Of the constructive processes three seem especially noteworthy: *growth, morphogenetic movements,* and *differentiation.* Growth will be used here in the sense of an increase in living matter; it involves the intake of energy and the storing of some of that energy by the synthesis of new protoplasm. This increase may be reflected in changes in size or weight, but such changes alone do not necessarily involve the synthesis of new protoplasm, and therefore may not necessarily constitute growth. Morphogenetic movement is the migration of protoplasm which gives rise to changes in form. Here there is no synthesis of living material, but merely its transportation from one region to another. Differentiation is an increase in the detectable differences in chemical composition (resulting from synthesis) of parts of an organism which occurs between one time during development and another time. These detectable differences in composition may concern cells alone, tissues, or the gross morphological pattern.

The limiting or checking processes are harder to classify, although in a general way we find that there are external limiting factors and internal ones. The external ones vary greatly from such matters as mechanical stress to food supply limits, matters which often are affected by the size of the organism. The internal limits also vary, for hormones and chemical inductors limit, as do the ultimate checking agents, the genes in the chromosomes. This book will concern itself primarily with these limiting processes and how they fashion the intricate pattern of living organism by guiding the constructive processes.

There are certain other manifestations of development that also must somehow fit into any generalized scheme. For one we have *polarity*, the fact that all organisms in some way manifest an orientation, a headness and a tailness, some sort of symmetry. And ultimately the important point will be to discover how the manifestation of polarity fits into the whole mechanism of development. Also there is the manifestation of *determination*, the fact that there are certain differentiations or polarities which have become fixed in the course of development, so that no experiment is at present capable of altering this course, although this may have been quite possible at an earlier stage.

Any theory of development must involve the coordination of the various parts of the organism which give the organism its unified character, and its consistent shape from generation to generation. I agree with S. J. Holmes (1948, p. 4) when he says that "a true theory of development must be primarily a theory of regulation." For it is the regulative or balancing properties which he so justly emphasizes that are central. And so we shall not overly concern ourselves in this inquiry with the mechanics of growth, morphogenetic movements, and differentiation, but rather with the way in which these processes achieve a pattern. If we knew and understood why for any one organism more growth occurs consistently at one place than another, and why the cells move from one place to another, and why cells in certain places take one path in their differentiation and others consistently follow other paths, then surely we would be close to a micro-theory. It may be that it is impossible to know these things without knowing the mechanics of each process also, and again we realize to what extent we are at the mercy of experiments, for only they will find this out for us.

In introducing the subject of development a few words should be mentioned concerning its relation to evolution and phylogeny. This has been most admirably discussed by de Beer (1940), and I wish merely to refer to some of his more general conclusions. Organisms possess not only adult traits but also youthful ones, and the latter may be quite as conspicuous as the former. For instance the larval characters of many forms may be as distinguishing as the adult characters, and furthermore these youthful characters may also be as important if not more important than the older ones in the progress of evolution. It becomes obvious that in speaking of phylogeny, the adult is of no greater consequence than all the developmental stages that lead up to it. We tend in our minds to think of individuals of a species as an object in an instant of time, and more than likely this thin slice of time is taken in the adult stage. That is, when we say "mouse" an image of a mature mouse is the most natural one to appear in our minds. But the logicians have often pointed out that "mouse" might more correctly refer to some longer segment of time, starting perhaps with a fertilized egg and ending with death from old age. Any organism is a living object that alters through the course of time by development, and the individual might be defined as the whole of these time-space events.

Such a procedure would not only please the philoso-phers, but also dovetail neatly with de Beer's notion of evolution. For, he quite rightly says, phylogeny is not merely a sequence of varied adults, but a sequence of varied individuals in the broad sense used here. The genes which are responsible for the variations and their inherit-ance do not give rise to final characters alone, but also control most of the characters appearing during the course of the life-history, that is most of the steps of the process of development. The genes are the prime intrinsic limits of development, so it may be that Morgan did not stray far from development by studying heredity, and it may be that any micro-theory or micro-theories of development are part of the gene theory of heredity.

2. Size and Pattern

TO INTRODUCE the subject of the development of pattern and to obtain a view of some of its facets, it may be helpful to examine at least one of its extrinsic limits and see how it varies within the boundaries of that limit. An easy approachable limit is that of size, for size does restrict the variety of patterns in living organisms.

There is no living form or structure that does not impinge on the problem of magnitude, but it must always be remembered that when we consider the size of an object we always compare it with something greater or smaller and that size has no meaning to us except by comparison. The natural impulse of a man is to use himself as a yardstick, and we call an elephant large and a mouse small. In experimental science there are rulers and balances, but even when one individual plant or animal is measured, it is compared to the ruler or the balance, and furthermore we cannot escape thinking of other plants or animals which are of a similar or of a different size. Such being the case, if we wish to speak of magnitude, we must compare organisms of different sizes; or if we speak of one organism, it must be of different stages in its development where again there are different sizes to compare.

The crux of the problem, and I use D'Arcy Thompson's (1942) example here, can best be visualized by examining a small and a large sphere. The volume of the sphere is a function of the cube of the linear dimensions (L^3) for the volume,

$$V = \tfrac{4}{3}\pi r^3,$$

and the surface area is a function of the square of the linear dimensions (L^2) for the surface area,

$$S = 4\pi r^2.$$

So in going from a small to a large sphere, the ratio of the surface to the volume becomes progressively smaller for

$$\frac{S}{V} \propto \frac{L^2}{L^3} \propto \frac{1}{L}.$$

This means that in similarly constructed bodies the relations of the parts will vary with the size, and this principle he calls the *principle of similitude*. It is used to a great extent in engineering, and there its study is referred to as *dimensional analysis*.[1] For instance in the use of aeroplane models for wind tunnel experiments it is necessary to construct a model which in every way has the flying properties of its larger prototype. This can be accurately determined mathematically by dimensional analysis, and it is not too surprising to find that the model appears in its linear proportions completely different from the actual aeroplane. No amount of common sense would have made one believe that they represent one and the same functional aeroplane.

The question, for living organisms, is what properties vary as the cube and what ones vary as the square of the linear dimensions; and then how do the relative sizes of the parts limit the shape of the organism? In addition to the surface area, the following vary as the square of the linear dimensions: the strength of bones, of muscles, of stems in plants, etc., the breathing mechanisms (surfaces of gas exchange), the surfaces of food absorption, and heat loss. In addition to the volume, the following vary as the cube of the linear dimensions: weight, tissue respiration or combustion, and heat production. While it is slightly aside from our main purpose (which is to examine development) let us look at some examples from D'Arcy Thompson's *Growth and Form* of these properties in similarly constructed mature organisms. In this way the workings of the principle of similitude should become abundantly clear.[2]

In mammalian quadrupeds the thickness of the legs and the thickness of the bones of the legs often reflect the size of the animal, for the strength of the leg varies as its cross section area (L^2), while the weight of the animal varies as

[1] See P. W. Bridgman (1931).
[2] See also A. V. Hill (1950) for a highly sophisticated analysis of the relation between locomotion in animals and the principle of similitude.

the volume (L^3). So in the elephant its legs and its leg bones are thick in proportion to its body; and comparatively those of a dog or of an antelope are thin. One must remember that pressure is in terms of weight per unit area, and the total weight of an animal rests on its four legs, therefore the cross section area of the legs (especially the bones of the legs) receives a certain pressure. The larger the animal the greater the weight and the pressure and since this rises as the cube, the area of the leg must become disproportionately large to keep pace with it. A similar example was used by Galileo and he drew a picture which is shown here (Fig. 1) of the proportions of the

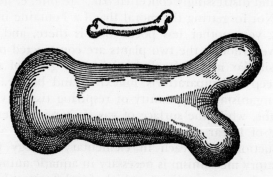

FIG. 1. A drawing by Galileo of which he says, "I have sketched a bone whose natural length has been increased three times and whose thickness has been multiplied until, for a correspondingly large animal, it would perform the same function which the small bone performs for its small animal."

thigh bone required to support a large animal as compared to that of a small one. The fact that an animal so large as a hippopotamus has weak, spindly legs and does not show compensatory thickening can be explained by its aquatic habit, and this, as Galileo and Herbert Spencer[3] knew is because in water the weight becomes negligible and has permitted whales and brontosaurs to achieve tremendous size. There are many other manifestations of the

[3] These references to Galileo and to Spencer in his *Principles of Biology* are of course in *Growth and Form* along with many others.

differential increase of weight and strength among animals which may in part account for their differences in construction and also for differences in efficiency of locomotion, but the reader must turn to *Growth and Form* for these many facets.

The same problem also arises in plants, and Ingold (1946) has made a study of mushrooms showing that the cross section area of the stalk follows the principle of similitude in its relation to the weight of the cap or pileus. Other problems arise when we come to bending moments and the problem of elasticity. In "Le Chêne et le Roseau," La Fontaine has the delicate reed say to the large and distressingly conceited oak, "Je plie, et ne romps pas." Not forgetting the moral that La Fontaine intended for us, yet another less poetic one is there, and that is that even though the two plants are constructed of somewhat similar materials, the weight and girth of the oak tree keep it comparatively inflexible and brittle.

In organisms the quantity of respiring tissues varies as the cube, while the surface of gas exchange varies as the square of linear dimensions, and this fact may affect its construction. We teach in elementary biology that no respiratory mechanism is necessary in aquatic animals that are less than one millimeter thick, for diffusion alone will allow gas exchange to take place sufficiently rapidly for metabolism.[4] In this way protozoa, sponges, coelenterates (the jelly in coelenterates has little need of oxygen, and the active tissues are less than one millimeter from the surface) and even flatworms (by virtue of being flat) require no gill or lung or circulatory system. But with increasing bulk existence would be impossible without these systems. The same argument applies for the ramifications of the gut canal, the great extension of the small intestine and the projecting villi which do so much to increase the surface of food absorption.

We have now come to our main point, which concerns

[4] For a more careful and concise discussion of this point see Adolph (1931, pp. 159-161).

the whole question of division of labor in organisms—the fact that in some simple organisms all the functions are fairly well performed by all the cells, and in others certain cells become differentiated to perform specific functions, giving us muscle cells, nerve cells and so forth. It is generally believed that those organisms which have the least degree of division of labor are the most primitive and lowly on the phylogenetic tree. The paleontologists do not find this invariably true, but it is true that wherever there is an increase in bulk (especially when over the limit of about one millimeter in thickness) then there invariably will be some degree of division of labor. I do not say that some organisms smaller than the limit will not also have elaborate differentiations, but these could be explained away with no difficulty (e.g. that they stem from larger ancestors).

It is customary to think that in the course of evolution there arose a progressive division of labor because the organisms thereby became more efficient and better adapted in the perilous process of natural selection. There is no question but that these specialized forms have been successful, and we ourselves are such a form, but we must not forget that the lowly, minute, and often highly undifferentiated organisms have also been successful, existing everywhere in the world in great abundance, apparently since the very beginning of life on the earth. The difference is that the larger forms with divided labor do not compete directly with the smaller ones; they occupy different niches in the environment. They differ in that some are large and the others are small (albeit there are many grades of largeness and smallness) and they have virtually separate micro and macro environments. Thus size alone, as Simpson (1949)[5] makes clear, is an aspect of adaptation, a vital cog in the wheel of evolution. And with increase in size and magnitude come progressive division of labor, progressive differentiation.

[5] On page 151 he says, "The rule of size increase in evolution operates in general as if it were thoroughly adaptive."

It is possible to lay down a rule or law that division of labor among cells within an organism is no more than the result of the principle of similitude. To be even more specific one can say that with increasing sizes of organisms, those parts (and their associated processes) which vary as the square of the linear dimensions will show corresponding increases in their division of labor. This principle might be called the *principle of magnitude and division of labor*.[6] From it we can expect and do find differentiation into all the structures associated with gas exchanges: lungs, gills, tracheae, circulatory systems, the spongy mesophyll of plant leaves, and many more such examples. With strength we find muscle, bone, chitonous exoskeleton, tendon, and in plants various types of supporting fibers. For food absorption and distribution there are elaborate gut canals, again a circulatory system, and the vascular system of plants; even eating mechanisms are involved here. Finally it seems likely that nerve cells and the progressive centralization of the nervous system of animals bear a relation to size. It is not that nervous activity or centralization varies as the square, but the nervous system coordinates other processes that do, and with the increased diversity that comes with the increased size, greater coordination is required to keep the diverse parts functionally together, and for this a centralized nervous system is more efficient than a diffuse one.

Certain organisms, such as many coelenterates and higher plants, have solved the problem of increased bulk in another way. Instead of increasing the area involving those functions that vary as the square, they have decreased the volume of materials involving those functions

[6] This principle was recognized in essence by Sachs. For a short general discussion of this and references see Haberlandt (1914). F. O. Bower (1930) has made the most important contribution to this principle in his book *Size and Form in Plants*, where he shows the relation between the size and the structure of ferns in the course of their evolution. Also I should mention here that this principle does not apply to unicellular organisms which often possess complex differentiations. The division of their labor may make them more efficient, but it is not imposed on the organisms by size, at least in the manner that this principle implies.

[16]

that vary as the cube, and in this way avoided extensive division of labor. In both cases a large part of the bulk is inert, nonliving, nonrespiring material; in coelenterates it is jelly, and in higher plants it is wood. Since respiration is not involved in these massive dead parts, despite the fact that it varies as the cube of the linear dimensions, it does not increase disproportionately with increased size, but tends to keep a more or less constant ratio with those structures that vary as the square of the linear dimensions.

Avoiding any discussion of the cell theory and its many interpretations, a few words should be said here of the problem of cell size. As is well known, the size of the cells of most organisms are reasonably within the same range. The botanist Julius Sachs in his concept of "energids" thought of the nucleus and its surrounding cytoplasm as a metabolic unit. If this is so, then there may be an optimal size for the most efficient execution of metabolism, and this optimum may be within the range of known cell sizes. Such a notion would complement admirably the whole conception of division of labor and cellular differentiation presented here. It would give us a clue as to why individual cells differentiate as a unit in shape and structure, a process which we term cellular differentiation. The cells or energids must exist for reasons of efficient metabolism, according to Sachs' hypothesis, and for this they are confined to a certain limited range of magnitudes. It is not surprising then that differentiation also respects this magnitude, and each cell differentiates in a unitary fashion. But there is a facet of differentiation that transcends the cell, and that is the differentiation of tissues, of organs, and ultimately of the whole organism. Of this the efficient metabolic size of cells tells us nothing.

I should now like to turn to the problem of changes in magnitude that take place during the course of development of any one organism. It is usually true that during development growth takes place, and size increases between the beginning and the end of development. The important question here is what happens during development to those factors which are differentially affected as one would expect from the principle of similitude. We have seen that in the grand picture of evolution increased size has gone with increased differentiation in mature forms, and now we must see if this is also true of their development.

There are certain structures which appear during the course of development, like lungs in a mammal, that are not used by the embryo, but are used only after birth. Development, however, will hardly cease at birth for a mammal, and from birth to maturity there is an increase in size. So any structure such as the lung will require critical proportions following the principle of similitude only in that part of the development in which it functions. The old concept of a prefunctional embryo has long been abandoned, for it is quite obvious that some functions such as metabolism and all its manifestations go on through all the development, while other functions or activities appear and sometimes disappear on the long road to maturity.

So likewise in development our new principle of magnitude and division of labor applies, and that is with increase in size, those functions which vary as the square of the linear dimensions differentiate and divide the labor. In the egg or in the gastrula of an amphibian embryo there is no specialized circulatory system, but very early in the development a functional heart and circulation arise which serve to distribute the food and eliminate the wastes. Food is first supplied by the yolk, but the supply is not inexhaustible and eventually, as the bulk of the organism increases, a whole feeding device, mouth, gut, and all its accessories, is required. The early embryonic life of the amphibian can take place without any muscular movements, for there is no necessity of catching food, but the time comes when survival depends on movements, and for these a highly elaborate musculature is differentiated. Many of the muscles cannot act, nor could the growing animal support itself, without a rigid frame, and for this a skeletal system is differentiated. I give here a few aspects of one type of embryo, but the principle is very general.

An interesting instance of the principle of magnitude and division of labor is seen in the case of land plants, especially of trees. In plants, growth takes place largely through the activities of meristems or growing zones, zones of active cell division. These are either *apical*, at the tip of the root and shoot; or *intercalary*, found for instance at the base of the leaves of many monocotyledons; or *lateral*, that is the cambium which is responsible for the increase in girth of woody plants and trees.[7] These meristems represent a division of labor, a kind of differentiation, for only certain specific cells do the dividing. In parts of very young seedlings, such as for instance the oat coleoptile which is so much used in plant physiology, cell division occurs everywhere in the coleoptile and is not confined to any special region or meristem.[8] Or in the case of the shoot of early *Brassica* seedlings, Havis (1940) has shown that while there are regions of high and low cell divisions and cell elongations, these regions are diffuse and ill defined until later stages. Later all the cell division takes place in the apical meristems of the root and the shoot.[9] Surely this is no more than another manifestation of our new principle, for the strength of the plant varies with the cross section area or the square of the linear dimensions, and the weight by the cube. The larger the seedling becomes, the greater must be its strength in proportion. For this it must harden its tissues by the deposition of rigid secondary wall material, and the cells that do this sacrifice their ability to divide and to grow. This differentiation into a meristem, this division of labor, is necessary if the plant is to stand erect. The plant can increase in size by having an accretionary type of growth, and constantly adding at the tips of the rigid and congealed stem and root, but there is a very definite limit as to how tall a

---

[7] There is also a *cork cambium* which gives rise to cork, but it does not enter our argument here.

[8] Avery, G. S., and P. R. Burkholder (1936).

[9] Or in the intercalary meristem, but the problems raised by the intercalary meristem are similar to those of an apical meristem.

slender stem can be before it will sag under its own weight. So again, following our principle, with increasing size a further differentiation arises, that of the cambium, which serves to increase the thickness of the tree. The cambium also gives an accretionary type of growth, for the xylem or wood cells laid down inside the cambium turn hard and die to become the skeleton of the tree. D'Arcy Thompson discusses the shapes of different trees, the flying buttresses of large trees showing the same engineering principles as the Eiffel Tower, and the general characteristics and requirements of taper to assume maximum strength. Since the cambium lays down an extra layer of wood each year, and at the same time the apical meristem is active, one has in essence a series of cones one fitting over the next. It is like making a candle, where each dip of the string into the tallow is deeper so that the candle shows finally a tree-like taper.

In the instances given it has always been true that with increased size during development there is increased division of labor. There are, however, certain specific functions or activities of organisms which require differentiations only when the organism is still small, and they are lost, becoming useless as the greater size is attained.

A good case of this is seen in the osculum of sponges. As G. P. Bidder (1923) shows in his remarkable paper, it is of vital importance to the sponge standing in still water not to use the same water over and over again, since it naturally must become poor in food and oxygen. The prime factors in preventing such inefficiency are the mass of water and the velocity with which the water is ejected through the osculum, for, to put the matter simply, with a greater inertia the waste will be squirted farther away. Since this inertia is directly proportional to the total amount of flagellated collar cells as well as the osculum size, it is clear that in large sponges with many collar cells the inertia will not only be great but sufficient. In small developing sponges, which are not touched upon by Bidder, the inertia would presumably be far too low to

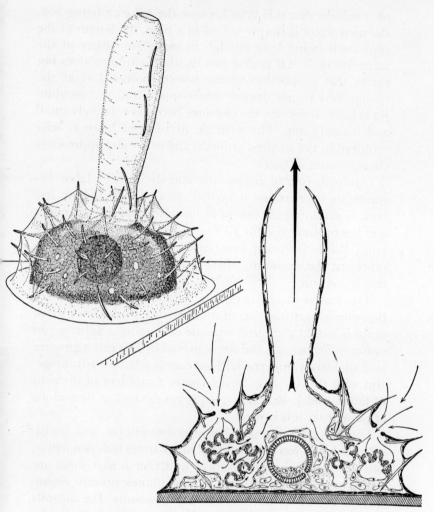

Fɪɢ. 2. A young fresh water sponge (*Ephydatia fluviatilis*) showing the large osculum chimney. *Above*: an external view. *Below*: a diagrammatic cross-section. (From Ankel, 1948.)

avoid this re-use of water; but a distinguishing feature of the very young sponges is a gigantic osculum chimney in relation to the size of the sponge. (Fig. 2)[10] It is hard not

[10] See, for instance, W. E. Ankel (1948).

[21]

to conclude that this is so because the velocity being low, the used water is simply led off in a pipe, the length of the pipe itself being long enough to make any re-use of the water unlikely. Of course this osculum chimney does not retain this proportion to the whole sponge, but as the sponge gets bigger during development and the osculum jet velocity increases, the chimney becomes relatively small and insignificant. The extreme division of labor is only required in the smallest animals, and as the size approaches the optimum, it fades.

Our principle of magnitude and division of labor becomes, as we examine it further, more subtle but no less true. It cannot apply except in terms of a specific function, and the optimal size for all functions is not necessarily the same. While for many functions the size of cells seems to represent the optimum, there are many others for which this is not true.

The matter of size is especially important in the evolution of multicellular organisms from unicellular ones. Here again it would seem that separate cells remain adhering to one another because the size achieved by this cell aggregate is of adaptive value, and will have some selective advantage. But with this increase in size comes a problem of division of labor, and J. R. Baker (1948) has devised an ingenious argument on this subject.

Undoubtedly the gap between unicellular and multicellular forms has been bridged many times independently, but one interesting thing noted by Baker is that there are many more colonial forms among photosynthetic organisms than among particle-feeding organisms. He suggests that the problem is one of a feeding mechanism; in the green colonies (and also in saprophytic forms) food is taken in everywhere, all over the surface; but in particle feeding forms a special feeding device is needed. It may be that each individual cell of the colony possesses such a device, but it is a major evolutionary step to divide the labor and create a communal feeding apparatus.

There are some particle feeding organisms that have circumvented this problem in a curious way. Two good examples are in the true slime molds (Myxomycetes) and the amoeboid slime molds (Acrasiales). In the life history of both these organisms there is first a vegetative stage during which all feeding takes place. The feeding is by pseudopodial engulfing, although the Myxomycetes possess one large multinucleate plasmodium, and the Acrasiales consist of separate independent amoebae, each of which feeds by phagocytosis. In the Myxomycetes the plasmodium becomes large, and in the Acrasiales the separate amoebae become very numerous. The feeding and growth period in both cases stops after a time, and fruiting, that is pure changes in form unaccompanied by growth, occurs. In the Myxomycetes the plasmodium humps up into knobs, each of which by morphogenetic movement rises into the air to produce a mass of spores held on a rigid stalk of nonliving exudate.[11] In the Acrasiales the amoebae stream together to central collection points to form a mass of cells which, by morphogenetic movement, also pushes up into the air. Here some of the cells become stalk cells, and the others form the mass of spores at the apex.

In both these slime molds we have complex differentiated structures, the fruiting bodies, and these structures have no feeding mechanism. They simply do their feeding before they differentiate. But in order to have their cake and eat it too (as a matter of fact they eat the cake before they have it), in order to avoid the complex problem of constructing a feeding device and yet be colonial, they have morphogenetic movements. For it is only by these movements that they can rearrange their parts from the feeding condition to the mature differentiated condition. There are, of course, many assumptions in such a scheme, such as the selective advantages of the slime mold fruiting structure over the simple amoeba or plasmodium, but it is elaborated here merely as an interesting possibility.

[11] Not all species develop stalks.

Our argument has been that size imposes certain mechanical limitations on the development of living organisms, and we have seen how some of these limitations might have affected development. The variety of patterns in living forms may be great but it has its bounds.

3. Physics and Chemistry in Development

IT IS now time to examine the development of pattern itself—to find how it does its job, to assess all the information we have that might tell us something of its inner mechanism. The first step in this direction is quite clearly marked. Cells and tissues, in fact all living objects, are matter and energy, and therefore during development the changes which we wish to understand involve changes in energy and in matter. The physicist and the chemist know many facts and many principles of these changes which must be operating during development. If we have isolated some of these, talked about them and discussed their limitations, then later when we enter more directly on the characteristics of development, it might be possible to see what biological processes could or could not at the moment be accounted for directly by specific physico-chemical processes.

The most general laws of physics that must be dealt with are those of thermodynamics. It is hardly to be expected that energy is either created or destroyed during development, or that any reactions during development are improbable. But at first it seems paradoxical that development starts in an apparently simple indifferent group of cells, or a single cell in the case of an egg, and in a rapid and determined way elaborates itself into a complex structure. In a remarkable and frequently quoted passage in *De Generatione Animalium* Aristotle says of development: "It is possible, then, that A should move B, and B move C; that, in fact, the case should be the same as with automatic machines shown as curiosities. For the parts of such machines while at rest have a sort of potentiality of motion in them, and when any external force puts the first of them in motion, immediately the next is moved in actuality."[1] Here he also saw this progression of development and ascribed it, as we do today, to a series of causes, similar to the course of a chemical reaction.

[1] 734^b (Translation by A. Platt).

We are reminded of the principle of Clausius and Carnot, or the second law of thermodynamics, which says that in any system all the reactants tend to go from a less probable to a more probable condition and that the free energy decreases, making energy less and less available for work in this downhill course. How, then, can we reconcile the apparent building up from germ to adult with this universal law.

The second law of thermodynamics applies in a whole system, and in the case of an embryo we must consider both the embryo and its environment. If we manage by a little mental acrobatics to picture an isolated section of environment containing first an egg, and later a mature organism, it is absolutely true that in that overall space or isolated system (that is the embryo and the environment) the free energy will have decreased, and the system will have become more random and more probable. But this does not mean that the free energy in the mature organism might not be much greater than the egg, as the environment would be especially depleted of free energy. Likewise, of course, the mature organism could be less random, less probable, and more orderly than the germ. Suppose for instance that the embryo could feed during development (or use its yolk which was also derived from the environment), then the free energy is being transformed from the environment to the embryo. The second law states only that the free energy of the *whole system*—embryo and environment—decreases, and the successful embryo sees that the environment pays the debt while it actually gains.

An interesting parallel is seen in the case of the growth of a crystal. Here also order seems to spring from chaos, and this is perhaps even more remarkable as the crystal has no metabolic machinery, and cannot capture and store energy. In fact the total energy of a crystalline or solid state is less than that of a liquid. But here we are reminded that order strictly speaking is not dependent on the energy, but on the entropy, and while the entropy increases in all spontaneous reactions, and therefore the crystal and the environment show an increase in entropy during crystallization, the entropy of the crystal alone may decrease. It does so by virtue of loss of heat to the environment (heat of crystallization) and therefore randomizing the heat in the whole system of the crystal and its environment.

Even though, in a sense, neither development nor crystallization are downhill processes, each will occur spontaneously and go at a steady, measured pace. They are machines, as Aristotle thought of them, but unlike clocks or mechanical devices, they do not decrease their thermodynamic order, but increase it by bleeding the environment. Developing organisms are endowed with the even greater accomplishment of being able, by means of their metabolism, to store free energy.

We cannot in any way analyze or explain development by considering its energetics alone. Could we measure it, we might find out something of the energy we started with and that which exists after development is finished; we would have an energy bank balance before and after but nothing in between. And there are other aspects besides energy, even though it is true that all processes or changes involve changes in energy.

Of these other aspects the laws of surface tension, as D'Arcy Thompson has shown, have a very direct bearing on development. We are interested in change of shape, and anyone who has watched drops pull away from a dripping faucet, or a solid column of water streaming from a garden hose break up into droplets, has seen surface tension act and do its work of changing shape.

Surface tension, or capillarity as it is sometimes called, depends on the attraction between the molecules of a liquid. If one imagines a molecule in the middle of a solution, then it will be pulled equally in all directions by the similar molecules completely surrounding it. For that reason it will not tend to go in any particular direction, but will remain suspended because the pulling forces will neutralize each other. But if the molecule is at the surface, then the other molecules that pull it will be only on one side, and it will no longer be in an equalized field of forces. As a result the surface molecule will be pulled inward. This means that no molecules are under any tension except those at or near the surface which are being pulled inward. The force on each molecule is the same regardless of the size of the globule, and since the surface tends toward minimum potential energy, the shape of the globule tends to be spherical. This is why rain drops and so many other small quantities of liquid approach the shape of minimum surface, that is, the shape of a sphere.

The surface tension itself is dependent on the attraction force between the molecules, and this in turn depends on the nature of the liquid. In addition, Gibbs showed that certain substances accumulate at the surface by adsorption and in so doing lower the surface tension. But for any given liquid the tension is always the same irrespective of the configuration of the liquid, and in this respect it differs completely from elastic or membrane tension, which is illustrated by the case of a rubber balloon, where the tension of the membrane varies with the size of the balloon.

It was for Laplace to show that in any liquid body bounded by a surface the internal pressure, P, is directly proportional to the surface tension, γ, and to the sum of the reciprocals of the radii of curvature, R, R':

$$P = \gamma \left(\frac{1}{R} + \frac{1}{R'} \right)$$

The molecular basis for this relation is quite simple in the light of our previous description of the forces between molecules at the surface. If the surface approaches a plane and therefore the radii of curvature become very large then the internal pressure will be extremely small. For any one molecule at the surface will be pulled inward by a hemisphere of molecules about it. If the surface is highly curved then there no longer will be a complete hemisphere of molecules beneath it, but a smaller portion of a sphere.

Hence the inward pull on the molecule will be greater, for the direction of the pull of the various surrounding molecules will be more uniformly in one direction. Remembering that the strength of the attraction between any two molecules is a function of the surface tension, it is clear that the effect of this pulling will be greater (and therefore the pressure will be greater) in small, highly curved drops.

It is unfortunate that these properties of liquid surfaces serve only as a model, as an analogy (with all the dangers of an analogy) to what actually exists in cells and organisms. The main reason for this is that the membrane about the cells shows elasticity and therefore does not exhibit true surface tension, as K. C. Cole and others[2] have demonstrated. That is, the tension at the surface varies with the internal pressure, as it does in a rubber balloon.

The second difficulty is that the equation of Laplace applies for a perfect liquid or a liquid film, and protoplasm, cell walls and cell membranes are hardly perfect liquids or liquid films, but are made up of solid gels, crystals, and paracrystals interspersed in the liquid.

Another great difficulty in interpreting the form of cells and tissues is that, as E. N. Harvey, K. C. Cole, and more recent workers have shown,[3] the tension at the surface of cells is too low to attribute any shape or change of shape to it. Conceivably it is of such a magnitude (about 0.1 dynes/cm.) that it could round off some corners, but it is certain that the different shapes of cells, the appearance of pseudopods in amoebae, and the shape changes during cell division—all these are not molded by tensions at the surface.

How, then, are we to reconcile the fact that D'Arcy Thompson was so successful in showing that many shapes within cells and tissues are identical to "surface tension shapes." For instance he takes Plateau's figures of revolution and for each one he shows examples among simple organisms: *Protococcus* for the sphere, *Spirogyra* and other filamentous forms for the cylinder, flagellates, Foramini-

[2] See the review by Danielli (1945).   [3] Again see Danielli (1945).

fera, and others for the unduloid; *Trichodina pediculus*
approaches the unstable and transitory catenoid, and finally
as a real *tour de force*, the nodoid is seen in *Paramecium*
and other ciliates with their gullets (Fig. 3). It is clear
how surface tension makes the sphere, but in others, such
as the cylinder, the problem is more subtle. There it must
be assumed that the tension is greater in the long axis, than
it is at right angles, around the long axis, for if the tension

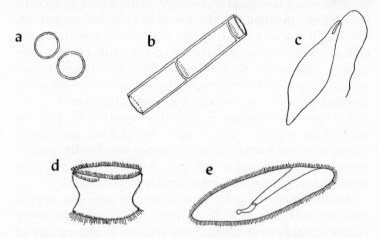

Fig. 3. The shapes of organisms which approximate Plateau's figures of
revolution: a, *Protococcus* as a sphere; b, *Spirogyra* as a cylinder; c, *Eu-
glena* as an unduloid; d, *Trichodina pediculus* as a catenoid; e, *Paramecium* as a nodoid.

is equal in both directions all we can have is a sphere. In
fact it is impossible to make this figure with a soap bub-
ble even by supporting its ends with a wire. But we have
said previously that surface tension is negligible in organisms and therefore cannot account for the shape of
cylindrical forms such as various filamentous algae and
fungi, and if this is so we may rightly ask how is their ·
shape achieved. It is probably because there is near the
surface of the organism a rigid structure of a cylindrical
shape which gives the cell a solidity. It is not that the
tensions are different in different directions, but that the

cell actually has a skeletal framework, and that this framework has different properties along its radii of curvature. There is no reason why the shapes achieved by surface tension cannot be imitated in many other ways. It is true that surface tension must always be present in all living organisms, for it is a property that every liquid has. But obviously, for the many reasons we have mentioned, we must look for other forces to explain the fact that *Protococcus* is a sphere and *Spirogyra* a cylinder.

What we have said here must also be true for all that D'Arcy Thompson finds of the direction of the cleavage planes, and the configurations of cells within cell aggregates. In each of these cases other forces must be involved. Surface tension may guide the process to some minor extent, but it is not strong enough at the surface of protoplasm to be responsible for the shape and the deformation of the shape of cells. Again, the fact that the laws of minima of Lamarle[4] (which describe the most efficient configurations) are observed by both liquid films and by cells does not mean that they are controlled in the same way, but only that other things besides surface tension observe the principle of least action.

If surface tension is to be relegated to a minor role, what forces can we look to that might mold the shape of living things? The forces of crystallization for one deserve careful scrutiny.

It is now a well-known fact that all cells contain crystals in some form or other; it may be that they possess true crystals or liquid crystals (i.e., paracrystals). The distinction between these two types of crystal is very simple. True crystals have a space lattice; that is, like the pile of cannon balls at a monument, no matter from what side (or axis) one examines it, the parts (the molecules or the cannon balls) are oriented and symmetrically lined up. Crystals have perfect orientation in all three dimensions. Liquid crystals, on the other hand, are oriented only along one axis, like a log jam headed for a saw mill.

[4] See D'Arcy Thompson (1942).

There are an infinite number of different possible crystal shapes but only a limited number of possible symmetries, for all crystals fall into thirty-two classes of symmetry. Long ago R. J. Haüy showed that there was a simple law limiting the variety of shapes (the law of rational indices) and that the reason for this law lies in the fact that crystals are made up of identical units, of blocks, and that there is a limited number of ways in which similar blocks can be stacked. The fact that crystals were made up of units became clear with the discovery of x-ray diffraction—where the actual molecules and their relations to other molecules were revealed. The x-ray technique depends on the fact that the molecules of the crystal are arranged in an orderly space lattice.

Concerning the growth of crystals it used to be thought at one time that there was some mysterious force that governed the shape of crystals as they grow. In fact even in the late nineteenth century O. Lehmann, the discoverer of liquid crystals, talked of a *Gestaltungskraft*, a determinant which gave a "wholeness" to crystals. The view now is more prosaic but easier to understand—that the crystal shape is entirely interpretable in terms of the shape and character of the molecules. The protuberances of each molecule and the attractive forces between molecules (which act over very short distances) govern their position of stacking and this in turn governs the whole shape of the crystal.

I realize that the explanation of the smooth and continuous growth of crystal faces is not yet complete. With some cubic children's blocks one can build many structures—houses, towers, even arches with some careful balancing. It is very unlikely that one would build a large cube, but molecules do just this unlikely thing. Crystals form in a slightly supersaturated solution where there is insufficient solvent to carry the solute in a liquid state. The solute molecules begin to cling together to form aggregates, that is, they stack. But once an aggregate is started certain regions of the small crystal have a stronger pulling force to take new molecules in than others. The reason for this is easy to see in a commonly used diagram (Fig. 4). In position *a* the new molecule will adhere on three surfaces, in position *b* on two, and in position *c* on one only. Obviously position *a* will be filled first, for the attraction forces there are that much greater and only after all such three sided positions are filled will position *b* be filled, leaving finally position *c*. So in this way a crystal will

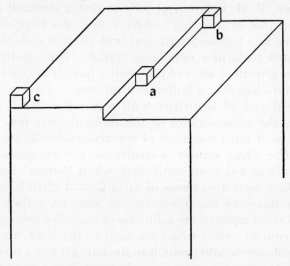

FIG. 4. Diagram illustrating sequence in which new material adds to a crystal surface in an ideal growth process. (After Egli, 1949.)

grow regularly in layers and the reasons for this involve no *Gestaltungskraft* but are determined solely by the individual molecules. This is a clear and striking case, of which we will say more much later, where a whole shape (the crystal) has a wholeness, an individuality, and where this is felt to be completely understood in terms of its constituent parts, the molecules. We have here a complete and satisfying micro-theory of crystal shape. It is true there are many fine points which still bother the crystallographer, but the general concept is well established.

A further example of the stability of the whole crystal shape is seen in the phenomenon of crystal regeneration. If a crystal is broken and a part is placed in a supersaturated solution, growth will occur fastest at the ragged edge and soon it will be smoothed over and later, whatever the shape of the missing part, it will have been restored. The reasons for this are the very same we have just discussed. In the manufacture of large crystals for electric circuits, which has recently become of interest and importance, P. H. Egli (1949) tells us that a standard technique is that of "capping" where a slice of a large crystal is placed in a bath as a seed, and both the lost ends are regenerated to form a new large crystal. (Plate I) In this case the growth of some of the smaller faces is so rapid that they may close over a hollow central area.

The degree of sensitivity with which the crystal form reflects the idiosyncrasies of the molecule was not fully appreciated until the work of the remarkable Louis Pasteur. The whole subject of enantiomorphy or optical isomerism was unknown until 1848 when Pasteur[5] showed that there were two forms of tartaric acid crystals, one a mirror image of the other, and by separating these two crystal types and making solutions of each, one solution in a polarimeter would rotate the light to the right, and the other solution would rotate it to the left. (While a mixture of equal parts of the two showed no rotation, i.e., racemic tartaric acid). Later it was shown that this difference is entirely the result of the distribution in a molecule of the atoms about one asymmetrical carbon atom. That is, if a carbon atom has four different groups attached to it, there are two different ways in which these groups may be spaced about the carbon atom, one of which is a mirror image of the other. So the molecules whose atomic structure gives mirror images has crystal forms whose facets also show mirror images (Fig. 5).[6]

[5] See Gause (1941) for the references to Pasteur's work on isomerism.

[6] There is another kind of isomerism—namely "steric isomerism" which involves the different arrangements of groups attached to $>C=C<$ where the double bond prevents rotation.

This fact is interesting enough, but Pasteur found one other thing which convinced him that he was close to the very core of some key problem bearing on the nature of life. It was that when any of these substances that are optically active are produced or fermented by living organisms, either the right- or the left-handed form only

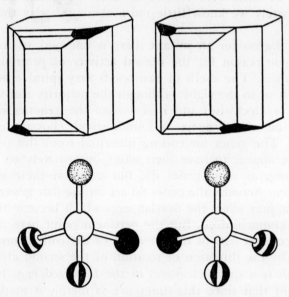

FIG. 5. Mirror images in chemical substances. *Above*: Left- and right-handed crystals of the sodium ammonium salt of tartaric acid. (From Perkin and Kipping, Organic Chemistry, Lippincott, 1932.) *Below*: Models of left- and right-handed molecules of lactic acid. The central white ball represents carbon, and the other balls represent H, OH, COOH.

is affected, and not a mixture of the two. He found this first in the fermentation of racemic tartaric acid by the mold *Penicillium glaucum* which fermented the right-handed tartaric acid only, being therefore a convenient method of isolating the left-handed tartaric acid. Now it is known that many of the substances within protoplasm, such as various amino acids, various sugars, and so forth, all occur in nature asymmetrically, that is, in either the right-handed or left-handed form and not in the racemic mixture. The curious part is that in the laboratory, by means of simple reactions it is usually impossible not to get both, but with the help of specific enzyme systems, this asymmetry is maintained by living organisms. Pasteur may have been quite correct in believing that the significance of this, were it known, must be great, but unfortunately we know little more about it today than he did.

To digress for an instant there is one odd attempt to see some reason for the optical activity of protoplasmic substances. The shells of gastropods may spiral either to the left or to the right (although the majority run to the right or clockwise) and in *Limnaea* the genetics of the direction of coiling is well understood (Boycott et al., 1930). The genes for coiling inherited from the parents do not appear to have their effect immediately on their offspring, as most genes do, but only on their grandchildren. Actually the genes do act on the first generation in that they affect the ovarian eggs which become the altered grandchildren. But the pertinent point here is that the very first sign of the direction of the coil is foreshadowed by the direction of rotation of the second cleavage (which is a spiral cleavage) of the fertilized egg. It was thought that since this difference is merely a matter of rotation that there may be a difference in the optical activity of the amino acids of a sinistral or dextral snail. But the sad fact is that this scheme was too perfect and like so many of its kind there is no truth to it.[7]

One interesting property of enantiomorphic or "mirror image" substances is the frequent occurrence of twins, where one has a crystal possessing one half laevo form and one half dextro form. Twinning is by no means confined to enantiomorphic substances but many other simple substances exhibit this property, quartz and gypsum being

[7] See the review by Gause (1941) on "optical activity and living matter." Actually the studies of the amino acids on snails were not on *Limnaea* but *Fructicicola*.

excellent examples. Some crystals, which are named hemi-morphic, have what amounts to a head and a tail end, for although they may be symmetrical about a main axis, the ends of the crystals differ in shape. These hemimorphic crystals also occasionally give twins (Fig. 6).

Another important aspect of crystals that should be men-tioned, since we will later talk of analogies between grow-

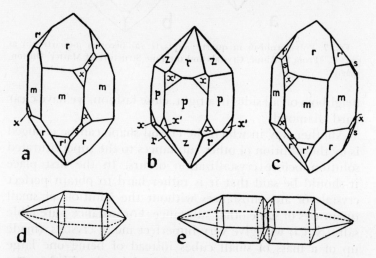

FIG. 6. Crystal twins. a, left-handed quartz crystal; b, twinned left- and right-handed quartz; c, right-handed quartz; d, hemimorphic crystal of succinic iodimide; e, twin of succinic iodimide. (From F. Rinné, Crystals and the Fine Structure of Matter, Dutton, 1922.)

ing crystals and developing organisms, is that of poly-morphism. Many crystals are polymorphic, that is they have different crystal forms. These different forms rep-resent different kinds of packing of the molecules which in turn depend upon the temperature at which crystalliza-tion takes place. Quartz again is a good example of this (Fig. 7) and has two such polymorphic forms, but ice does far better with five different crystal shapes. A familiar ex-ample is carbon: in one form the atoms form rings which slip by one another readily and we have black, slippery graphite; in another, where each atom is locked with its

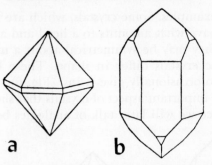

FIG. 7. Polymorphism in quartz, α-quartz (a) becomes β-quartz (b) at 575° C. (From F. Rinné, Crystals and the Fine Structure of Matter, Dutton, 1922.)

neighbors on all sides in a tight, close fashion, we have clear hard diamond.

Another way in which the crystal shape can be changed is by the addition of other substances to the supersaturated solution before crystallization occurs. In the first place it should be said that it is rather hard to obtain perfect crystals of any substances without the addition of small quantities of some other substance. For instance pure table salt (NaCl) will give very imperfect messy crystals (made up of a mass of small cubes instead of being one large cube) but if a small amount of lead ion is added to the solution, then large, almost perfect cubes are formed. With other substances NaCl can be made to assume many different shapes (Fig. 8).

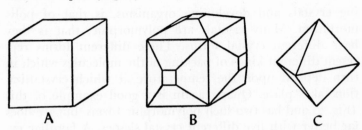

FIG. 8. The effect of extraneous substances on the crystallization of rock salt. a, from a pure salt solution; b, from a solution containing glycocoll; c, from a solution containing formamide. (From F. Rinné, Crystals and the Fine Structure of Matter, Dutton, 1922.)

The explanation for this phenomenon is that the molecules of the foreign substances also become adsorbed on the surface of the crystal during its growth, and these foreign molecules will in some way modify the normal processes. The crystal then becomes in reality a "mixed crystal," and this is what it is called. The shape of the NaCl molecule affects the manner in which the contaminant is deposited, and in turn the contaminant guides the NaCl.

If colloids are used as a contaminant then the effects may be even more marked and the shapes produced more remote from our simple idea of crystal shape. Again in the case of NaCl, if gum arabic is added in increasing concentrations, the crystals will assume a progressively more feathery appearance until finally all suggestion of the cube is gone. In other cases extraneous substances produce rounded lobular crystals, and here as before, the reason is that the contaminant adheres to the crystal planes and all traces of crystal faces often become obliterated (Plate II).

In some cases where two substances are mixed, they separate so that one has a large crystal made up of the two separate crystal types. A good example of this is the mineral rutile which is found studded on another mineral called iron glance, very much like jewels set in a large ring (Fig. 9). One interesting thing is that the rutile crystals are oriented with respect to the planes of the iron glance and this again is an important phenomenon in collective crystallization, where if two substances of moderately similar molecular structure crystallize near each other, they will orient with respect to one another. It is difficult to see, in the case of the iron glance and the rutile, how the molecules of each mineral found each other and then arranged themselves in such a beautiful symmetrical pattern, but we must imagine that the answer involves some simple physics and chemistry.

So that we do not forget that this book is about living things let us examine the various types of true crystals that are found associated with organisms. They are mainly in the form of spicules or shells and their variety is tremendous.

There are a number of cases where true crystals, with crystal facets, are found inside living forms, but invariably these crystals do not bear any relation to the shape of part or of the whole organism. Instead they are usually inclusions in or between cells. In higher plants one frequently finds crystals in the cells of various tissues, and a good ex-

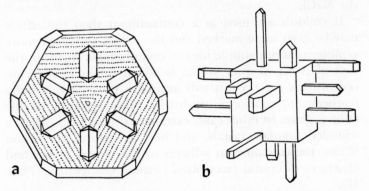

FIG. 9. Parallel outgrowths in crystals. a, the mineral rutile deposited symmetrically on another mineral, iron glance. (Drawn after Rinné, Crystals and the Fine Structure of Matter, Dutton, 1922.) b, Urea crystals on ammonium chloride. (From Bunn, Chemical Crystallography, Oxford, 1945.)

ample among the animals is the accumulation of uric acid crystals in the Malpigian tubules of many insects, this being their method of elimination of waste nitrogenous material.

In the case of spicules (spines) and skeletons, although they possess a space lattice and are truly crystalline in substance, their external contours are strictly not those of any crystal. The proof that this is so, that the external shaping of spicules cannot be by the forces of crystallization is elegantly and masterfully presented by D'Arcy Thompson. He says (1942, p. 679) of them: "The spicule is a true crystal, and therefore its existence and its form are *primarily* due to the molecular forces of crystallization; moreover it is a single crystal and not a group of crystals, as is seen by its behaviour in polarized light. But its axes are

[40]

not crystalline axes, its angles are variable and indefinite, and its form neither agrees with, nor in any way resembles, any one of the countless polymorphic forms in which calcite is capable of crystallizing. It is as though it were carved out of a solid crystal; it is, in fact, a crystal under restraint, a crystal growing, as it were, in an artificial mould, and this mould is constituted by the surrounding cells or structural vesicles of the sponge."

These skeletons and spicules are constructed primarily of two substances—the diatoms and the radiolarians use silica; the foraminiferans, coelenterates, and molluscs use calcium carbonate (calcite); and finally the sponges use both, depending upon the species of sponge (Fig. 10). There are a few species of radiolarians that use strontium sulphate. The curious thing is that a number of animals in widely divergent groups make spicules almost identical in shape using different chemical materials. This is true for instance of certain sea-cucumber spicules made of calcium carbonate and others of sponges made of silica. This point is an integral part of D'Arcy Thompson's argument, for it is clear that the shape of the spicule is not being determined here by the molecules (as they are in crystal forms), for the molecules are quite radically different yet the external shapes are the same.

In a second argument D'Arcy Thompson shows that these skeletons (at least some of them) are certainly not crystal forms. There are certain radiolaria whose shells are regular dodecahedra, that is, composed of twelve regular pentagon faces, and others whose shells show regular icosohedra, that is twenty faces of equilateral triangles. It so happens, and it was discovered by Haüy in the eighteenth century, that certain shapes, including these, are impossible crystal shapes; they do not satisfy the law of rational indices. It is impossible by the mere stacking of molecular blocks to achieve these shapes, and therefore D'Arcy Thompson shows us they must have been carved out or molded by forces other than those of crystallization.

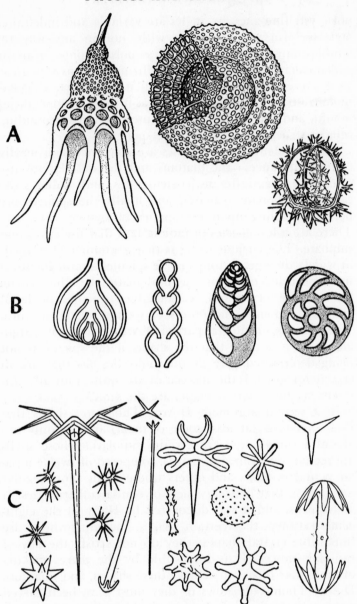

Fig. 10. Spicules and skeletons. A, radiolarian skeletons; B, foraminiferan skeletons; C, sponge spicules. (From Hyman, 1942.)

He attributes this great variety of spicular and skeletal form to the distribution of vacuoles and cell interstices. The protoplasm forms the mold; the surface energies between the crystal and the protoplasm guide the final shape. In this way the spikes and the barbs of the sponge spicules, the plates and anchors of the sea-cucumbers, and the beautiful cages of the radiolarians are all interpreted in a common way. The sad part is that although we think we understand how a crystal makes its shape, how it is that from generation to generation a sponge will make one particular kind of elaborate spicule is still totally unexplained—our insight into crystal form has only shown us that it will give no insight into skeletons and spicules.

I have often been struck by the fact that so many of the most elaborate forms, the radiolarians and the diatoms, are made of silicon, and that this element is so close to (in fact is a congener of) carbon. Henderson (1913), for one, asks why organisms have used carbon instead of silicon. Silicon being just below carbon on the periodic table, their physical and chemical properties are very similar; they both have four electrons in their outer ring, giving a valence which apparently is especially successful in making compounds. Both elements are found in great abundance on the surface of the earth, but why is it that carbon instead of silicon became the key element in protoplasm? The answer is not far to see, for as Henderson points out there is greater flexibility in the types of compounds carbon makes, all the sugars, amino acids, proteins and so forth, but silicon produces only rock. But it does seem to me that silicon has had some success in living forms, for it is used in the shells of radiolarians and diatoms. It is used there in a great variety of shapes, shapes consistent with what we expect of an element with four electrons in its outer ring. The suggestion, then, is that somehow silicon itself is important and responsible for the form of these shells and their great variation. But this faint hint may well mean nothing, and if it does it must also apply to calcium carbonate and strontium sulphate.

Before leaving the subject of silicon I would like to mention one interesting experiment of N. I. Hendey (1945),[8] who managed to cause some marine diatoms to eject their protoplasm from their shell. He then raised them for nine months on silica-free media and they grew and reproduced as elliptical globs of protoplasm. When they were returned to water containing silica they immediately started to rebuild their shells, and the intricate shape and design was identical to that which they possessed many generations before. During cell division, and especially following sexual fusion, parts of new shells or entire new shells are formed *de novo*. In this sense these experiments show nothing new, but still the experiments give us a strange feeling of wonder, for the explanation seems so obscure and distant, yet we also have the feeling that the answer, if only known, might be marvelously simple.

There is another whole group of crystalline skeletons that we have not yet mentioned: the deposition of primary cellulose in plant cell walls.[9] From the work of the British crystallographers, mainly W. T. Astbury and others,[10] we have now a considerable knowledge of the crystalline nature of many plant walls. One of the important facts that has emerged is that there is a spiralling in the axis of orientation of the cellulose molecules. This is especially clearly seen in multinucleate algae such as *Valonia* or *Cladophora*. There are usually two separate spirals, a dextral and a sinistral one, that is, two layers of cellulose oriented at different angles. This will give a crossed fiber appearance at any one point, except at certain points where the spirals become so small and tight that they have the appearance of rings—these points are the branch points. Astbury has asked the question that is crucial here: what is it that determines the position and the shape of these cell walls? It was Julius Sachs, the great botanist, who said

[8] This is not the first case of such an experiment, but it is used here as a good example.

[9] As a matter of fact there are many other examples besides this. See L. E. R. Picken (1940).

[10] See Astbury (1945) and Frey-Wyssling (1948).

that the protoplasm determines the shape of the cell wall, and not the reverse, and Astbury's hypothesis abides by this dictum. He finds that the spacing between the nucleotides on the nucleoproteins is virtually the same as the spacings of the cellobiose units of cellulose; and he suggests that the nucleoproteins which are known to be so important in the cytoplasm and the nucleus, and which are believed to be tied up with the mechanism of inheritance, are actually responsible for plastering the sugar molecules into oriented cellulose on the inside of the secondary wall. He cautions wisely that he has only referred the problem to another chemical substance, and we cannot forget that this is a mere hypothesis, but it does seem sensible and helps us to see at least one possible link in the chain of events. What gives the nucleoprotein its power to do this and its power to orient the successively laid down spirals (if they actually do this) is hard to see.

From all this we learn that true crystals are only a part of organic form in that the skeletons and spicules and cell walls have crystalline space lattices, but their contours are as D'Arcy Thompson said, molded, and this molding is not at all understood. Even if Astbury had found the nucleoprotein to be responsible, we still would want to know what makes the nucleoproteins behave as they do.

Leaving skeletons, spicules, and other hard structures, we may now consider liquid crystals, or paracrystals as they are sometimes called. J. Needham has introduced the matter by saying, "Liquid crystals, it is to be noted, are not important for biology and embryology because they manifest certain properties which can be regarded as analogous to those which living systems manifest (models), but because living systems actually *are* liquid crystals, or, it would be more correct to say, the paracrystalline state undoubtedly exists in living cells."[11] We have, in the very

[11] Needham (1936, p. 157); and also (1942, p. 661). In much of the discussion that follows it would often be more correct to term the structures referred to as "anisotropic structures" rather than "liquid crystals," since the latter term has a rather specific meaning (see Frey-Wyssling, 1948). There is no evidence that cells possess "liquid crystals" in this narrow sense.

[45]

beginning of this section on crystals, distinguished between true crystals and liquid crystals, the later having no three-dimensional space lattice, but being definitely oriented in one axis. There is another important characteristic: the molecules that comprise a liquid crystal are long, that is pencil-shaped, and when their long axes are lined up they show beautiful birefringence. (This birefringence, or power of double refraction, is revealed with polarized light and is the only real means of detecting liquid crystals.) To those who have not tried it, I strongly recommend mixing a little oleic acid and ammonium hydroxide, which will give liquid crystals of ammonium oleate; with two pieces of polaroid and an ordinary microscope one can see (upon occasional heating and cooling) the most beautiful and varied liquid crystals dance about.[12]

Liquid crystals possess many of the properties of true crystals; for instance they can regenerate upon breaking. But even more remarkable, as their discoverer, O. Lehman, showed, they can fuse so that two small crystals can merge to form one large crystal (Fig. 11). Apparently then, the molecules are not held rigidly together, but they form what some have called a "swarm," and others have called the mass of molecules a "tactoid." Whatever name we use, the forces between the molecules appear different from those of a crystal (whether they can act over any great distance is still a matter of debate), but somehow these masses of large molecules manage to keep together even though it be in a loose, malleable, in fact liquid-like state.

There is a clear distinction between liquid crystals and true liquids, for the molecules of the latter are oriented in no particular direction. It is true that if the liquid contains long molecules and if it is set in motion, the molecules will line up and give flow birefringence, but this is only momentary and stops when the motion stops. If the experiment is done carefully, all true crystals when they

[12] It is best to dissolve the ammonium oleate in some 95 per cent ethyl alcohol and then allow the solution to partially evaporate on the microscope slide before placing a coverslip over it.

pass (by heating) from the solid to the liquid state or in the reverse direction (by cooling) do not go directly from one state to the other, but pass through so called meso-forms. In the mesoforms the molecules may pass from orientation in all three axes (crystal) to orientation in two, then

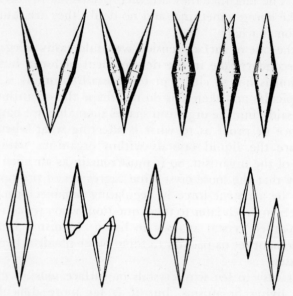

Fig. 11. Liquid crystals of ammonium oleate. *Above*: The fusion of two crystals to form one large crystal. *Below*: Regeneration of the crystals after breaking. (After Lehman.)

one axis to finally the unoriented liquid. From this we see that the paracrystalline state is a sort of intermediary between solid and liquid.

The evidence that liquid crystals (or more correctly, anisotropic structures) exist within cells comes largely from the fact that with a polarizing microscope all sorts of birefringent structures can be seen; as for instance in the cortex of cells, in the cytoplasm, in the nucleus, in astral rays and spindle fibers, etc. It is often true that the birefringence does not stay but comes and goes as the cell activities become modified either through cell division or in other ways. It is also known that some of the key substances in protoplasm, namely proteins, are likely in some cases to exist in an oriented form, but farther than this we cannot go. That is, we do not know or understand to what extent these molecular alignments regulate form, if at all. The fact that they are there leads one to feel they must be *doing* something, and no doubt they are, but the question is what?

In the case of surface tension we could easily relegate it to a secondary role in the development of form, but the situation is not so clear cut for crystallization. It is true that spicules and skeletons do not shape the organism (as Sachs said), but the organism shapes them, but we have no evidence or proof as to what is affecting what when we compare the liquid crystals within organisms with the shape of the organism. So it must remain as an open possibility that the loose crystalline aggregates of protoplasm might be a potent force in regulating organic form. We will return much later to these questions when we consider the so-called crystal analogy to living organisms, but for the moment let us pass on to some other physico-chemical processes.

It is easy to see why crystals or surface tension might shape living organisms, but it is far more difficult to imagine the process of diffusion as performing any task so active. I do not believe it would ever have occurred to me as an actual possibility were it not for the work of N. Rashevsky (1938), and even though he definitely neither demonstrates nor proves anything concerning what really takes place in living cells, he does show that at least theoretically diffusion can do a remarkable number of things, especially in the way of shaping and growth movements. I do not pretend to even begin to be able to follow Rashevsky's mathematics, but he has stated many of his assumptions and conclusions in simple words easy to comprehend. Before discussing these let us say a few things about the nature of diffusion.

The explanation of diffusion rests upon the kinetic

theory of gases, for the inherent motion of the molecules, so pronounced in gases and less so in liquids, is responsible for the diffusing. The molecules move in random paths, jerking aimlessly about, the jerks being the result of collisions between molecules. As is well known, Brownian movement is produced by this motion of molecules, where the colloidal particles in suspension are large enough so that they can be watched bouncing about under the microscope.

Imagine now that a given quantity of some gas is liberated in the corner of an enclosed room. Where the molecules are most numerous they will be knocking against each other frequently, but elsewhere in the room, they will be floating about almost free and unhindered by one another. Just as water seeks its own level the gas molecules will, given enough time, progressively even their distribution about the room. This will be the equilibrium. It may be well to take an example which has more biological meaning and instead of a room filled with gas, consider a tube partitioned off into two halves, one half of which contains a protein solution, and the other pure water. Then, as shown in Figure 12, after removing the separating partition one can follow and measure through the course of time the relative concentration of protein at different points in the tube.

The rate of diffusion may be expressed in a deceptively simple mathematical relation.

$$\text{Rate of diffusion} = -DA\,\frac{dc}{dx}$$

where A is the cross sectional area, c is the concentration of the given substance, and x is distance; therefore dc/dx is the concentration gradient. D is the diffusion constant or coefficient of the particular substance. This coefficient is concerned with mobility and therefore size, which is clearly shown if one compares the coefficient and the molecular weight of a few substances, for the larger the molecule, the smaller the diffusion constant.

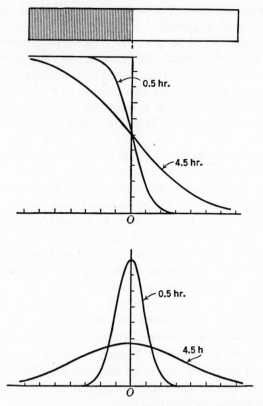

FIG. 12. The relation between the concentration and the distance of migration of a protein in solution in a diffusion column. *Top*: Graphical illustration of the diffusion column. *Center*: The relation between the concentration and the distance of migration. *Bottom*: The relation between the concentration gradient and the distance of migration. The curves refer to diffusion times of 0.5 and 4.5 hours respectively. (From Bull, Physical Biochemistry, Wiley, 1943, after Neurath.)

It is always a little difficult to visualize how diffusion acts when we consider chemical substances, but we are helped by the fact that heat also diffuses and can be treated mathematically in an identical fashion. The mathematics are very cumbersome and hard, but we all know how one can heat one end of a glass tube red hot and still be able to hold the other end, for the glass conducts heat poorly, that

[50]

is the heat's coefficient of diffusion in glass is small. We know, too, that if we held a copper tube similarly in a flame we would soon drop it in pain, for it conducts heat well. It is also easy to see that if we heat one end of both tubes for a few minutes and then take the flame away, both will eventually reach an even temperature throughout, although the copper tube will do so far sooner. And finally if we heated one end of the copper tube continuously and cooled the other end continuously by leaving it, for instance, under a running cold water faucet, then we would have a steady state, a constant temperature gradient. Also with the diffusion of a substance in solution, if one has a constant source of the production of the substance at one point and the constant elimination at another, a stable concentration gradient will be established.

It is upon just such a system as this that Rashevsky bases his whole argument, for he imagines that a certain substance is produced at one region within a cell and that it is constantly produced by the metabolism of the cell. Furthermore he assumes that the site of production of this substance is not in the dead center of the cell, but in some acentric position. These assumptions do not in any way disturb the biologist, for it is expected that substances are produced during metabolism, as our respirometers for example tell us. And furthermore it is not surprising that different parts of the cell might produce special substances or different amounts of substances, since the cell is not homogeneous throughout but has the nucleus (rarely in the dead center), the golgi apparatus, the mitochondria, and so forth.

The important thing is to maintain a concentration gradient across the cell, and this involves the elimination of the substance. It might be by diffusion through and out of the cell membrane or it might be by the breakdown of the substance, either by simple oxidation or by the help of specific destructive enzymes. Since it is a gradient that is required, it should be mentioned here that to obtain one it is not necessary to have a specific site of production, but one might have a site of destruction. Or there is another possible variable and that is if one side of the cell were permeable to the key substance and the other not.

The problem now is how to get from this gradient a force sufficient to make the change in shape from the outward diffusion of this substance given off at an acentric point. For this Rashevsky further assumes (again not unreasonably) that the protoplasm is a network of solid gel pierced with interconnecting holes of liquid. The diffusion outward is a flow of substance, of molecules, and the spongy medium exerts a force resisting this diffusion flow. According to Newton's third law, where every action has an equal and opposite reaction, the flowing molecules exert a force on the medium in the direction of the flow. Since the gradient (i.e. the force) is acentric within the cell, the cell will be deformed. With these basic assumptions, and a few more concerning magnitudes such as the amount of the substance produced, Rashevsky has been able to show by purely formal analysis that cell shape, cell division, cell movement (amoeboid or pseudopodial motion), and cyclosis or protoplasmic streaming could all theoretically be accounted for by diffusion. I cannot help but believe that Rashevsky's hypothesis is helpful and constructive, has broadened our view, and may well guide us to the facts.

One need only thumb through the table of contents of a treatise of physical chemistry to see that there are many physico-chemical phenomena that can and surely do in some way contribute to the shaping of organisms. For instance electrical forces, osmosis (which is a case of diffusion), adsorption, chemical combination, hydrogen ion concentration, etc., etc. Really the whole book applies to the problem of living form in some fashion, and this is what makes it all the harder to try and isolate any one phenomenon as we have just done.

The problem may perhaps be brought into better focus by examining the properties of one chemical substance, say sodium chloride, which should simplify the problem. We may first look into the handbook and find its characteristics

—its color, its crystalline shape, its melting point, its boiling point, its solubility in various solvents, and then if we search further elsewhere we might find that it has an odor (or an absence of odor), a piezoelectric effect in crystalline form, an effect on the electrical conductivity of solutions, an ability to combine with other compounds, etc., etc. But these properties are for one substance in all different conditions, and in living cells, while the condition is not uniform, it does keep within a limited range. For NaCl is dilutely dissolved in water and with other salts is a key factor in water balance and the maintenance of osmotic pressure. Also its Na^+ and Cl^- ions are involved in various chemical reactions; it will affect the solubility of certain proteins; it has many properties and many effects within living cells.

But this is just one substance, and a very simple one at that, which exists among a plethora of different kinds of substances; many other salts, all the different proteins, fats, carbohydrates, each of which has its special properties and all of which somehow exist together harmoniously to give a living organism. One thermodynamic property of the living, to return to where we started, is that a stable equilibrium is not achieved (this is better approached at death), but instead we find a steady state where energy pours in and pours out, and the internal machinery which we call metabolism keeps it so. To say that living cells are dynamic may be misleading to some because the word has become so shopworn, and so often improperly used to mean interesting as opposed to dull; nevertheless in its strict sense it is apt, for the wheels are constantly in motion. This means that all the chemical substances within cells, all the liquids and all the solids, all the huge and minute molecules, are in a constant fever of activity and each with their own properties, which for each will change as the conditions change from second to second, and this in turn will change others. Yet from this appallingly complex and minute engine comes order, come cells and organisms which respire, assimilate, reproduce, locomote, and develop. If we put the matter this way it does seem presumptuous to ask what special physico-chemical processes are particularly important for the development of shape. It appears, as it actually is, an abstract question, for how can we isolate any one process in development when all the other physico-chemical processes are related and interconnected with it? It may be true that this can be done only in abstraction, but for myself I still see value in it, and I still cheer myself and others to look for physical and chemical mechanisms in biological processes, even though we may never, in this way, see the whole of the process.

In the case of NaCl, or still better in the cases of the elements themselves, we can from the remarkable work of Mendeleev and later of many others predict on the basis of the periodic table and the electron structure of the atoms, many properties of the elements. This is one of the few outstanding cases in science where because of the periodicity of properties as the electron shells become progressively filled, one can predict events at a higher level from those of a lower level. This applies also, to a minor extent, for compounds or groups of compounds, but the problem soon becomes fuzzy and indistinct. When one arrives at the level of cells and protoplasm any consideration of the structure of atoms or molecules tells us ridiculously little of life; the predictions become quite impossible. Instead we satisfy ourselves with generalizations we call *biological* and do little else but throw small pebbles to fill the great chasm between the structure of molecules and the properties of cells. It may be that some day there will be a periodic table from which the living functions could be predicted from levels below, but for the moment this is only a dim hope for the future.

4. Patterns of Growth

TO DEFINE the word "growth" precisely is a perplexing problem because it is used, and quite usefully, in a number of different ways. It is perhaps best to employ the word in the most general possible fashion and to describe, by various examples, the type of phenomena it may include. A very loose statement might be that it is an increase in size in living matter (we are talking now of biological growth and not growth of civilization or of a bank account), but I shall show that this definition raises a few problems.

Mechanically there are two ways in which growth may be accomplished, one by cell expansion without cell division, and the other is by expansion with cell division. The difficulty is that it is always assumed that the increase is a result of an increase in protoplasm, the constructive metabolic synthesis of new living stuff. If a dog takes a large drink of water and swells a bit as the result, or if a dessicated plant is watered and the shrivelled leaves fill out regaining their turgor, this is not, by any stretch of the word, to be considered growth. But when the plant physiologist measures the growth curvature of a young shoot (as in the *Avena* test) then there may be little else than the addition of water to one side of the plant, yet this he calls growth. It is true that there is some increase in the wall material as the cells swell, and there must be some slight increase in protoplasm, although the volume change is largely water. So perhaps, because of these small additions in living matter this may be considered growth. Often the physiologist takes pains to make a clear distinction between volume or wet weight increase and dry weight increase to show the different steps of the growth process.

Another problem arises in some cases where cell division is involved, as for instance in the early development of the echinoderm egg. There, after fertilization or parthenogenetic activation the egg begins to cleave, the cells and the nuclei becoming smaller and smaller, first the blastula

[55]

appears and later the gastrula, leading finally to the motile larva. Until the larval stage is reached no energy is brought in from the outside, but only the reserves laid down within the egg are used. The cells themselves become smaller with successive divisions, and the whole structure, while it changes in shape, hardly increases, but probably even decreases in size. For a moment it might appear that this is not growth according to our definition, but upon reflection it is obvious that there are some synthetic processes taking place—for one there is a vast increase in the amount of membrane since, with division, the cell surfaces have multiplied, and then there must be other constructive processes associated with differentiation. The yolk has become depleted and this food energy has been converted into new material by protoplasmic synthesis. This is the basic requirement of growth in the sense it is to be used here.

There is another problem in cases where dead or inert material of some sort is accumulated, such as the wood of trees, the shells of snails and other molluscs, the horns, teeth, and claws of many mammals. This involves an increase in size, but not necessarily in living matter and for that reason this special type of accumulation is given the term "accretionary growth."

This increase in size, this growth, has been probably one of the earliest things to be measured in the history of the civilization of man, for everyone has wondered at the extraordinary growth of human beings, through infancy, childhood, youth and maturity. It is hard to believe that parents even in the days of prehistoric man did not pride themselves and vie with others about the growth of their children, and still today the proud parent watches the progress of his offspring by marking their height every year on the back of the door of the hall closet. So much, if not all of science, reflects the foibles of man's thinking, man's desires, man's psyche, that it is not alarming to find this same primitive urge to measure in our most modern, so-called, quantitative biology. There is a great feeling of satisfaction, that no one can deny, in being able to take a living phenomenon and apply the ruler and balance to it. Our rational minds tell us that we do this to learn and penetrate deeper into the phenomenon, and often this is true, but this never removes the aboriginal pleasure of measuring.

And so we have curves of growth, cartesian plots in which the quantitative progress of growth can be drawn, and we have some other mathematical ways of expressing the same thing. Perhaps the best and easiest way to introduce this subject is to consider, for a moment, banking and compound interest, for this really is (from a quantitative view) growth. In compound interest at regular intervals a certain per cent of the capital is added to the capital, and therefore as the process continues at each interval (be it a month or a year) the added amount will be greater, and if this is shown on a graph it will give a series of increasingly steep steps (Fig. 13, a). Some organisms which have seasonal growth, such as trees, do increase in size just this way, by a series of steps, but others are not affected by seasons and have no periodic growth, so there is a further problem of describing them. This case is analogous to continuous compound interest, where the compounding does not occur in steps but all the time. It is easiest to think of the time interval between taking the interest as becoming shorter and shorter so that the compounding is not done yearly, or monthly, but say each second, and then the curve will be smoothed out to an even line (Fig. 13, b). Within this explanation of continuous compound interest lies the very basis of calculus, and the growth curve may be expressed

$$\frac{dy}{dt} = ry$$

where y is the amount, be it the length or the weight of an organism, or dollars in the bank, t the time, and r the rate constant, or the per cent interest. This may be integrated

$$y_t = y_0 e^{rt} \qquad \text{or} \qquad \ln\frac{y_t}{y_0} = rt$$

[57]

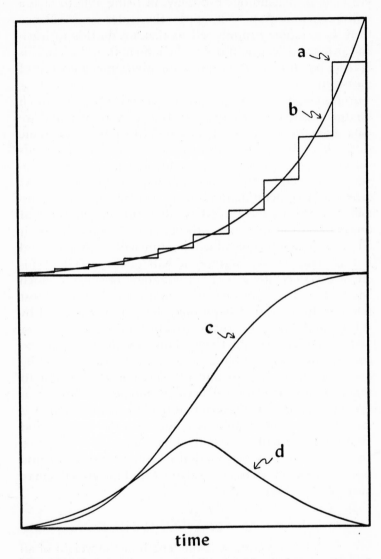

Fig. 13. Growth curves. a, compound interest; b, continuous compound interest; c, the "S" shape growth curve; d, the growth rate (i.e. acceleration) involved in the "S" shape curve.

where y_t is the amount of y in a given time t, and y_o is the initial amount of y.

It so happens that the growth of any living organism never follows the curve expressed by this formula—that is, it may do so for a short period only, and that period is called the logarithmic phase of its growth. For growth does not increase to infinity, but is curbed and controlled. Mathematically, the limiting of growth can be expressed by modifying the previous differential equation slightly,

$$\frac{dy}{dt} = ry(b-y)$$

where b represents the limiting factor in some way, by being for instance the original concentration of the food supply. So in a given time t the food will have dwindled to $(b - y)$ and this in turn gives the S-shaped growth curve so characteristic of organisms (Fig. 13, c). Note that if the first derivative of this curve is taken, that is if the slope of the S-shaped curve is plotted against time, one obtains the acceleration, the rate of increase or decrease of growth. This is very similar to the bell-shaped probability curve, or the Gaussian curve; it rises to a peak at the center and tapers off evenly at both ends (Fig. 13, d).

There are many ways in which the subject of growth could be approached. One of the central aspects we would like to know more about is the chemistry of the synthesis of new protoplasm, for there is really no more intimate and profound a problem. Energy is poured into the organism in the form of food, and with this energy new proteins, often new fats, carbohydrates, vitamins and so forth are made, and they are arranged within the cells in such a manner that we may say that the amount of living matter has increased. This is a biochemical problem which has received and is receiving much attention, but the task is tremendous and progress necessarily slow. The work began not long ago with the discovery of cellular enzyme systems and the whole special problem of cellular respiration, and only in the last few years have we obtained a clear idea of how energy, by means of the high energy phosphate bonds, is exchanged within the cell. It is known that certain substances for certain organisms, such as vitamins, some amino acids, and specifically those with sulphydryl groups, limit these synthetic growth processes; but exactly why, or to what step in the whole series of enzyme reactions they apply is more often a matter of conjecture. There are other organisms, and often very primitive ones as Lwoff (1944) shows, that can synthesize almost all these substances, and their growth cannot be limited by their absence. In fact, Lwoff argues that one of the striking things in the evolution of the flagellates is the loss of these synthetic abilities. There are others who are studying these biochemical steps by examining the limiting effect and action of certain growth hormones, and we will return later to their consideration. Some have been particularly absorbed in the problem of the synthesis of new proteins. It is suspected that the nucleoproteins are of key importance here, and also they are presumably connected in some way with the genes, or hereditary substances, although this is no absolute certainty. Viruses are also mainly nucleoproteins and they also grow and accumulate new nucleoproteins. It is common parlance to talk of template reactions, where somehow the parent nucleoprotein adsorbs on itself amino acids in just such a way that, like a template, a new molecule, identical to the parent, is synthesized. All these matters concerning the actual mechanism of growth are vitally important, and it would be foolish to deny that until they are completely and satisfactorily known we cannot claim an understanding of growth; until then it will remain unexplained. It is a biochemical problem and we will only be satisfied by a biochemical answer. There is, of course, a great deal more known today than I have given any intimation of in this paragraph, but it so happens that this large subject is one that I do not intend (perhaps wrongly) to include in this book. It is partly that there are many others who are far better equipped than I to discuss it, and partly because the way is still so foggy, so unsure, that the time may not be ripe to bring these things together.

The way I should like to approach the matter of growth here is to consider in what fashion growth is controlled and governed—to consider the pattern of growth. Of all the qualities that are "living," there are none which seem quite so unexplainable, so mystifying yet so characteristic as *regulation*, for so many processes, such as growth, are perfectly regulated; they start and they stop in harmony to give the organism certain proportions, proportions that remain constant from generation to generation. If we knew how this pattern was achieved, then we might not be so bothered by—we might even explain—the wholeness of the organism, and not be driven to entelechies. It may be false to assume that we will ever be able to have any understanding of this pattern until we completely know the biochemistry of growth. But I think, after we have surveyed the facts, that the whole subject of growth will seem bigger than the chemistry of synthesis, and that it will be more likely that this latter will seem a small (although important) part of a larger scheme in which growth is used here and there, sometimes encouraged, sometimes discouraged, and in such a way that a consistent, whole, individual organism is created in an orderly and masterful fashion.

Growth can be controlled in many ways. The rarest and most difficult condition to achieve is that in which there is no control at all, and this would be portrayed in Figure 13, b, where there is an unchecked logarithmic increase. In order to obtain such growth in yeast cells or in bacteria, for instance, it would be necessary to constantly add new nutrient and constantly remove toxic waste products. But even then a limit of some sort must be reached, most likely the size of the vessel will finally be unable to hold all the organisms. Even though these checks (which we see drawn in the S-shaped curve, Fig. 13,c) are somewhat artificial and not intrinsic in the organisms, they do demonstrate the impossibility of completely uncontrolled growth.

[61]

Tumor or cancer cells are often referred to as exhibiting uncontrolled growth, and in a relative sense this is true, for the main characteristic in which they differ from the surrounding normal cells is that their growth rate has changed and they begin to grow way out of proportion. Of course eventually they are limited in some way, either by the blood supply being inadequate or often by the death of the organism. Such limits as these would be considered superficial or extrinsic. There are other more internal limits, and in the course of our discussion we shall run the gamut between these two extremes.

It is well, in the beginning, to make a distinction between control with respect to size limits, of which we have been speaking above, and control with respect to shape (i.e. pattern). The two may, although not necessarily, be similar, for if the extent of growth in different parts is controlled, the shape will be controlled. But often shape is more than the amount of growth, but involves also the direction of the growth.

A simple case of superficially controlled growth is seen in colonies of bacteria. There the shape of the colony is determined by the shape of the bacterium and the nature of the gum or exudate that surrounds the bacterial cells. The latter may be altered by the medium upon which the bacteria are grown. Also it may be altered by mutation, and it is well known that such mutant variants will give "rough" or "smooth" or some characteristic colony shape. There is, in fact, a fair number of distinct colony types that can be identified and are used constantly by the bacteriologist as diagnostic features. Recently it has been shown by H. Bloch (1950) that extractable substances from one colony type of the tubercule bacillus which has ropy "chords" of cells will cause (by adding the substance) a diffusely growing type to assume the ropy shape. Apparently in some way the substance, which is lipid in nature, affects the adhesion between the cells. To show to what extent the physical environment, especially the structure of the surrounding medium, affects colony shapes, the work of J. Schachner (1928) is most interesting. He inoculated stiff gelatin just below the surface with bacteria (or yeast) and as growth ensued, the shape of the colony was like a small dowling peg sticking straight out of the agar into the air. If the surface of the agar was disrupted with a needle, then the colony would have a more usual, spread out appearance (Plate III). The explanation of the peg shape is very simple. When growth first begins in the cells locked under the surface of the gelatin, pressure is exerted in all directions, but a break-through occurs only at the upper part, weak because it is so near the surface. The cells continue to grow and expand and so they begin to be extruded through the break-through hole. Growth takes place largely at the base near the nutrient jelly, and so by force of circumstance this becomes a growth zone, a meristem, and the cells become pushed upward. The peg shape is really a product of a circular break-through hole imposing a constriction on the exuding bacterial mass. It is just like the worm of tooth paste made by squeezing the paste through the circular orifice of the tube.

This is a clear and easy example of how the physical environment may produce a definite shape; Schachner has managed to artificially induce a meristem and an external form in a simple mass of bacterial cells. All order is maintained by the stiffness of the gel and the location of the inoculation point. Any variation of these will produce another shape; in fact, as we have said, even disrupting the surface will do it. Another potent factor in making this shaping possible is the gumminess of the cells that sticks them together. This is obviously a prime requisite for any multicellular organism.

The physical environment of the specific functions within that environment also often affect the shape and the structure of an organism, and this is true of those cases which are called *functional* or *direct* adaptations. There is no question here of Lamarckian inheritance of acquired characters, but rather that the characters are assumed as a result of the functional activity of some organism during its lifetime, and not passed on.

A good example is the case of compensatory hypertrophy of the kidney where, if in mammals one kidney is removed, the other increases radically in size. The reason for this apparently lies somewhere in its functioning, for when the one kidney is left to do a double load, the organ is stimulated to increase in size so that it may comfortably handle its new task. E. S. Russell (1945) has argued elegantly that this compensation in the kidney shows that there is some directiveness, some purpose, some sophisticated teleology in nature, but of course this can only be an opinion, and even though I admire Russell's work greatly, I do not feel a strong necessity to share this opinion. It is simply that his metaphysics are different from mine, and I do not see that one is better than the other.

Another example, equally to the point, is that of the increase in size of muscles with their use. Everyone knows that if one exercises certain muscles they will grow and enlarge. The very fact that one's favored arm, be it the right or the left, is larger than the other is a case in point, and this may become quite exaggerated, as for example in championship women tennis players who often have delicate female features except for the arm they use to swing the racket. The legs of ballerinas show the same thing, as do the biceps of boxers, and the arms and shoulders of men crippled and forced to use crutches. It may be that people with certain physiques are predisposed to certain types of physical activity, but still functional adaptation exists and operates. The advertisements saying that the thin and spindly can become human gorillas by using a certain type of exercising machine may exaggerate, but there is enough truth in what they say so as to allow them to remain legally in business.

D'Arcy Thompson discusses with other examples this same phenomenon.[1] He says, "The soles of our boots wear

---

[1] I. I. Schmalhausen (1949) also discusses a variety of cases of this phenomenon and in particular discusses their rôle in evolution.

thin but the soles of our feet grow thick, the more we walk on them, for it would seem that the living cells are 'stimulated' by pressure, or by what we call 'exercise,' to increase and multiply."[2] He talks of experiments on plants which show this same thing, where Hegler, Pfeffer and others loaded the young shoot of a plant with weights so that it approached its breaking point, and then a few days afterwards its breaking point was redetermined. The sunflower, for instance, will break with a load of 160 gms so it was loaded with 150 gms and then after a few days its breaking point was redetermined and found to be as great as 250 gms. By continuing the process at intervals, a weight as great as 400 gms was tolerated.

The general phenomenon has a parallel in the physical world (of the kitchen) as D'Arcy Thompson shows. He discusses the making of candy from boiled sugar or treacle where the "taffy" is drawn out in a rope and continuously pulled and folded. As the process is repeated it becomes more and more difficult to pull until finally, "all the man's force is used to stretch the rope." The explanation of this adaptation in taffy is that by the pulling in one direction alone the molecules become oriented, lined up in that direction and this gives the rope much greater strength. "For increase of strength by rearrangements of the particles we have already a rough illustration in our lock of wool or hank of tow. The tow will carry but little weight while its fibers are tangled and awry; but as soon as we have carded or 'hatchelled' it out, and brought all its long fibers parallel and side by side, we make of it a strong and useful cord."[3] We have then an explanation (orientation of the molecules) as to why certain structures are stronger and more efficient, although the exact mechanics in the case of the kidney or muscle hypertrophy is not quite so clear. But the fact that the explanation can be simple gives us courage to hope that some day we will fully understand all these functional adaptations.

There are certain cases in living organisms that are not

[2] Thompson (1942, p. 1018).   [3] Thompson (1942, p. 987).

much different from the case of taffy. They concern the orientation of nerve and some other animal cells during growth. The work was originally conceived by R. G. Harrison (1910) following his classic discovery that it was possible to grow cells in tissue culture, and later P. Weiss (1929, 1934, 1945), through a series of ingenious and fascinating experiments, became the leader in this particular subject. Harrison observed that as the axones of the nerve cells in culture grow out, the direction of growth was determined in the small advancing pseudopodial tip. Its course was guided by surfaces or solid structures with which it came into contact and he called this orientation to solids, thigmotropism. Weiss first made a series of studies with the cells grown on fibrin clots in the culture chamber. His important discovery was that if the fibrin was stretched so that it clotted while under a strain, then the nerve or mesenchyme cells which grew on it were always oriented in the direction of the stretch, while if no tension had been exerted on the clot, the orientation of the cells was at random. It was, in effect, the same thigmotropism of Harrison except of a much more sensitive nature than had originally been imagined, for here, as Weiss pointed out, the outgrowing cells are sensitive to the orientation of the molecules or micelles of the fibrin, and follow along this ultrastructure as though the micelles were arrows pointing the way (Plate III).[4] In later work this sensitive contact guidance, as Weiss calls it, was revealed in other ways and he showed that the outgrowing cells will follow the flow path of exudate given off in front of the cells, and in this way they may become, in the living organism, oriented into places where there is no guiding ultrastructure. Weiss has produced, on a sound experimental basis, a whole concept of the control of growth, where there are stresses and strains set up within the body of a growing organism (Fig. 14).

[4] The growth pattern of bacterial colonies may be, in some instances, governed by the stress and strains artificially set up on the surface of the gel medium. This was discovered independently by Jacobsen and Sergent. See Stanier (1942) for references.

The growing cells, being acutely sensitive to these tensions, work their way along them so that the final whole organism has its perfect shape. The control of growth here is referred back to molecular orientations, and forces within the or-

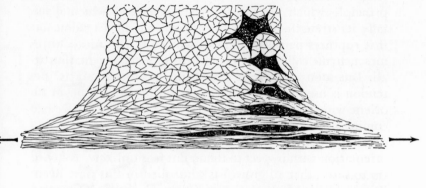

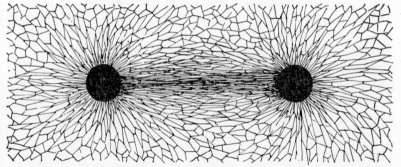

FIG. 14. Diagrams of P. Weiss, indicating his theory of the effect of the configuration of the ultrastructure of the medium on the orientation and shape of the cells. *Above*: The effect of graded stretching (in the direction of the arrows) of a reticular matrix on the shape of mesenchyme cells. *Below*: The orientation of a reticular matrix along the connecting lines between two centers of contraction. (From Weiss in Parpart, Chemistry and Physiology of Growth, Princeton University Press, 1949.)

ganism, a theory which, although far closer to experimental fact, is very similar to T. H. Morgan's (1901) old idea of development—where again he spoke of tensions set up within the germ that became slowly satisfied during development.

A very excellent example, which Weiss used to support his thesis, is that of repair in the tendons. Tendon cells are highly oriented with respect to their direction of pull, that is their fine attenuated processes run up and down the length of the tendon using, no doubt, exactly the same principle which we have already discussed which gives taffy its strength. If a hole is gouged out of a tendon, or if it ruptures partially, the gap will be filled quickly with mesenchyme cells which at first will show no orientation at all. But soon as they fit closer into position, and as the tendon is used and pulled, the mesenchyme cells begin to orient with respect to the direction of tension, finally becoming quite perfect tendon cells. There is no doubt concerning the reality of these tensions and the reality of the orientation with respect to them, but it is unlikely, as I will try to show, that all growth is controlled in this way. Even if it were, would we not immediately ask how is it that the tensions and the molecular orientations arise within the organism? Some are clear, such as a tendon doing its work, but others such as those that guide an outgrowing motor nerve fiber to its muscle are harder to see, and their origin is harder to explain.

Of all the cases of functional adaptation, that of the bone trabeculae which has been discussed by Weiss (1939), D'Arcy Thompson (1942), and many others is perhaps the best known. The point is that in the spongy "cancellous tissue" within a bone there are continuous small ridges called trabeculae that may be seen in bones, especially well in the femur, when it is sawed longitudinally, down the middle. D'Arcy Thompson tells the whole history of the discovery and understanding of these trabeculae; and quite appropriately, their significance was first seen by an engineer, Professor C. Culmann of Zurich. He was at that time (1866) in the process of designing a crane, and during a visit to the laboratory of his friend and colleague, Professor Meyer, the anatomist, he saw the trabeculae in the head of a bisected femur (Fig. 15). With a sudden flash of insight he exclaimed, "That's my crane!" He under-

stood well the principle of the crane, for had not he himself designed it, and now he saw the almost identical design in nature. The theory behind the crane is briefly
this. Any solid structure which has to perform a function
of pushing or pulling will internally be pulled and pushed.
By understanding the direction of these forces, it is pos-

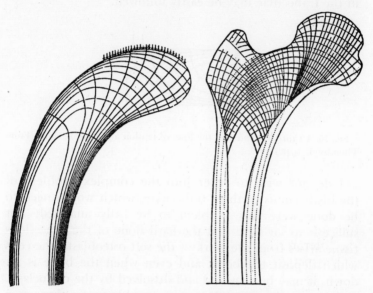

FIG. 15. A comparison of the crane-head (left) with the head of a femur
(right). (From Thompson, 1942, after Culman and Wulff.)

sible to build the structure so that it will be especially
strong. It is easier to comprehend in the simple example
of the bracket or cantilever, how these forces operate. If a
block is attached by two screws to a wall and a weight
suspended from its outer edge, obviously it will tend to
pull away from the wall at the upper screw, and push into
the wall at the lower screw. With this as a basis, the lines
of equal compression within the block may be drawn, and
running perpendicularly (or orthogonally) at all points
will be the corresponding lines of tension or pulling (Fig.
16). These lines are especially stable in that they are devoid

of any shearing forces. Clearly as the shape of the block becomes modified, so will its lines of tension and compression, and thus we see the trusses on one type of bridge being quite different from those of another. But the head of the femur is not greatly different from our simple block cantilever, and the tension and compression lines as seen in the trabeculae may be easily followed.

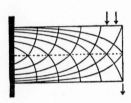

Fɪɢ. 16. A cantilever showing the lines of tension and compression. (From Thompson, 1942.)

I do not wish to enter into the complex problem of the histogenesis of these trabeculae, which would need to be done were this problem to be fully analyzed; but suffice it to say here that the hard bone of the cancellous tissue arises from the work of the soft osteoblasts, the cells which deposit the bone, and even when the bone is set down, it may be removed and dissolved by the osteoclasts, and later redeposited by more osteoblasts. So there is a rigid structure that is laid down by soft and no doubt sensitive cells, sensitive to tensions and compressions; and it is no wonder that, like the tendon cells, they deposit bone with respect to these lines of force.

But all we have shown so far is that these trabeculae are in the most advantageous position for maximum strength with a minimum of material, and there has been no demonstration that they arise as a result of function.[5] This evidence comes, for instance, from cases where the bone is broken and reset badly so that the original configurations of the trabeculae will no longer follow the lines

[5] See Murray (1936) for a general review of these problems concerning bones.

of tension and compression. Then the old trabeculae will slowly disappear, and new ones appear, perfectly arranged to give greater strength to the defectively set bone. Another case is that of ankylosis or ossification of the knee joint. In this pathological condition of humans the leg stiffens with the knee slightly bent, and within the newly ossified knee there are beautiful trabeculae, perfectly engineered to optimally fulfill their function.

Most of these growth patterns that we have discussed so far are limited by extrinsic factors, by some property of the environment, and now we begin the more subtle and difficult problem of intrinsic or internal factors affecting growth patterns where the organism itself appears to lay down the rules governing its course of growth.

Plants, with their rigid cell walls, often offer an almost diagrammatic representation of their growth, for no change in shape is obscured by cell movements. The plant cells divide and enlarge and the whole course of growth may be followed through these processes. There is a neatness and an order in the process, and therefore this will serve well to start our discussion. It should be said in the beginning that although there is a good deal known about the variability in size and the size or growth limits of individual unicellular organisms, reviewed by Adolph (1931), this material will not be considered here largely because of the unsatisfactory state of this knowledge: it is known that there are persistent inherited size differences, but other variations in size appear less persistent for obscure reasons. Instead we will concentrate on the patterns involved in the shaping of multicellular forms.

There is one factor of absolute importance in the growth of any multicellular organism and that is the adhesion between cells. Without this the cells would merely fall apart. It may be that the cell walls are closely cemented together, as they are with pectin in plants, or that the cells are loosely embedded in a jelly, but in any event they are held together. There are some special cases that we will consider shortly, where the adhesives do not surround the cells but are localized in one specific region and this has a rather special effect on the growth of the colony.

With these nonmotile, somewhat rigid plant cells, the most obvious factor which might affect the shape during growth is the direction of the cleavage planes. This is really a problem in geometry and in discussing it it is easier to talk of the direction of the spindle axes during division rather than the orientation of the division plate.

Let us take the simplest example, that in which the spindle axes are *all* along one axis or a line. This can only produce a line of cells, or a filament, and the algae *Ulothrix* or *Spirogyra* would be excellent examples of this type of cleavage. The filament is really a basic structure in the plant kingdom, and most all the cellular structure of higher plants presumably stems from it. Its mechanical advantages as a structure are easy to see and were well recognized by the older botanists.[6] There is no real way of knowing the channel through which it originated in the early history of the earth, for the lower the organism, the more hopeless it becomes to determine its phylogenetic relations. There is a series of organisms that exist today that suggests a possible route from the isolated cell to the filament, but we must guard ourselves not to be too taken with the idea for it is so very hypothetical. In the life cycle of the unicellular *Chlamydomonas* there is the so-called palmella stage, in which a number of nonmotile cells are embedded together in a jelly (Fig. 17). This cell mass arose from a single cell that first lost its flagella and then secreted a coat of jelly. This was then followed by a series of rather haphazard divisions; the lack of orientation is no doubt partly accounted for by the fact that the cells twist about, giving the irregular palmeloid stage. Other forms, closely related to *Chlamydomonas*, namely *Palmella*, have lost the typical flagellated freeswimming stage, and now exist permanently in the jelly. There is another form, *Geminella*, which is similar to *Palmella* except that the cells are in a line, although sepa-

6 E.g., see Haberlandt (1914).

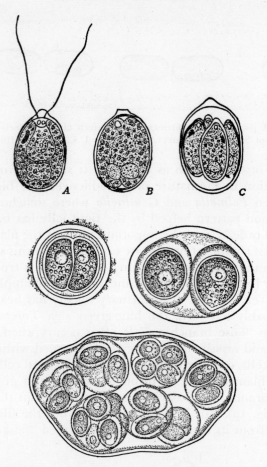

FIG. 17. Different stages in the life cycle of *Chlamydomonas. Above*: (A) a normal motile individual which undergoes division (B, C). Each of the daughter cells (C) forms a new cell wall and breaks free of the mother cell wall. *Below*: The progressive stages in development of the palmella stage of *Chlamydomonas*. (From Brown, The Plant Kingdom, Ginn, 1935.)

rated by a considerable space of jelly, and the reason for this is, of course, that the spindle axes of the cell divisions are in a line (Fig. 18). It takes no stretch of the imagination to bridge the gap between the separated cells of *Geminella* and the closely adhering cells of a true fila-

[73]

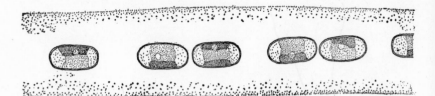

FIG. 18. A portion of the filament of the green alga, *Geminella interrupta*. (From Smith, Freshwater Algae of the U.S., McGraw-Hill, 1933.)

mentous organism such as *Ulothrix*; it simply involves a modification in the nature of the adhesive. The big step is between *Palmella* and *Geminella* where somehow the cell division pattern helped by the rigid jelly has become fixed and orderly, and the important result is the filament.

The first complication that we can impose on this simple picture is the advent of branching, although it is true that there are forms which branch and yet remain simple filaments. Every student of elementary botany has heard of, and probably has seen, the blue-green alga *Tolypothrix* which has "false branching." It often occurs when those peculiar and mystifying heterocysts are formed within the chain of cells, or sometimes where there is a dead cell. The growing filament plunges through the wall and gives all the appearance, at a hasty glance, of a branch in the filament (Fig. 19). But it is really nothing but the filament bursting from its seams and is rightly termed "false."

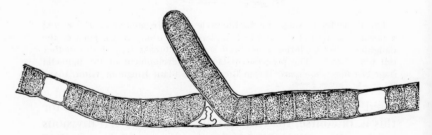

FIG. 19. False branching in *Tolypothrix*. Note the remains of the dead cell where the branching occurred. The two clear cells are heterocysts. (From Brown, The Plant Kingdom, Ginn, 1935.)

[74]

It is more common among the algae to have true branching, where one individual cell in the filament divides so that its spindle axis is at some angle from the main axis of the filament. But the point here is that this aberrant division is not successively repeated but recurs intermittently; that is, once a branch is initiated by such a division, the branch itself continues as a straight filament with its spindle axis of division again in a line. Branches may and do have further branches, but they are always separated by periods of straight filament growth. There are many examples of such branching algae, *Stigeoclonium* and *Cladophora* (Fig. 20) illustrating these features well. The branching of each species is quite specific, showing that

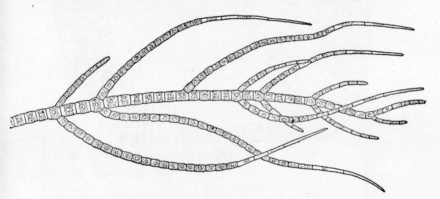

FIG. 20. A branched thallus of *Stigeoclonium*. (From Smith, Cryptogamic Botany, McGraw-Hill, 1938.)

somehow the periodicity of the aberrant branch-making division is controlled and characteristic of the organism.

There are many other forms in which the filamentous nature has become so modified by what amounts to repeated branching that it consists finally of a flat sheet of cells. *Coleochete*, which grows on flat surfaces and enlarges by radiating outward as an enlarging disc, is a good case in point, for one can follow the outgrowing filaments like the spokes of a wheel, and the lateral branches fill up the ever increasing gaps created by the outward spreading (Fig.

21). The spindle axes are in the direction of the radii for the most part, and those that are not are all at right angles to the radii, parallel to the perimeter of the disc.

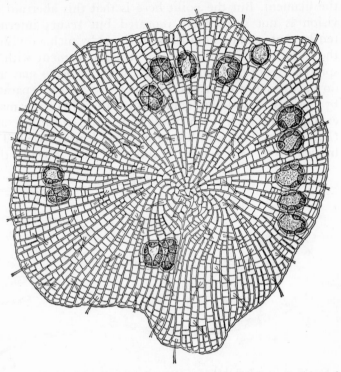

FIG. 21. The thallus of *Coleochaete*. Note that it is composed of branching filaments which are so close together that the appearance of a solid sheet is produced. The dark bodies are fertilized eggs which are overgrown to various extents by the surrounding cells. (From Brown, The Plant Kingdom, Ginn, 1935.)

Another instance of this tendency to broaden and thicken is seen in the case of *Schizomeris* a green alga that resembles *Ulothrix* except for the fact that many of its cells have divided with their spindle axes perpendicular to the plant, giving a thick appearance (Fig. 22). In both this case and *Coleochete* it appears as though all the space between the cells must be filled so as to give a solid mass of cells. Because the young embryonic plants of the higher

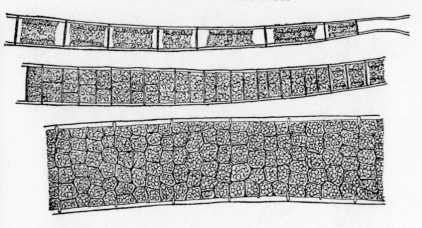

FIG. 22. *Shizomeris*. Portions of the thallus at three different levels. (From Smith, Cryptogamic Botany, McGraw-Hill, 1938.)

Ulvales are quite identical to *Schizomeris*, it is presumed that they at least have common ancestry. But *Ulva* the sea lettuce, with its large broad green blades, and *Entero-morpha* with its long green tubes have elaborated into a sheet of cells (Fig. 23). The basic plan is thought to be that of *Enteromorpha*, a tube of single cells. In a certain species of *Enteromorpha*, *E. Linza*, the tube has become very flat and has a central hollow only at the edges, and finally *Ulva* which has no rounded edge left, that is, it consists of two sheets of cells stuck firmly together (Fig. 24). In the blades of these algae, the cells have lost their filamentous character (although it is still visible in the stalk), and they appear like an irregular honeycomb or froth (Fig. 23). The spindle axes are random, but only within one plane. So, in a sense, the forms of these algae are determined by the cleavage planes. Even the difference between *Enteromorpha* and *Ulva* could be accounted for in this way, for if the cell divisions are in the direction of the main axis of the plant, a long thin plant will arise giving *Enteromorpha*, and if on the other hand the broad-ening becomes excessive in the direction perpendicular to the main axis of the plant, then it is no wonder that the

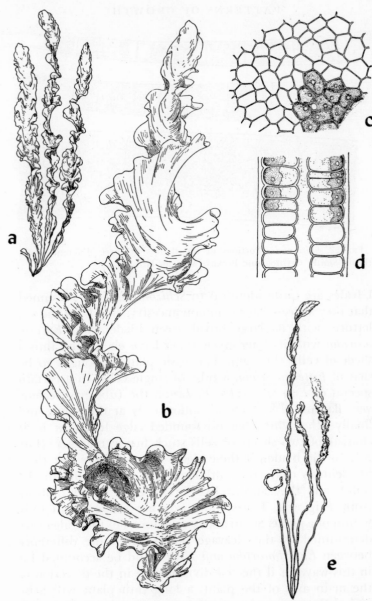

Fig. 23. The structure of *Ulva* and *Enteromorpha*. a, *Enteromorpha Linza*; b, *Ulva Lactuca*; c, a surface view of the cells of *Ulva*; d, a cross section of the thallus of *Ulva* showing the two layers of cells; e, *Enteromorpha intestinalis*. (From W. R. Taylor, Marine Algae of the N.E. coast of N. America, Michigan, 1937.)

great wide cylinder will collapse to two sheets of cells, and as it is thrashed about in the water, the edges become frayed, as has happened with *Ulva*.

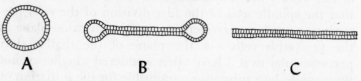

A   **B**   **C**

FIG. 24. Diagram to show the construction of different Ulvales. A, cross section of the thallus of *Enteromorpha*; B, of *E. Linza*; C, of *Ulva*.

The hardest thing to account for is the fact that the thallus is cylindrical rather than a single sheet of cells, as is found, for instance, in the related *Monostroma* or in the convergent red alga *Porphyra*. The answer may be that the spindle axes must always be parallel to the surface of the plant, and if such is the case in a form such as *Schizomeris*, a hollow will form in the center of the filament to give a cylinder. The idea then is that the *Schizomeris* form is not really dividing towards a plane, but rather towards a cylinder and that the factor which affects cleavage planes, which in turn affects the shape of the plant, is the surface. At first there appears to be an exception to this hypothesis in the development of *Enteromorpha minima*. In that particular species Bliding (1938) found that the swarmers which settle to the bottom to produce new plants do not start the usual *Ulothrix*-like filament, but form a flat irregular mass of cells. Then a number of these mats from different swarmers will start growing upward and fuse into an irregular tent-like structure that finally rises higher and higher to form the normal cylinder of *Enteromorpha*. This early development is different from other species of *Enteromorpha*, yet the end result is essentially the same. But if we examine it closely we see that our rule about cleavage planes being parallel to the surface still holds, for this is the way the mats form. The only additional feature in *E. minima* is the fusion of the numerous mats to form one whole plant.

[79]

Some years ago I became interested in the production of swarmers by *Ulva*, which occurs in all the cells in a band around the edge of the thallus, and although little came of the work I did notice one interesting fact, and that is that the spindle axis of the first division of the cells preparing to produce swarmers was not in the same plane as the vegetative cells (in the plane of the thallus) but perpendicular to it. I have often wondered whether or not there might be a substance responsible for the initiation of swarmers which diffuses inward from the edge between the two sheets of cells; for here the division line between reproductive and vegetative cells is so sharp, and in *Enteromorpha* where there is the central hollow, the line of demarcation is irregular—scattered patches of vegetative cells among the reproductive cells and vice versa. The idea is that the substance will slush about more inside the *Enteromorpha* than in the *Ulva*, and that the substance itself determines the cleavage plane. But such unbridled speculation is not too fruitful, although it sounds a note that we shall hear again, the idea of chemical substances, hormones, being involved in the control of growth.

We have fashioned, by pointing to where and in what direction cell division shall take place, a line of cells (filament) with and without branches, a flat disc, a cylinder, and a broad irregular sheet of cells. There are more shapes than these within our reach.

The square (or rectangle) is best shown in the blue-green algae, most especially *Merismopedia* (Fig. 25) and *Tetrapedia* (Fig. 26). The spindle axes are in one plane, but now they must be extremely regular, and successively at right angles to one another. The cells of *Merismopedia* are small spheres and separated from one another by a considerable extent of jelly. As the cells divide, which they all do simultaneously, they become elongated and capsule-shaped, and then finally pinch off into spheres. The next division will be the same except for the fact that the divisions will be at right angles to the previous ones. If one follows the course of a single cell dividing a number

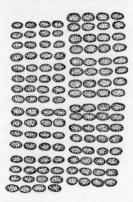

FIG. 25. A colony of the blue green alga *Merismopedia*. (From Brown, The Plant Kingdom, Ginn, 1935.)

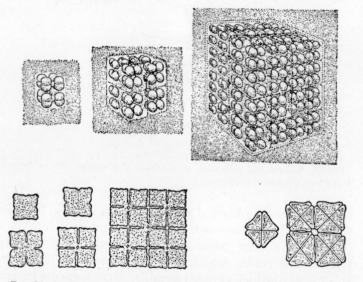

FIG. 26. Square and rectangular colonies of blue green algae. *Above*: Various stages of development of *Eucapsis*. *Below*: The stages of two species of *Tetrapedia*. (From Brown, The Plant Kingdom, Ginn, 1935.)

of times, then one can easily see that the colony will only be a square between every second division, that is when it consists of 4, 16, 64 cells, and the colony will be a rectangle when it consists of 2, 8, 32 cells. While these flat sheets of *Merismopedia* are quite frequently found in fresh water ponds and puddles, *Tetrapedia* is rare and I have never observed it. But from the published drawings, the striking simple symmetry of the cells really has no parallel in organic form. They are almost too geometrically simple and perfect to seem real and living. There are other examples of such regular sheets of cells, and *Gonium*, the colonial green alga, is one (Fig. 27). Each of sixteen cells,

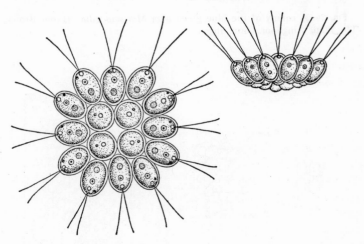

Fig. 27. Surface and side view of a colony of *Gonium*. (From Brown, The Plant Kingdom, Ginn, 1935.)

which are also embedded in a gelatinous matrix, has two flagella, and the colony actively swims about.

The blue-green algae provide another particularly symmetrical colony which forms a perfect box or cube. It is *Eucapsis* which closely resembles *Merismopedia* except for the fact that instead of the spindle axes of cell division remaining in a plane, they occur at successive right angles to one another in three dimensions (Fig. 26).

The sphere, especially the hollow sphere, is an extremely common shape assumed by a mass of dividing cells. It is characteristic in the early development of many animals and is referred to there as the blastula. The cleavage planes are such that, as in the Ulvales, the spindle axes are parallel to the surface, so the cells, which become smaller and smaller with repeated division, come to enclose an increasingly large cavity or blastocoel. Among the algae, *Volvox* shows much the same thing in the formation of its daughter colonies, although in this colonial green alga the cells are bi-flagellate, resembling those of its relative *Gonium* (Plate IV). There may be from 500 to 2,000 cells, each separated some distance from one another by jelly, giving the whole colony a size of 0.5 mm. in diameter. The cells usually although not invariably are connected to each other through the jelly by fine protoplasmic strands (or plasmodesmida). In asexual reproduction certain large cells in the posterior half of the colony, the so-called gonidia, start dividing, with their spindle axes parallel to the surface. As the successive bipartitions continue, the daughter mass begins to bulge inward, and is held fixed by a little hole or mouth (the phialopore) to the mother colony (Fig 28). Again here as division ensues the cells become smaller and the central cavity larger, giving what is essentially a blastula. In the sexual development, the sperm mass forms in just the same way from the male initial cell; and in the development of a zygote after various resistant and motile stages, the final zoospore, floating free in the water, divides rapidly and also forms such a hollow structure. This behavior is not confined to this genus of the Volvocales, but there are also others, for instance *Pleodorina*. The colonies there consist of much fewer cells, and the central cavity is correspondingly smaller. In *Pandorina*, where there are only 16 (rarely 8 or 32) cells in the colony, the cavity is not even demonstrable.

In reviewing all these many cases, it would seem that the direction of the cleavage is a key determinant in the shapes of many lower organisms. The next problem would be to

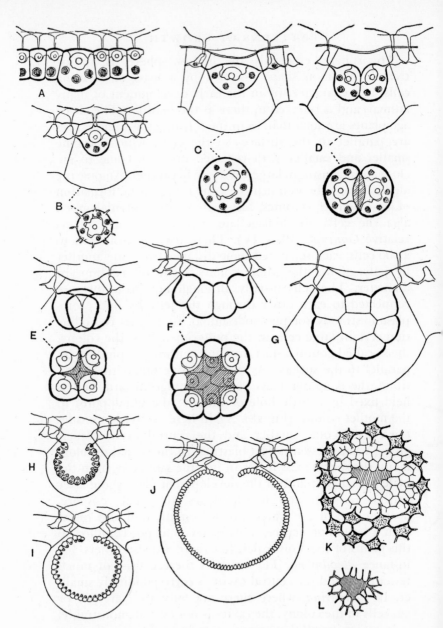

Fig. 28. Daughter colony development in *Volvox*. A, Gonidium and somatic cells of a young colony; B,C, side and surface views of enlarging gonidia before and after loss of cilia; D-F, the same of 2, 4, and 8-celled stages; G, 16-celled stage; H-J, sections of the developing embryo to show the formation of the free lip of the phialopore; K,L, the phialopore on completion of cell division; in K the surrounding cells of the parent colony are shaded. (From Pocock, 1933.)

find what factors in turn determine the direction of cell division, but unfortunately we immediately dive into pure speculation here. It is possible in some cases that the environment of the cell is a factor, for if a cell near the surface is surrounded on all sides but one by other cells, it will have an asymmetrical *entourage* and this may have its effect. This difference might be in the concentration of a chemical substance, leading to the idea suggested previously that certain substances might, by their position in relation to the cell, be effective. Another idea, much championed by R. A. Harper (1908, 1918a), is that of pressure-contact stimuli where growth pushes in the direction of compression. There is a great deal of information about both animals and plants concerning the factors which determine the first cleavage plane in the cleaving egg. Of special interest is the study of the egg of the brown alga *Fucus* in which Whitaker[7] has shown that a whole variety of factors will guide the direction of the first cleavage, but we will return to this problem later. It must be clearly kept in mind that we are concerned here mainly with a growth process and that the cell usually enlarges or elongates before it divides. Sachs laid down the rule that the cell plate (or division furrow) crosses the cell across its long axis, so that the direction of growth of the cell and the direction of the spindle axis must be one and the same. And Hertwig added a corollary to this rule for yolk-laden cells of animals, where he pointed out that division was not necessarily across the long axis of the whole cell, but across the long axis of the area of yolk-free protoplasm. Suffice it to say here that the whole problem concerning directions of growth is an aspect of the problem of polarity, and later in this book the general problem of what gives orientation, symmetry, headness and tailness in organisms will be considered.

Just as there are numerous cases where the cell division direction reflects the form, there are, if anything, many

[7] See the review by Whitaker (1940) for references to the work on *Fucus*.

more examples where this is not the case. Before discussing the variety of other cases I should like to take those where the shape of the organism, or better, the colony, is a function partly of the direction of cleavage planes and partly of the specialized and localized nature of the adhesives between the cells.

This really amounts to a collection of oddities, a Rogues Gallery of organisms with unconventional growth habits, all of which are living organisms and therefore we are bound to include them. There is one particular type that is found among widely dispersed groups of organisms: in the colonial ciliates, and the colonial diatoms. It involves the adhesive or exudate being given off from one end of the cells, and by a combination of repeated cell divisions and the continued production of the exudate, to which all the cells are attached, a tree-like branching colony is produced. In the ciliates, *Zoothamnion* and *Epistylis* are good examples (Fig. 29). Fauré-Fremiet (1930) shows in the case of *Zoothamnion* how a migrant ciliospore comes to rest on the bottom, begins to exude the adhesive at its lower surface, and in this way raises the cell into the water (Fig. 30). The cell then eventually divides and each daughter cell continues to add to her separate adhesive stalk, and later there is bifurcation as a result of further cell divisions. In *Zoothamnion* and other related forms there is a contractile element, the myoneme, which lies in the center of the stalk, and when the colony is disturbed this miniature muscle contracts violently to pull the cells from harm's way. There are other colonial ciliates, such as *Epistylis* that lack this myoneme.

The colonial diatoms, that possess this growth habit, also lack any ability to contract. Of these forms the most beautiful is *Licomorpha*, especially *L. flabellata*, for the beautifully sculptured wedge-shaped cells will form fans held together by the thin exuded stalk, giving the whole colony a delicate oriental quality (Fig. 31). There is basically no difference between the method of development of these forms and the colonial ciliates.

[86]

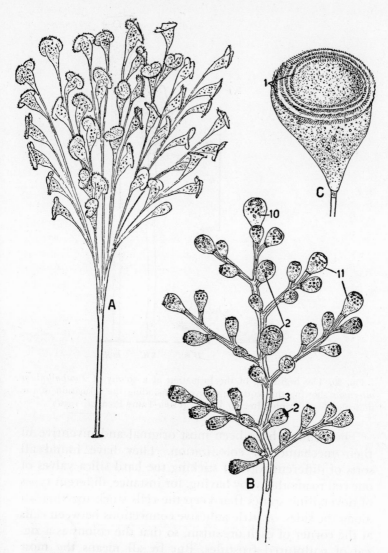

Fig. 29. Colonial ciliates. A, a colony of *Epistylis*; B, a colony of *Zoothamnium arbuscula*; C, one cell of *Epistylis* (not the same species as A). 1, adoral zone; 2, presumptive migrant ciliospores; 3, myoneme or muscle fiber; 10, apical cell; 11, terminal branch cell. (From Hyman, 1940.)

[87]

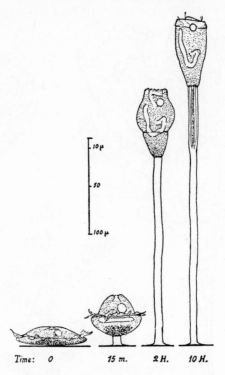

FIG. 30. The beginning of the formation of a colony of *Zoothamnium alternans* showing the sequence of events including the formation of the muscular fiber visible after 10 hours. (From Fauré-Fremiet, 1930.)

The diatoms have been most original and inventive in their mechanics of colonization. They have found all sorts of different ways of sticking the hard silica valves of one cell to another—by having, for instance, different types of dovetailing spines that keep the cells stuck together all along the sides, or little adhesive connections between cells at the corner of each organism, so that the colony is a zigzag of sculptured frustules. But by all means the most remarkable of all is *Bacillaria paradoxa* which is a series of pencil-shaped cells that lie parallel to one another (Fig. 32). The cells, unlike other diatoms, are not securely fixed in one position, but each cell may slide freely with

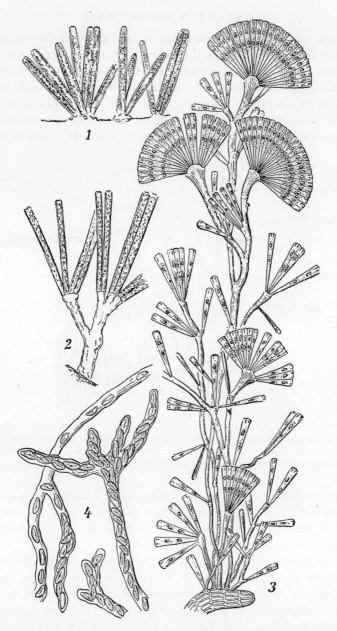

FIG. 31. Various colonial diatoms. 1, 2, two species of *Synedra*; 3, *Licmorpha flagellata*; 4, *Cymbella*. This latter form is composed of a branched gelatinous sheath which encases many individual diatoms. The sheath itself may be quite large and give the whole colony a bushy appearance. (From Oltmanns, Morphologie und Biologie der Algen, Fischer, 1904, after Smith.)

its neighbors. This means that at one moment the colony may appear as a collapsed carpenter's rule, and later it may stretch way out like an extended rule. As one observes this strange phenomenon under the microscope, the cells appear to do this so suddenly and with such rapidity that the effect is quite startling. In all these cases of colonial diatoms where the cells merely stick together, there is no

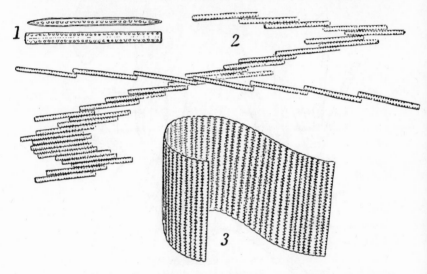

Fig. 32. The colonial diatom *Bacillaria paradoxa*. 1, the side (below) and surface (above) view of one individual; 2, the cells in an expanded condition; 3, the cells in a contracted position. (From Oltmanns, Morphologie und Biologie der Algen, Fischer, 1904, after Smith.)

real overall colony shape, as there is in *Licmorpha* where one has a clear distinction between the proximal and distal end. Instead they are more a collection of cells and therefore are certainly primitive colonizers.

In sharp contrast, there is another type of colonial diatom which involves exudate in a yet unmentioned way, that gives the most elaborate colonies of all the diatoms. It is not infrequent, when collecting algae in the sea, to come upon a delicate hair-like tuft of algae, a few centimeters long, perhaps attached to the thallus of some large and leathery brown alga. At first glance the fine strands of the tuft will look like some wispy brown alga, but when, in the laboratory, you have time to examine them more closely, you can see inside a cylinder of what appears as tinted plastic material, small boat-shaped diatoms quite widely separated. This may be a species of *Navicula* or *Cymbella,* and the outside cylindrical tube is the exudate given off by the cells (Fig. 31). The cells are capable of moving freely about within this housing that they have built, and which they keep enlarging by dissolving and extending the ends of the rigid tube. They will sometimes, if two cells are lodged at the tip, start a branch in the cylinder, and in fact branches are quite frequent. If the tube is broken, the cells wander out apparently unconcerned. O. T. Wilson (1929) has described the formation of new colonies, where first the cells will simply divide, and later begin to form a thin sheath of mucilage. The striking fact here is that these separate cells can build a large elaborate colony. They do so mainly by molding the external sheath, and in this case the cleavage planes must be of very little importance. It is true that the sheath will be extended where the cells are, and the cleavage will affect this, but the overall complexity of the colony appears to be far too great a task for simple diatoms.

In the golden algae there are also good cases of colonial forms in which the daughter cells, after division, have not separated. A common form of this is *Dinobryon* where each cell is surrounded by a small wine-glass-shaped shell called a lorica (Fig. 33). This shell has its lower end attached to the substratum, and after cell division one of the daughter cells retains the parental lorica, while the other builds a new one which attaches to the upper edge of the older one. By repeating this process numerous times a pie-shaped colony is formed. *Ophiocytium* is another example of the same general phenomenon, but there the contents of each pencil-shaped cell divide into a number of daughter cells, all of which emerge simultaneously through a hole at the tip of the parent cell, attach there, and form a fan of new

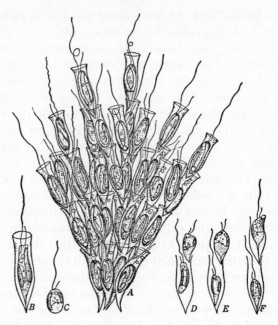

FIG. 33. *Dinobryon*, a colonial golden alga. A, a large colony; B, an individual cell; C, a free swimming individual that is capable of initiating a new colony; D-F, cell division. (From Brown, The Plant Kingdom, Ginn, 1935.)

daughter cells, hinged to the empty cell wall of the parent, like a bouquet of flowers in a vase (Fig. 34). This case differs from *Dinobryon* in that there are a number of daughter cells and that the only living cells are at the periphery of the colony, but the process by which the daughter cells use the parent cell as a point of attachment, a pedestal, is the same.

The path we have begun to follow started with a consideration of the extrinsic factors that limit and control growth, and now we have taken a first glance at those that are intrinsic, more intimately bound up within the cell. Of these intrinsic ones, the simplest and easiest to grasp involve shapes predictable on the basis of cell division planes, and shapes predictable on the basis of certain types of

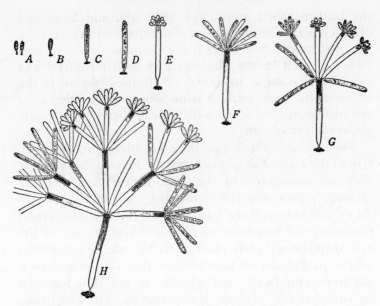

FIG. 34. The successive stages of development of a colony of the golden alga *Ophiocytium*. (From Brown, The Plant Kingdom, Ginn, 1935.)

localized adhesives or exudate. I do not say that all these things are explained, but we seem to feel that to explain them is not out of the question, not unreasonable. At least in the case of the localized adhesives the most immediate (but not especially satisfactory) explanation is known. Concerning the direction of cell division, there are some further facts which put the matter in a slightly different light.

There are great numbers of plants whose form is distinguished by the fact that it can in no way be interpreted in terms of planes of cell division. Obviously, for instance, all the multinucleate coenocytic forms which do not even possess planes of cell division, but have only nuclear divisions, must fall under this category. In the algae the Siphonales and their relatives are good examples; there is the common fresh water *Vaucheria* which is a thin green filament, and then of the salt water forms there is *Bryopsis*,

[93]

the feather-shaped green alga (Fig. 35), and large and often elaborate forms such as *Caulerpa*, and others (Fig. 36). Also among fungi this is the common situation, seen especially well in the Phycomycetes both terrestrial and aquatic. The basic structure of all these forms is the filament, but each nucleus is no longer surrounded by a cell membrane and a cell wall; instead they wander freely about the cytoplasm.

The special problem that these organisms present (relative to the control of growth) may be better understood if they are considered in the light of the fact that the cleavage planes only reflect the directions of the growth. As we said before, if the long axis of a cell lies in a certain direction, which is achieved by the increase in size of the cell, then the cell plate must by Sachs' rule lie perpendicular to it. This means then that the direction of growth is the important factor, and whether or not it is followed by oriented cell division is superfluous. The obscuring, outer shells of the problem seem to have been peeled off, and now the question is resolved to what controls the direction of growth; is it by gradients of food, or other limiting chemical substances, is it by some internal orientation of the molecules which requires that addition can only take place in certain directions (much as a crystal can accumulate molecules on certain faces faster than others), is it by pressure-contact stimuli the explanation of which would still be required, or is it something else we have neither mentioned nor imagined? I believe that it is most likely more than one of these factors, and that there are many ways of controlling the direction of growth. It is hard for me to believe (although any guess including this one is dangerous) that the mechanism whereby the regular right angle turns in the growth of *Merismopedia* and *Eucapsis* is governed can be the same as that which governs the more haphazard pushes of growth in other forms. It may be that there are potentially in all organisms numerous methods of control, and some are more im-

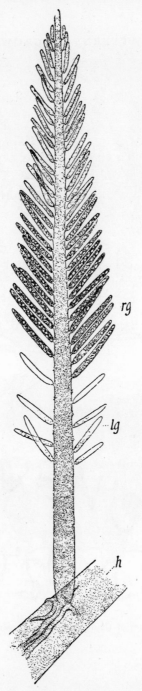

Fig. 35. *Bryopsis*, a coenocytic green alga. rg, plumules that have begun to form gametes; lg, empty gametangia; h, rhizoidal attachment. (From Oltmanns, Morphologie und Biologie der Algen, Fischer, 1904.)

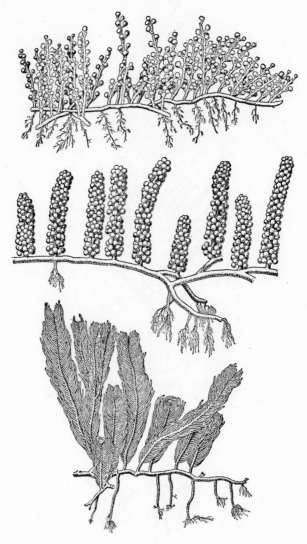

FIG. 36. Three species of *Caulerpa*. (From Brown, The Plant Kingdom, Ginn, 1935.)

portant, more pronounced than others, depending on the species.

It is quite enough to contend with the idea that whatever controls the growth in a plant filament does so within each individual filament, for this in itself seems a considerable task, but there are many plants which consist of an aggregate of filaments, and the aggregate has a consistent form, a consistent shape. Already an example of aggregation has been given among the algae (p. 79) where a number of young plants of *Enteromorpha minima* fuse to form a single complete adult. There are many instances among the fungi (as well as others in the algae) both simple and complex; let us first start with the simpler ones. The brush-like fruiting bodies of *Penicillium* are known to all (especially in this era of Penicillin). They stand small and erect from a tuft of cottony mycelium, and on top of the single stalk filament there is a cluster of pegs, each of which bears a row of small spherical airborne spores or conidia. The whole appearance gives the impression of a minute skeleton of a hand, with the carpals and the phalanges. There are certain genera of fungi related to *Penicillium* which do not consist of isolated fruiting bodies, but of aggregates of fruiting bodies (Fig. 37). This general form is often called a coremium, of which the genus *Coremium* is an excellent example. This aggregation, loose though it may seem, is well proportioned; the stalk is made up of the collected bundles of filaments like Roman fasces, and the conidia are at the top in a coherent mass.

A more common and more ostentatious example of the same phenomenon is the mushroom. It is an easy matter to tease apart any mushroom or toadstool and see that its flesh and in fact all its parts are made up of a sometimes tight, sometimes loose weft of hyphal filaments. The mushroom itself, the part that is edible, is the fruiting body, the spore-bearing body, and from the gills or pores (depending on the species) minute basidiospores are shed to be carried away into the air. These spores will germinate and

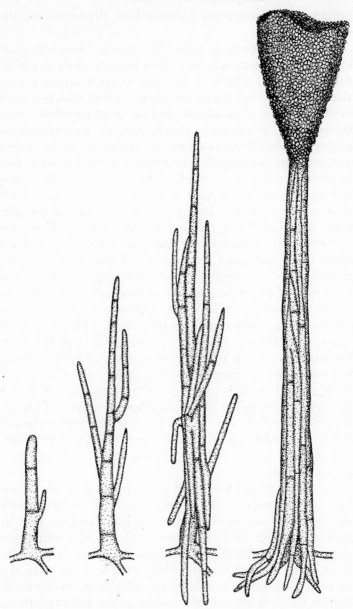

FIG. 37. Successive stages of the development of a coremium type fruiting body.

produce vegetative hyphae that spread and grow in the ground or in the rotten wood, feeding on organic materials. When the vegetative hyphal mass has achieved considerable size (and sexual fusion taken place) little knots of hyphae will begin to grow together to form the germ of the mushroom. Then, often at a tremendous rate and hence to "mushroom up," the ball of hyphae will enlarge, become delineated into stalk and cap and spore-bearing regions, shoot into the air and simultaneously expose the gill to the air (Fig. 38). There perhaps should be a word of caution here in that the growth largely takes

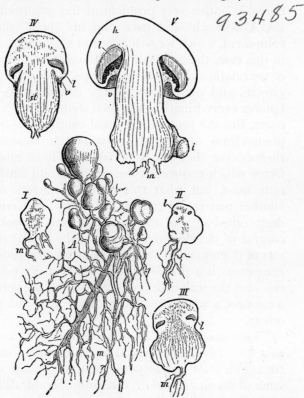

FIG. 38. Different stages of development of the common mushroom, *Agaricus campestris*, starting with a mycelial mat (A) and ending with a mature mushroom (V). (From Sachs, Botany, Oxford, 1882.)

place during the vegetative period, and the fruiting must involve a transfer of the protoplasm from the old hyphae into the new central collection points. Since new cell wall is laid down during the fruiting, there is some growth, but the protoplasm must come largely from the old store. In this way it resembles the fruiting of Myxomycetes, and it makes it easy to understand how some large mushrooms seem to appear overnight.

The remarkable aspect of their development is that this mass of filaments becomes controlled and rounded off so that there is a smooth stalk, an even cap, and gills or pores. It is this very problem of the mushroom that puzzled Gurwitsch[8] and gave him his "field" theory of development, which we will mention again later. Apparently, in this case, the cell wall, the filament, as a unit has little or no relation to the overall shape. The protoplasm in its growth, and perhaps to a large extent in its movement, ignores everything but the final shape of the whole mushroom. But the protoplasm is not continuous, as it is in the plasmodium of the Myxomycetes; it is separated into threads, yet they act as a whole. There must be some factor which transcends the cell wall and unifies this cottony mass, but what this factor or factors might be is another matter. Already in this book we have come to a deep-rooted sign of the least understood problem of the control of development, for it is the explanation of this sort of phenomenon that makes us say that growth and development is a problem. Really it is many problems; but this one, the unification of great masses of protoplasm into a oneness, a wholeness, has us more mystified than all the others.

There are myriads of other forms that have this same character involving hyphal aggregations: some algae, as for instance *Batrachyospermum*, a large share of the thousands of Ascomycetes with their innumerable different forms (for instance the fleshy cup fungi), then the many Basidio-

[8] See Bertalanaffy and Woodger (1933) for references and a good discussion of Gurwitsch's work.

mycetes besides the mushrooms, such as the puffballs, the stinkhorns, the bracket fungi, etc., and also the lichens, those fungi which live communally with algae. Each has its characteristic shape and differs in small and large ways, but they all have one thing in common, and that is the problem of how their growth is controlled.

Let us turn now to another matter, that of meristems, or growth zones. In the evolution of the higher plants, one of the major steps concerning growth was the appearance of a meristem, a specific region where cell division takes place. The reasons for the importance of a meristem have already been discussed, that they are required of organisms that reach a certain size, for rigidity is necessary in large organisms, and cell division and growth cannot occur within the rigid portion.

No doubt meristems originated independently in a number of different ways among the algae, for even today there are various types of meristems that do not appear related. It is, of course, far more common to find algae with no meristem; and in simple filaments such as *Spirogyra* or *Ulothrix*, where any cell which has reached the necessary size is likely to divide, there is no specific region of division or growth. In some of the brown algae there are filamentous hairs given off which possess a meristem. Cell division takes place only at the base of the filament, adjacent to the larger thallus, and cells elongate and become progressively larger the more distal they are (Fig. 39). This general picture of a meristem is the usual one, that is a zone of division and beyond this a zone of elongation.

In the case of flat sheets of cells, some rather large algae, such as *Ulva*, have no meristem. Again any cell in any part of the broad thallus may divide. This must mean that in some way the cell walls are flexible enough to yield, and to accommodate the general expansion. Also the adhesives between the cells must be sufficiently fluid to allow some cell slipping.

In some algae, for instance the brown alga *Sphacelaria*, there is an apical meristem, that is, a meristem where the cell division takes place at the tip of the plant, and the enlargement of the cells occurs below this. In fact *Sphacelaria* is a fine example of an apical cell; all the cells of that branch of the thallus arise from the division of one cell (Fig. 39).

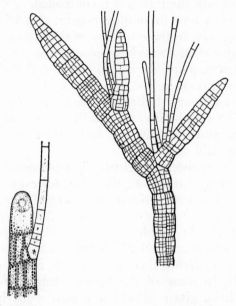

Fig. 39. The thalli of two species of Sphacelariales, a group of brown algae characterized by having an apical-cell meristem on the main stems and intercallary meristems on the fine hairs. (From Taylor, Marine Algae, Univ. of Michigan, 1937.)

The largest of the algae, the kelp or *Laminaria* (and other related genera) have, as would be expected from their size, an extensive meristem and it so happens it is an intercalary meristem, not found at one end of the plant, but somewhere in the middle. *Laminaria* has a long stalk, sometimes achieving incredible length, for its use seems to be to keep one end of the plant firmly attached to the bottom of the ocean by the holdfast, while the other, the flat blade, must lie near the surface to catch the sun's energy for photosynthesis (Fig. 40). Between the

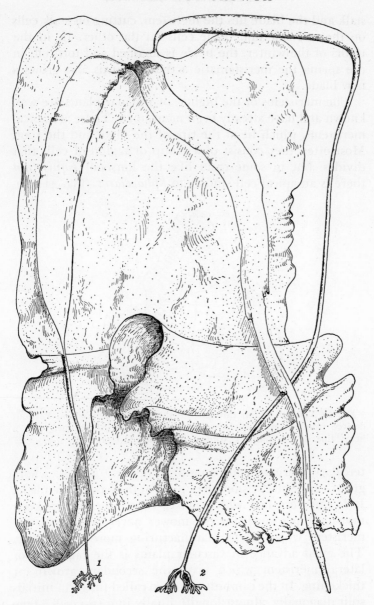

FIG. 40. Two forms of *Laminaria*. (From W. R. Taylor, Marine Algae, Univ. of Michigan, 1937.)

stalk and the blade lies the meristem, cutting off stalk cells on the one side and blade cells on the other. If, in the rigors of the winter, the blade is smashed and torn off, in the spring the meristematic activity returns and grows a new blade.

The meristems of the higher, or vascular plants are well known and have already been mentioned. There are apical meristems, which lie at the tips of the shoot and the root. Most often they consist of a group or region of cells that divides, but in some cases like the horsetail *Equisetum* there is an apical cell similar to *Sphacelaria* (Fig. 41). In-

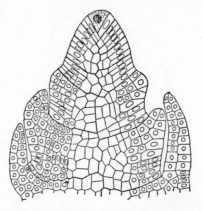

Fig. 41. Vertical section through the shoot tip of *Equisetum*. Portions derived from successive divisions of the apical cell are outlined with a heavy line. (From Smith, Cryptogamic Botany, McGraw-Hill, 1938.)

tercalary meristems are found in delicate grasses, where growth and cell division takes place at the base of the blade. It is this very fact which makes it so necessary to keep mowing one's lawn, for the mower never takes away the meristem which keeps manufacturing more grass blade. The great advance in vascular plants is the cambium or lateral meristem which gives the secondary growth or thickening. In the cambium long, so-called fusiform initials split diagonally, almost longitudinally into two cells.[9] One

[9] This is a classic exception to Sachs' rule concerning cell division.

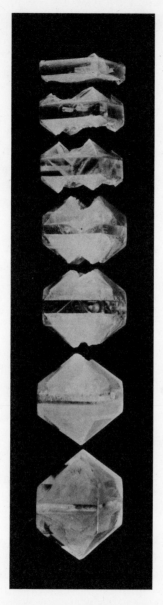

PLATE I. Successive stages of the capping process in the growth of a crystal of ammonium dihydrogen phosphate. Growth occurs primarily at the perimeter of the seed plate (the center of the plate can be cut out without effect) and the enclosed pyramids are hollow. (From Egli, 1949.)

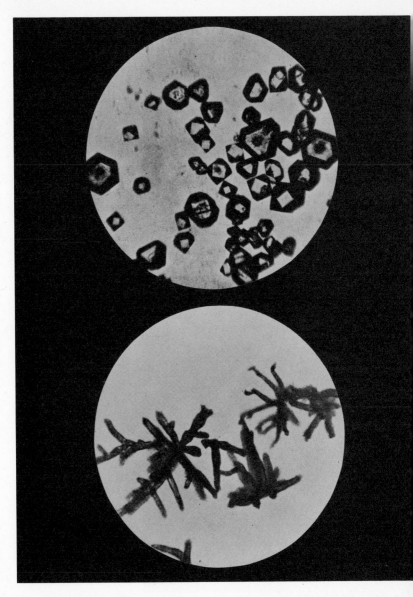

PLATE II. The effect of a foreign substance on crystal shape. *Above*: Pure silver chloride crystals. *Below*: Silver chloride crystals formed in the presence of methylene blue. (From Reinders, Zeitschr. physik. Chemie, 77, 1911.)

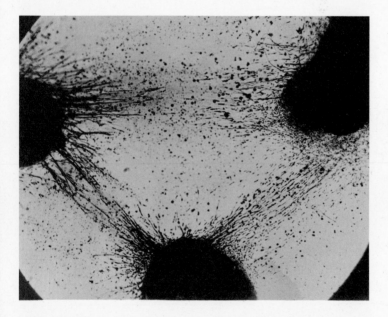

PLATE III. *Above*: A bacteria colony grown on stiff gelatin and inoculated below the surface (from Schachner, 1928). *Below*: Oriented cell growth between three explants cultivated in a thin film of coagulated blood plasma. (From Weiss in Parpart, Chemistry and Physiology of Growth, Princeton University Press, 1949.)

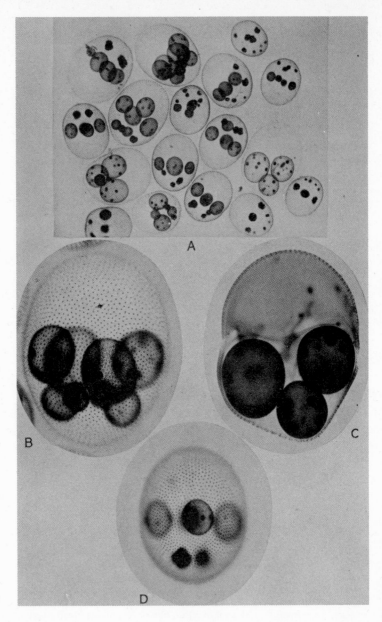

PLATE IV. *Volvox*. Various views of asexual development in *Volvox africanus*. Note that the daughter colonies form only within the posterior half, and often one sees daughter colonies within daughter colonies. (From Pocock, 1933.)

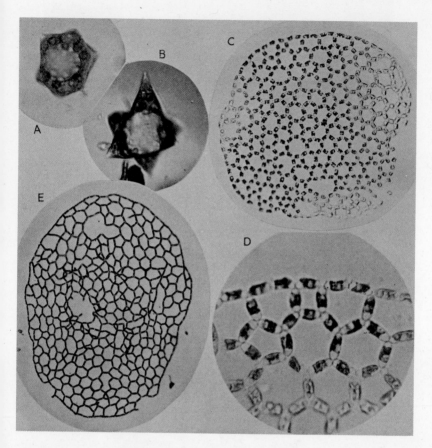

PLATE V. Colony development following sexual reproduction, in *Hydrodictyon*. A, B, Polyhedra; C, a young net, recently formed, showing barrel-shaped uninucleate cells; D, a small portion of the edge of C (top left) enlarged; E, an older net showing parts of the center two-layered. (From Pocock, 1937.)

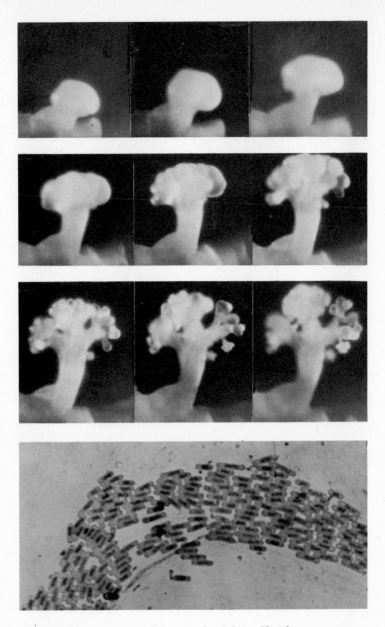

PLATE VI. Development of the myxobacterium, *Chondromyces crocatus*. The upper six photographs show various stages of the fruiting taken at approximately hour intervals. The lower photograph shows the bacterial rods (which have been prepared by Rabinow's technique using Giemsa's stain) streaming towards an aggregation center. (Original photographs by E. A. Wheaton.)

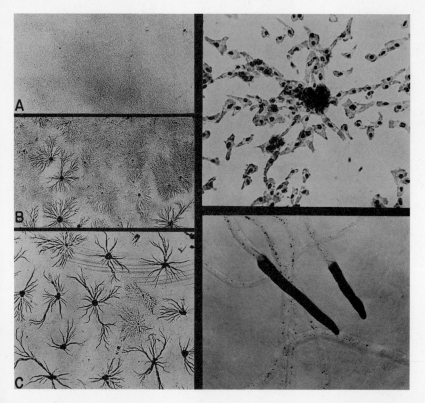

PLATE VII. Different stages in the development of *Dictyostelium discoideum*. *Left*: Three stages of aggregation of the amoebae. (From Raper, 1940a.) *Upper right*: A preparation stained by silver impregnation showing a young aggregation stage (the amoebae are about 15 to 30 micra long). (From Bonner, 1947.) *Lower right*: Migrating cell masses showing the slime tracks deposited behind them; the large one would be about 2 cm. long. (Photograph by K. B. Raper.)

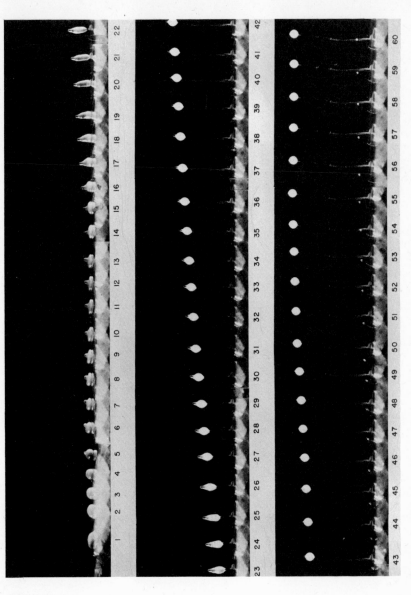

PLATE VIII. The final fruiting or culmination of the slime mold *Dictyostelium discoideum* taken at 15 min-

PLATE IX. Resting trout lined up in regular rows. (From Gudger, 1949. Originally from Field and Stream, 1929.)

of the cells will retain the ability to divide and the other will become some part of either the xylem or phloem depending on whether it is cut to the inside or the outside (Fig. 42). The shape of the cambium itself may consist of a complete cylinder or it may be part of a cylinder broken up into bundles of various designs. The pattern of the phloem and xylem may be further altered by changes,

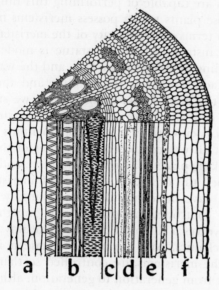

FIG. 42. Diagram illustrating the lateral meristem (cambium) of a woody plant, and the tissues produced by the cambium. a, pith; b, xylem; c, cambium; d, phloem; e, pericycle; f, cortex. (From Brown, The Plant Kingdom, Ginn, 1935.)

during the course of growth by alterations in the extent of the cambium, and this, as a rule, varies in different parts of the plant. It must always be remembered that meristems give rise essentially to accretionary growth for there is only the meristematic region itself which produces new tissue, and once the tissue is formed it does not contribute to further growth but only to the total bulk, be it dead as in the case of wood, or living as in parts of the phloem. In this respect it more closely resembles simple interest than compound interest, for unless the meristem itself enlarges, the capital remains the same and the income is kept elsewhere (in some old sock) in no way helping to make new tissue, or enriching the capital.

Meristems represent a kind of division of labor, which if the argument be correct, is a concomitant of increased size. It is a division of the labor of growing, for now only certain cells are capable of performing this function. The form of those plants which possess meristems must be interpreted in terms of the activity of the meristems, for this really is an instance where the statue is modeled by the sculptor adding more and more clay, and the way in which the clay is added, that is the amount and the location, determines the final shape. Before, when we summed up the case for control of growth in plants with simple cleavage patterns, coenocytic plants, and filamentous aggregates, we said that all we see are manifestations of the fact that growth is taking place in an orderly fashion, and we simply had described the order. In the case of meristematic organisms we have done just the same thing, we have described the controlled progress of the growth which in this case involves a different and in some ways more specialized mechanics. And again in this case it is far from clear how the meristems are controlled so that the shape is consistent from generation to generation, although there is some helpful information bearing on this point.

The work of E. W. Sinnott[10] on the shape and size of fruits, mainly of gourds, squashes, and pumpkins or cucurbits, is pertinent even though the problem does not so much involve a meristem as it does a general consideration of the factors affecting shape and size in higher plants. One of the most important factors will be reserved until later in this chapter, for it involves a genetic control. But with these genetically different races Sinnott studied, by comparison, differences in the growth of large and small fruits, and differences in the growth of different shaped fruits

[10] See Sinnott (1939) for a partial review of his work. Also see Sinnott (1942, 1944, 1945).

(Fig. 43). There has been little more than a mention, thus far, of the subject of size limits, the fact that growth stops at a certain specific point, and this, as we have just said, may be genetically determined. The cucurbits have proved to be a good place to study the detail of this, for in large and small races there may be a tremendous difference in

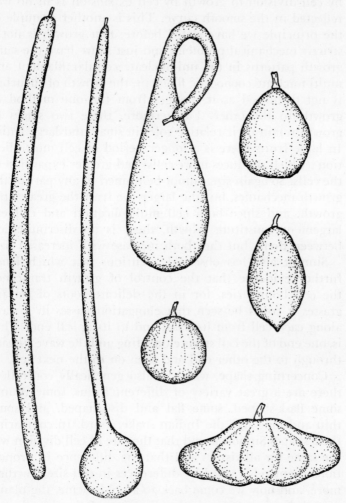

Fig. 43. Gourds of various shapes.

the mature size. In fruits Sinnott finds two periods of growth; the first involves cell division, and at a specific point cleavage stops and growth by cell expansion sets in. If the overall increase in size of the fruit is measured over these two periods, the growth increases logarithmically until the final leveling off, and the transition from growth by cell division to growth by cell expansion is in no way reflected in the smooth curve. This is another example of the principle we have stated before, that growth is not a strictly mechanical problem; and just as we have the same growth patterns in the uni-nucleate cellular filament and multi-nucleate coenocytic filament, the growth of cucurbits is not disturbed as it changes from the one method of growth to the other. Furthermore, these two stages of growth retain their relative roles in small and large fruits. In large fruits there is a longer period of cell multiplication (which produces more cells) and greater expansion of the cells. So again size cannot be pinned to any part of the growth mechanics, but the larger the fruit the greater the growth, and since both cell multiplication and cell enlargement constitute growth, there is no discrimination between them, but they both increase with increased size.

Sinnott also has observed a curious fact which lends further evidence that the control of growth transcends the cell boundaries, for in the delicate roots of certain grasses it could be seen that elongation passes in a wave along each cell from its basal end to its apical end. That is, one end of the cell starts elongating and the wave spreads through to the other end and then on to the next cell.

Concerning shape, which is also genetically controlled, there are a great variety of different forms, some round, some flask-shaped, some flat and disc-shaped, and some thin and long like the Indian snake gourd. In comparing these shapes Sinnott found that the rate of cell division was the same for all tissues and that the difference in proportions is entirely caused by differences in cell size. Furthermore, and now we come back to an old theme, the planes of cell divisions (that is the direction of the growth) are a key factor. In spherical races the mitoses are equally abundant in all directions, while in flat or elongate gourds the spindle axes line up in the direction of the distension of the fruit. Especially interesting is the case of the Indian snake gourd, which is as long as two meters and only a few centimeters wide, and there the majority of the new cell walls are at right angles to the main axis. If the orientation of the cells during various stages of mitosis is measured, in metaphase the orientation varied from 0° to 40° (0° being perfect orientation along the main axis); in anaphase the angles were "smaller and less variable," until finally they became almost negligible by telophase. Of this Sinnott (1940, p. 82) says, "The behavior of these figures resembles that of swinging magnetic needles which finally come to rest in a position determined by the magnetic field in which they lie." It is quite certain that there is no magnetism actually involved here, but whatever it is, like magnetism, it influences the whole structure, and not just isolated parts.

For some time it has been known that certain growth hormones, or auxins, exist in plants.[11] This raises a vast new subject concerning the control of growth, that of control by hormones. One of the first major steps in the history of phytohormones was the work of Went who established a bio-assay, a method of measuring the quantity of growth hormone by measuring the amount of growth it has induced. This test, the so-called "*Avena*-test" makes use of the young cylindrical seed leaf or coleoptile of the oat. It is cut on the upper surface and a small (standard size) agar block is placed on one side of it. If the block contains any auxin then it will move downward on one side of the coleoptile immediately below it and cause that side to grow more than the other. This, quite naturally, will result in a curvature, the angle of which can be measured with a protractor, and in this way the quantity of the

[11] Unless otherwise indicated, all references to plant growth hormones may be found in Went and Thimann (1937), which is still the best general review of the subject.

growth substance may be determined by the magnitude of the angle. There are now additional bio-assays of auxins known, but the *Avena*-test retains its usefulness and importance.

A word should be said concerning the chemistry of auxin for although it has a long and involved history, the final result is remarkably simple. Towards the beginning Kögl and Haagen-Smit isolated two substances (auxin *a* and *b*) and by some beautiful analytical chemistry found their chemical structure, and they were thought for a long while to be the only naturally occurring auxins in vascular plants. But it was found that a great many other substances also had growth promoting or auxin effects, and of these indole acetic acid was by far the simplest and most effective. Since this small compound is easily synthesized and readily obtainable, it became the commonly used substance for experiments on plants. And then, by a stroke of great good fortune, it became increasingly clear that indole acetic acid was in fact an important naturally occurring auxin, and that it is derived in the plant from the amino acid tryptophane.[12]

By placing various portions of a plant on agar blocks for a given period and then testing the block for its auxin activity, it is possible to find which parts of the plant are actively producing auxin. The tips of the plant, the root tip and the shoot tip, turn out to be by far the most important sites of production. The leaves and the fruit also produce fair quantities, but they do not compare with the tips. The tips also contain the apical meristem, and the relation between the activity of this meristem and the production of auxin is not known, that is it is not known which one causes the activity of the other. It is known, for other meristems, that auxin has a marked effect, but its effects are manifold. Let us examine them briefly but systematically.

Auxin stimulates growth in the shoot of the plant. It does so by stimulating cell elongation and cell division,

[12] See S. G. Wildman and James Bonner (1947).

that is it seems to affect all aspects of growth. Its effect on cell division in the shoot is seen primarily in the cambium, and presumably in the spring, when new leaves are formed and the branch tips become active, it is the auxin they produce that awakens the cambium to its job of cutting off new cells. Exactly how, chemically, the indole acetic acid promotes this growth is a subject that only very recently has received any attention, and the answers are a long way off. Thimann and his group[13] have begun to take up this problem, and their papers on the one hand reflect the magnitude of the problem and on the other seem to indicate that auxin itself is used in one of the many enzyme reaction wheels that lead to the synthesis of new protoplasm.

While it is an established fact, it is not at all understood why the effect of auxin should be the reverse on the root, that is, the concentration of auxin which stimulates shoot growth inhibits rather than stimulates the growth of roots. This may be demonstrated many ways, as for instance by cutting off the tip of the root, where the auxin is produced, and then the root increases its growth. And an easy way to curb the increase is to place an agar block containing auxin on the amputated surface at the end of the root.

These effects of auxin on the root and shoot are reflected in the response to light and to gravity. The shoot will curve toward light, and Went showed that if an *Avena* coleoptile tip is illuminated from one side, the auxin is destroyed on the light side and accumulates to a greater extent on the darker side. This unequal production of auxin causes the dark side of the plant to grow faster and the whole shoot will therefore curve towards the light. For the root the argument runs much the same except that the effect of the auxin is reversed; the tip grows away from the light rather than toward it. As for the response to gravity, the root of course grows downward and the shoot away from the center of the earth. Again it is assumed that this must be the result of the differential response to

[13] Reviewed by Thimann (1949).

auxin between root and shoot, but it is not clear how such a small molecule as indole acetic acid could respond to gravity. The fact is that in the shoot, for instance, the auxin accumulates on the lower side causing more growth there and creating an upward curve.

Of special interest to us is the question of apical dominance. If one examines the branch of a tree, the tip of the branch grows very actively. In the crotch above each leaf there are small axillary buds which are potential growth points, potential apical meristems, but they stand in abeyance as long as the apical meristem in the branch tip is active. But if the apical bud is removed, then one or in some cases two or more of the axillary buds will begin to swell and become active apical buds. This process is again tied up with auxin, for if the active apical bud is removed and auxin is applied to the tip in its place, then the axillary buds remain dormant. For some unknown reason, the presence of indole acetic acid itself has the power to do this, and once the substance is gone, the latent abilities of the buds are unchained. This dominance of the apex is not held to the same degree by all plants, and this difference of degree can alter the shape in ways easy to predict, for the greater the dominance, the greater the suppression of lateral branches. A conifer (a Christmas tree) which rises like a spire has a large amount, while a scrubby bush possesses little apical dominance. Gardeners have for centuries known of apical dominance, for the way to make a hedge thick is to clip it frequently so that many axillary buds will grow, and even in the case of trees, "topping" is often used for the same purpose. A similar phenomenon is found in roots, and we find tap roots and great bushy, scraggly roots.[14] Were it only known how the auxin inhibits the other buds, and therefore in what way the different species of plants differ, then we would be far along the road of understanding correlations of growth in different plant forms.

There are a few more effects of auxin that must be in-

[14] See Torrey (1950) for an experimental study of lateral root formation.

cluded. While the growth of roots is inhibited by auxin, the initiation of root primordia from a stem cutting is stimulated by auxin. It is, therefore, common practice now, in the propagation of plants from stem cuttings, to immerse the cuttings for some hours in a solution of indole acetic acid before placing them in the damp sand or soil. Auxin is also involved in the dropping off, or abscission, of leaves of deciduous plants. There is the "abcission layer" at the base of the leaf petiole which does not in any way separate provided auxin is passing through the petiole, and this is so during all the summer months when the leaf is healthy and synthesizing auxin among its many other metabolic activities. But come the first tinges of frost in the fall which paralyzes the enzymatic machinery (or mere old age will do the same thing), the auxin goes, the abscission layer tears apart, and the leaf falls. By applying auxin at the distal end of the petiole it is possible to prevent abscission, showing again that it is in fact auxin which is responsible. Finally I should mention that auxin is involved in the development of the fruit, and this may be shown by applying auxin to the ovary and obtaining growth without fertilization. It is quite easy to obtain in this way parthenocarpic tomatoes, cucumbers, peppers, watermelons, etc. But the exact role of auxin in the growth of the fruit itself is not known, and this is unfortunate for it would be most interesting to know the relation between auxin activity and fruit growth.

There is no doubt that auxin controls growth, and as far as the whole plant is concerned it must play a major role in governing its shape. However, when the growth hormone was first discovered it was imagined to be the whole answer, and the strange thing is that the more that was discovered of its manifold effects, the more it became obvious that auxin alone in no way satisfactorily explains the control of growth in the whole organism, although it does clear a great vista of understanding. The point is there is one agent, one common stimulus, but its effects depend on the part that responds; it is the specificity of the response of different parts of the plant that gives the plant its characteristic shape. It is quite true that the different parts react to only one stimulus, auxin, and it is therefore a master controlling agent, but what good is a master key without any doors to open; and here we must consider everything, the key and the many doors. Another analogy may be even more helpful. Imagine a garden in an arid country (and this garden is the whole organism). In it are planted a great variety of different flowers (which are the different parts of the organism with their specific differences). By carefully controlling where the water (which is the auxin) will fall, with the use of a garden hose, it is possible to bring forth some plants from the soil and keep others still dormant. It is even possible by overly saturating some areas to inhibit the plants if they are of a species that requires little water. In this way the shape of the whole garden is determined by the water, its distribution, and the types of specific flowers and their distribution. In the growth of plants there are the analogous determining elements, the limiting substance, auxin, its distribution, the specific responses and the location of the responses in particular parts of the plants. The shape of the garden is quite satisfactorily explained in terms of the character of various flowers, and of the gardener who planted them in specific places, as well as the effect of water on plants and the human will that guides the hose. But we fail to see how a plant derived from one single egg has achieved such differences in its parts. This really is a question of differentiation and therefore will be considered again in a later chapter, but here it bears directly on the problem of the control of growth. There also is the similar matter of the specific distribution of the sites of auxin production; another spatial problem, a problem of distribution of structures and functions within the space of the organism, that leaves us mystified. Again and again, at every turn, with every new example, we are faced with the fact that developmental processes are controlled and regulated within living organisms in a spatial configuration that respects the whole, and I believe that this aspect of development is the one in most need of a micro-theory.

Before leaving the subject of growth in higher plants there are a few other matters which show that by no means have all the aspects of growth been considered. In the first place, there are other substances besides auxin which limit growth, such as various vitamins which are produced in the leaf and are essential for the growth of the root, and other substances produced in the root which presumably limit the growth of the shoot.[15] In fact, it is thought that these two factors complement each other so that there is no great disproportion in size between the root and the shoot of any plant. Also the older leaves give off adenine, which is known to promote the growth of the younger leaves. Finally the leaves, stimulated by certain critical durations of daylight and darkness will produce the flowering hormone which alters the bud into a flower. There is really, then, a community of substances within the plant which stimulate and limit growth, but auxin far outshines the others in importance.

At this particular juncture I should like to shift the whole line of discussion from plants to animals. There has been no good reason why examples should have been taken first from plants to illustrate how growth is controlled, and the only reason that they have not been discussed simultaneously is that this might have been too unwieldy and might have obscured the argument. I believe firmly that it is wrong to talk of any major living activity such as development without considering both the plants and the animals (and the great hordes of algae and protozoa that lie somewhere between). It is one thing to study the development of one plant or one animal, for after all the number of experiments any one man can do in a lifetime is quite limited, but if one is to draw conclusions about development in general there is no excuse for setting such limits. There certainly is no reason why

[15] An excellent short review which includes this material is F. W. Went (1943).

we cannot talk of development in animals, or even limit ourselves to the development from eggs, or even, as Spemann did, to the embryology of the amphibian, for certainly this has been done in the past with great profit. But the point is that by comparing the development of larger and larger groups of organisms it is possible, simply by letting the comparison itself be the experiment, to find the common denominators of the developments of all forms.

Then let us consider animals, and yet keep close to what we have just said. The problems of control of growth by hormones will deserve some attention. This is again, like so many of the subjects touched upon here, a vast subject, a science within itself, the science of endocrinology. But for our purposes there are but a few essential facts and these alone should be plucked and mentioned briefly. In the first place only those hormones which affect growth concern us, and of these the growth hormone of the pituitary gland is the most important.

The pituitary, located at the base of the brain, has no parallel in the plant world, for here in this small body is a master controlling mechanism. It is rare, for instance, to find a hormone of another gland whose production is not stimulated and controlled by a specific hormone of the pituitary. There is, as is well known, a most elaborate interconnection between all the endocrine glands, and the pituitary is (without challenge) the headquarters, the control room. Among the hormones produced by the pituitary there is the "growth" hormone. The quantities of its secretion directly affect the quantity of growth; in fact Marx, Simpson, and Evans (1942) have obtained experimentally a good correlation between the amount of growth hormone injected and the amount of growth. This suggests that, like auxin, the growth hormone may actually be involved in some synthetic growth reaction and its effect is not simply that of starting a reaction which propels itself, but rather the hormone is part of the reaction.[16]

[16] Went and Thimann (1937) at the very end of their book make just this point for the action of auxin.

In human beings an insufficient amount of growth hormone produces midgets, and an excess produces giants. Because different parts of the body grow at different rates the pituitary dwarfs and giants do not have the same proportions and appear quite different in their general structure. Midgets may be cured, if discovered soon enough, by the injection of the growth hormone, but there is no known way as yet of preventing gigantism. One of the most interesting aspects of excess secretion is when the excess starts at or close to maturity. Then most of the growing regions of the bones have gone and the bones are fixed in length. But a few, especially those of the jaw, the fingers and some others are still capable of growth and the sudden gush of growth hormone spurs them on to renewed activity. The consequence is a considerable distortion of the human body and is known as acromegaly.

The thyroid also independently limits growth, for infants deficient in thyroid become cretins, dwarfs of peculiar crimped features. Here, unlike the pituitary growth hormone, the substance responsible is known, and it is thyroxin. This substance is intimately bound up with and necessary for cellular respiration and it is no wonder that its absence stunts growth. But an excess of thyroxin does not give gigantism, but instead has other effects centered around excessively high metabolic activity.

The secretions of the gonads are responsible for the secondary sex characters and these often involve growth. In the human male the growth of hair, and antlers in deer are good examples, and in the female the growth of mammary glands. But these are rather specialized types of growth and probably the overall size differences between sexes are not a result of sex hormones, but instead of a hereditary difference.

There are some obvious sharp differences between the way plant growth hormones and animal growth hormones operate. In plants there is primarily one substance which has a great variety of different effects, sometimes one the reverse of another, on different parts of the plants. Auxin is produced in different regions, but even the main source, the apical meristem, changes constantly as it grows. In animals there is also primarily one hormone, but its effect is rather uniform throughout, that of promoting growth. The only time its effects become markedly differential is when, in acromegaly, certain growing regions have become solidified into bone and have lost their capacity to grow while others continue to do so. Also the site of production of the growth hormone is at one place, a fixed structure that is not a meristem. If we look now mainly at the similarities in animals and plants, the common denominators, there is the fact that both have mainly one substance. It is probably false to imagine that all the tissues of a mammal respond equally to the growth hormone; for as we said before, and will have occasion to repeat later, the different parts of the body grow at different rates, and the proportions of a midget differ from those of a giant. There is then a specificity of response, a specific growth rate, so in fact there is a very broad, basic common denominator in these two extremely divergent groups. There are some lesser similarities also; the limiting effect of thyroxin might well be compared to the limiting effect of adenine, or the vitamins, or the root factor which limited the growth of the shoot. And also the growth-promoting effects of the gonads certainly bear much resemblance to the flowering hormone. The generalized picture of hormone control of growth in higher plants and animals has converged to the extent that there are relatively few substances upon which the ultimate control is completely dependent, and which cause certain regions to perform their specific tasks. The fact that all these manifold tasks of all the different parts of the organism work together to form one organism is immeasurably helped, but not explained, by the presence of such master hormones.

If plants and animals are compared in other ways it would appear at first glance that one of the unique features of plants is the meristem and that there is no real counterpart of this among animals. The fact is, however, that animals have rather perfect meristems, although they are not normally called that by zoologists. Before giving the best examples it might be well to examine the growth of certain colonial ciliates which already have been used as examples of growth forms involving localized adhesives. As has been said, meristematic activity gives rise to an accretionary type of growth, and also in the case of the ciliates the mucilaginous branching stalks are accretions. So in such forms as some species of *Epistylis* (Fig. 29) where all the cells divide equally abundantly, the row of advancing cells with respect to the whole colony, gives a perfect model of a meristem. It is only a model because all the living parts grow equally fast; there is no division of this labor. In *Zoothamnium* (Fig. 29) there are, as its tree-like form suggests, certain cells which divide and grow actively, and others that do not. The apical cell of the whole colony gives rise, after every division, to a branch; that is, both of its daughter cells continue to divide. One of these cells becomes the terminal branch cell, and it also continues to be meristematic, cutting off the branch cells which ordinarily do not possess the capacity to divide. So there is here a real division of the labor of growing, and it may be considered a meristem, although admittedly rather a rudimentary one.

It was Fauré-Fremiet (1930) who postulated that there were specific cell-division inducing substances that were retained by the apical and terminal branch cells, and not passed on to the branch cells. This hypothesis seemed most reasonable until the work of Summers (1938a,b), who showed that no such simple mechanism could account for this segregation of growth activity. He performed a series of experiments in which he cut off the apical cell, and the terminal branch cells, in fact even parts of the branches; and the existing cells, instead of continuing their old role, became modified and took on new functions so that the integrity of the whole colony was retained. If the apical cell was removed, the terminal branch cell of the uppermost branch assumed the function of the apical cell and began to cut off new branches. If the apical cell and the terminal branch cells were removed, then two things might occur; most often the branch cell just below the amputated terminal branch cell became the new apical cell; in other cases the terminal branch cell of the second branch became the apical cell. In cases where the colony was transected through the middle, the large presumptive migrant cilio-spores became the apical cells. The extraordinary thing here is that not only is *Zoothamnium* tree-like in appearance, and possesses an elementary meristem, but like higher plants it possesses apical dominance. However, in the plants there is auxin and it is known that the presence of auxin somehow inhibits the lateral buds (which would be analogous to the branch cells). In *Zoothamnium* there is not even any such a beginning of an explanation. The cells are connected by the mucilaginous sheath and by the contractile thread which lies in the center of the sheath, and it is quite possible that a chemical substance might, like auxin, pass from one group of cells to another, but until such a substance is demonstrated the matter is purely speculative. The work of Summers is especially interesting in that it shows how highly coordinated the growth patterns may be in what were imagined to be very loose and primitive colonies.[17]

Meristems of an even more definite and clear-cut nature are found in the coelenterates, especially the colonial hydroids. Again it is not surprising to find that the forms that they achieve closely resemble plant forms. A few elementary words should first be said of the structure of hydroids. To begin with, the fresh water *Hydra* itself is shaped like a vase, that is it has only one alimentary opening and this is surrounded by a corolla of tentacles. In cross section the whole body is seen to be made up of three layers: the ectoderm, the endoderm, and the thin middle layer or mesoglea. In the colonial forms a whole group of hydras are, to put the matter crudely, hooked together on a piping system, so that in *Obelia*, for instance,

[17] See Fauré-Fremiet (1925) on the various colony patterns of colonial ciliates.

at the base of each hydra or hydranth (or polyp), the gastro-intestinal cavity narrows into a hollow tube, which is connected to all the other hydranths in the colony. It is a communal intestine, where the meal of some fortunate polyp may be shared by his relatives (Fig. 44).

Recently it has been shown by P. Brien and M. Reniers-Decoen (1949) that *Hydra* itself grows in a meristematic fashion and that new cells are continuously laid down at the anterior or hypostomal end (Fig. 45). While the over-all length of an individual remains approximately the same, it grows continuously at one end and degenerates continuously at the other. The buds of young individuals that arise during the course of asexual reproduction give another instance of localized growth zones in *Hydra*. It is especially interesting that the buds appear successively at approximately 120° from one another descending the main axis of the parent, giving no less than a perfect "phyllotaxis" comparable to the leaf spirals found in higher plants (Fig. 46).[18] This is the first example (and more will follow) that shows that similar growth mechanisms, such as the meristem in this case, tend to give similar growth patterns.

As Kühn (1909) showed, these colonial forms also possess meristems, and if they are to be classified on the basis of their meristems, there are three main types. From a phylogenetic point of view, Libbie Hyman (1940) considers the most primitive to be those which possess what amounts to an intercalary meristem. Below each hydranth there is a growing zone which is capable not only of elongating but also of giving off new buds. This so-called monopodial form gives rise to successive ramifying branches, and *Pennaria* and *Tubularia* are good examples of this growth pattern (Fig. 47,A). The growth zone itself leads continuously from the base of one hydranth to the base of the new hydranth that it forms, so there is never any cessation or interruption of its activity. Since the zone is below the hydranths, this has the peculiar result that the terminal

---

[18] For other examples of "phyllotaxis" in coelenterates see Komai (1951).

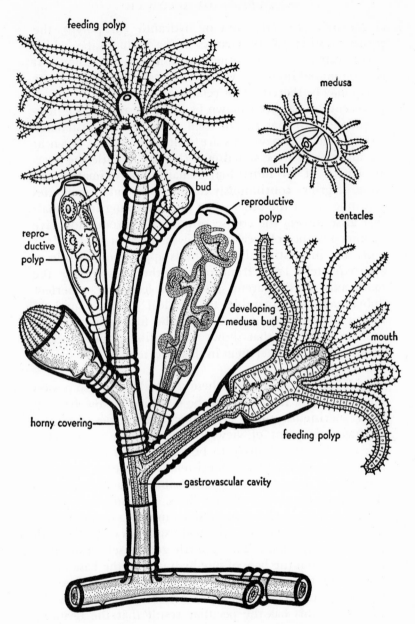

FIG. 44. Diagrammatic view of a colony of *Obelia*. (From Buchsbaum, Animals without Backbone, Chicago, 1938.)

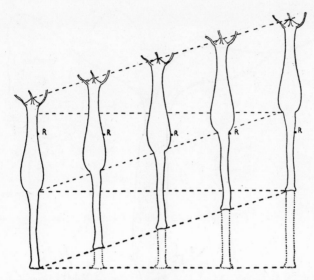

Fig. 45. Diagram illustrating the growth of *Hydra*. If the point R is a marked group of cells it will have the position indicated at successive time intervals showing that the growth occurs in the region just below the tentacles, and that the degeneration and loss of cells occurs at the extreme basal end. (From Brien and Reniers-Decoen, 1949.)

hydranth of a colony is the original hydranth, the hydranth from which the whole colony stemmed. The meristem itself, with continuous branching, becomes further and further subdivided so that as the hydranths increase in number so do the meristems.

The sympodial form differs from the previous type by having what amounts to a discontinuous meristem. That is a meristem rises and disappears with the formation of each hydranth. At a certain stage in the growth of a hydranth there is a zone below it which begins to grow actively and produce a new hydranth, which again at a certain stage gives rise to a further growth zone just below it (Fig. 47,B). The colonies that arise by this method of growth are often zig-zag, such as *Halecium* (Fig. 48,A), and others may become more elaborate and form branches, such as *Obelia* (Fig. 44).

[123]

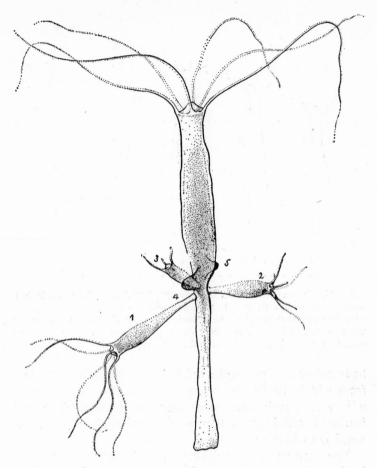

Fig. 46. A budding *Hydra* showing the spiral arrangement of asexual buds. (From Brien and Reniers-Decoen, 1949.)

The most advanced forms are those which have, precisely as plants do, an apical meristem (Fig. 47,C). These are most successful in the sea, in the sense that they give rise to the largest and most elaborate colonies. As the apical meristem advances it gives off buds which form lateral hydranths, and also it produces buds that remain meristematic and these become the lateral branches which in turn

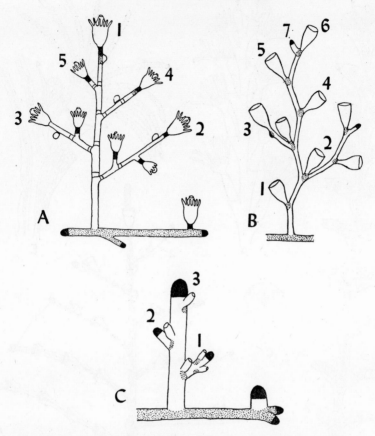

FIG. 47. Diagrams showing growth patterns in different hydroids. A, monopodial; B, sympodial; C, apical growth. Black indicates an active growth zone, and the stippling indicates a region that either has produced a bud or is capable of budding. (Redrawn from Bloch, in Kükenthal and Krumbach's Handb. der Zool., 1923-25, after Kühn, 1909.)

give off hydranths. If the leaves are considered to be analogous to the hydranths, the situation is quite parallel to that found in plants, again presumably because in both cases the growth is meristematic. There are cases where the hydranths clearly alternate, such as in *Plumularia* (Fig. 48,D), and others such as *Sertularia* (Fig. 48,B) where the hydranths arise in pairs and lie opposite one another.

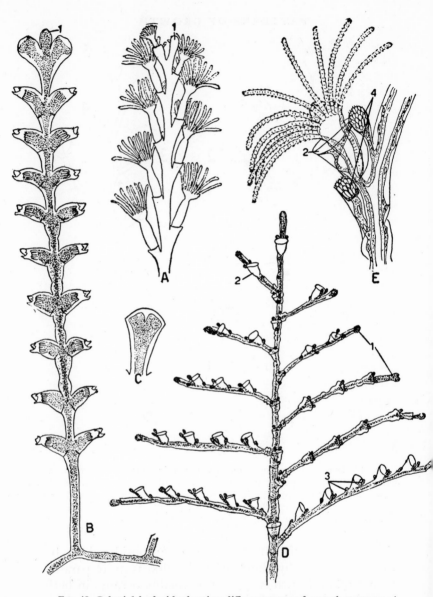

Fig. 48. Colonial hydroids showing different types of growth patterns. A, a branch end of *Halecium* showing sympodial growth; B, a branch of *Sertularia* showing dichotomous branching with an apical meristem; C, the growing point of *Sertularia* showing the beginning of dichotomy; D, *Plumularia*, showing apical meristems, E, a feeding polyp or hydranth of *Plumularia* surrounded by protective polyps; 1, a growing point; 2, hydrotheca; 3, 4, protective polyps. (From Hyman, 1940.)

The variety of shapes achieved by this type of meristem is great, for the problem is the same as that of the shape of plants, which may be varied depending on the type of branching and the position of the leaves.

There are no rigid cell walls in hydroids; the cells are typical of an animal, yet from this come devices and patterns of growth which are quite similar to those which arose independently in plants. It was said before, when meristems of plants were discussed, that meristems are but one of a number of methods of growth, and we are interested in meristems here because by examining the different ways growth does its work, we may perhaps understand what kinds of control would be required. Here again there is a need to find out how certain specific areas are designated meristematic, and how the direction of the growth of the meristems is controlled. For clearly by varying the location of the meristem and its direction of growth it would be possible to build all the different types of colonial hydroids that now exist, and many more.

In the filamentous algae and especially among the fungi a number of cases were given where the growth form was a result of the interlacing of many filaments which gave one aggregate pattern. In the hydroids there is a striking parallel, for certain forms are not made up of a single branching stalk or stolon, but a bundle of stolons. *Hydractinia* is a good example of a type where there is the least degree of organization of the mass of stolons. It is found on the shells of gastropods which are inhabited by hermit crabs and the stolon mass itself lies flat over the surface of the shell, like a covering of smooth dense moss. The small white hydranths rise up from this as though they were delicate bits of frost. The aggregate itself is no more than a mat of intertwined stolons. But in some forms the stolons are all more or less parallel and the mass has a definite finger-like shape. In others the stem appears quite thin and the stolons are tightly packed to form a perfect bundle. It is strange that such widely different structures as the plant filament and the hydroid stolon should produce similar types, the former being a linear series of cells or a multi-nucleate hard-walled filament, and the latter a multi-cellular hollow filament composed of ectoderm, endoderm, and mesoglea.

There are other kinds of animals besides the hydroids which show meristematic growth. Perhaps the best examples are the growth of bones, shells, and horns; for, as we have said, meristematic growth is accretionary growth and resembles simple rather than compound interest. The case of the horn of the rhinoceros has been used both by D'Arcy Thompson (1942) and by J. S. Huxley (1932) to illustrate the mechanism whereby the logarithmic spiral is achieved. A spiral differs from a helix or screw in that the radius of curvature constantly increases as one leads away from its center. For a logarithmic spiral this may be expressed in a more precise mathematical way, and for this and all the various geometric properties of the logarithmic spiral, the reader must consult D'Arcy Thompson. To return to the rhinoceros, whose horn is nothing else but a tuft of hair cemented together into a firm mass, the question arises, how is it that this horn curves to form a logarithmic spiral? To achieve this shape there are two requirements: one that the base which is actively involved with the deposition must become progressively larger. This alone will produce a cone-shaped accretion. The other requirement is a growth gradient, a gradient in the rate of deposition. In the rhinoceros the anterior end deposits at a faster rate than the posterior end, and this difference gives the horn its backward curve. The shell of the cephalopod *Nautilus* is laid down in the same way, that is it is secreted at the edge of the animal, at a faster rate on the upper and outer surface than on the inner surface, and as the *Nautilus* eats, it grows larger; and therefore the diameter of the area of deposition progressively increases. In the case of gastropods where the shell is not only a logarithmic spiral, but also comes off at an angle, or in the case of the horn of a ram which also winds outward, the growth gradient is no longer a simple uni-directional one, but has two components, a steep gradient in one direction and a less severe one at right angles to it (Fig. 49).

Although a great many accretionary growths are logarithmic spirals, by no means all are. There is, for instance, the curious and anomalous case of the tusk of the narwhal which is absolutely straight, having only screw-like grooves

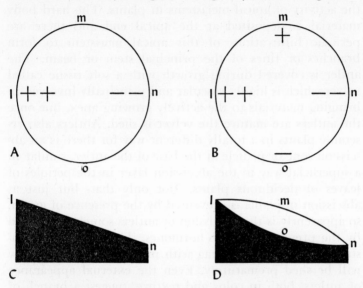

FIG. 49. Diagram to illustrate the growth gradients operating to produce the plane and the turbinate shells of molluscs. In A the growth gradient is from l to n only, giving C in a lateral view. In B there is a double gradient giving D in a lateral view. (Drawn from Huxley, 1932.)

running down its length. It is really the case of the cone in which there is a complete absence of a growth gradient; just an enlargement of the pulp which deposits the tooth. The whole problem of the narwhal's tusk, which is also the horn of the unicorn, makes a fascinating subject, but unfortunately this is not the place for it.[19] The point here is that within a limited range it is possible to produce accretions of various different shapes. It so happens that a great many accretions in animals have the fundamental

[19] Bonner, 1949.

[129]

character of a tube, or a rod, and by varying the diameter of the area of deposition and the growth gradients of deposition it is possible to produce a considerable variety of shapes.

The annual formation of antlers in deer (see Noback and Modell, 1930; Wislocki, 1942) parallels in some ways the activity of apical meristems in plants. The hard bony material is deposited at the apical end and there are periodic bifurcations of this apical meristem to form branches or tines of the principal stem or beam. The antler is covered during growth with a soft tissue called velvet which is highly vascular and principally involved in bringing materials to the actively growing apex, but once the antlers are mature the velvet is shed. Antlers also resemble plants in a totally different way for there is an abscission zone or pedicle at the base of the antler, similar in a superficial way to the abscission layer in the petioles of leaves of deciduous plants. Not only that, but just as abscission in plants is prevented by the presence of auxin, so apparently is the abscission of antlers somehow affected by the presence of male hormones. This can be demonstrated by castrating a stag with mature antlers, and they will be shed prematurely. Even the external appearance of antlers, both in color and texture, suggest a branch of a denuded woody plant, and, in fact, for many centuries the French have called deer antlers *"bois de cerf"* showing that this analogy between plants and antlers is hardly novel, although it may be more subtle than the early hunters imagined it.

While accretions in animals are rather specialized and are not too general in their occurrence (with the notable exception of bone and exoskeletons), growth gradients which are found in many of them are most common. They might be considered as a substitute for a meristem, or perhaps the degeneration of a meristem, a case where the growth is no longer sharply localized but simply has some regions which are more active than others with gentle gradations between them.

The matter of growth gradients seems to have been quite definitely recognized by Aristotle, who states in a number of passages in *De Generatione Animalium* the general principle of antero-posterior development, that is that the anterior parts of the body often grow faster than the posterior parts. He says, for instance, "First the parts above the hypozoma are differentiated and are superior in size; the part below is both smaller and less differentiated."[20] There have been in recent years many studies which not only support this view but supply figures to make the fact even more satisfying.

There are many instances in the development from the egg where the growth rate is different in different parts of the embryo. For instance in the amphibian, Bragg (1938) measured the mitotic activity in different regions and found that in the early development the cells at the animal pole divided at a consistently higher rate. This is undoubtedly correlated with the presence of yolk, for the yolk lies nearer the vegetal end where the cleavage is slower.

It is difficult, if not impossible, to attribute the form of these developing embryos entirely to growth gradients and differences in growth rate, because all embryologists now agree that the mass cell movements or morphogenetic movements are in many instances (at least in the early development) extremely important. Cell movements are something quite different from growth and they will be discussed in a separate chapter. But there are many instances in animal embryology where the shape is thought to be primarily the result of differential growth; one such is the growth of the optic vesicle from the neural tube in amphibians.

It has been shown that in the neural tube, in the region of the optic vesicles, mitosis becomes suddenly very active, and in fact there is a perfect correlation between mitotic activity and the opticle vesicle formation.[21] The mitoses

[20] 741b.
[21] See Weiss (1939) for a general discussion and references, especially to the work of G. M. Frank.

themselves are tangential to the surface of the tube, so that the vesicles come off in two flat fingers, one on each side. There apparently is little or no cell movement here, and the entire shape is a growth shape.

In his book on relative growth, Huxley (1932) devotes some attention to the problem of growth gradients, giving a number of excellent examples which I shall briefly mention here. He points out that the crustaceans are especially suited for study, for their skeleton (their armor plate) comes in pieces, each one of which can readily be measured. The body segments themselves are useful and even the lengths of the antennae or leg segments do admirably. In both these cases it is sometimes found that segments nearest one end grow faster, and the rate tapers off as one approaches the other end, but in other cases (like the formation of optic vesicles on the nerve cord) the growth center is somewhere in between and tapers off to both ends.

The whole subject of growth gradients brings us directly into the work and the ideas of C. M. Child (1941), who has championed for so long the importance in development of gradients. His great contribution has been to establish the empirical fact that metabolic gradients do exist in nearly all developing organisms—plants and animals, cryptogamic and vascular, invertebrate and vertebrate. His methods have varied; the early work was done by placing the organism in lethal solutions of cyanide and observing the course of destruction. The argument was that cyanide is an inhibitor of respiration, of metabolism, and therefore those parts which disintegrated first were carrying on the most active metabolism. This method was criticized for it was felt that the method was too crude, too brutal, and did the differential deaths of different parts really reflect their activity while living? Child then began a similar series of studies with vital dyes, such as methylene blue or janus green, which have a color reaction upon oxidation and in this way it was again argued that those regions which are most active metabolically will oxidize and alter the color of the dye first. There is still some discussion of the exact meaning of the color changes in the dye with respect to the metabolism, but it is now generally agreed that metabolic gradients do exist and are, as Child has shown, very widespread. For particular organisms or parts of organisms there are a number of cases where it has been impossible to establish any evidence of a gradient, but these are not so frequent as to impair Child's empirical principle.

Growth itself, the synthesis of new living material, quite obviously depends on metabolism and it is reasonable to expect that high metabolic activity might in some cases be correlated with high growth rates. Since our concern is the control of growth the question here is how are the growth gradients determined, how are they laid out. Child himself has a very definite theory; he believes that the whole explanation of development lies within these metabolic differences. Quantitative differences of various substances which must necessarily result from such metabolic differences account for all the differential growth and differentiation. I have no argument with the idea of small differences in the amount of any one substance creating all sorts of differences that might result in differentiation; this is an hypothesis that seems plausible and reasonable to me, but the question here is how are the quantitative differences established in the first place. It is one thing to say that water runs down a hill because the hill is inclined, and it is another to explain why the hill is inclined. Every step we take drives us back to the problem of the spatial arrangements within the organism and here we now ask what is the cause of the distribution of metabolic gradients. Child does not leave this matter entirely unanswered; he suggests in some cases that it might be the immediate environment (a note which we have already sounded) and that for instance if a developing organism is sitting on the bottom of a dish, the upper side will have more oxygen than the lower, and once this establishes a metabolic difference between the upper and lower side, it is easy to see how the condition may be maintained. He uses here his concept of "dominance" to signify the ability of an active region to maintain its supremacy and subordinate the surrounding territories. We already have talked of apical dominance, and I cannot see that there are any great difficulties in understanding how such a mechanism might operate, although we do not know any of the real details of the process. But it seems to me impossible to attribute all the many growth configurations that we have talked of as being ultimately determined by the environment. It may be that this will explain many simple cases, such as the direction of growth in the *Fucus* egg, but there are many others so vastly complex that they belie this. Quite obviously there must be some mechanism whereby certain growth gradients, and for that matter the locations of certain meristems, are controlled intrinsically within the organism, and the very fact that these growth patterns are so constant from generation to generation indicates that the genes are involved somewhere. I do not in any way want to dwarf Child's contribution, for I admire it greatly, but it does not seem to be *all* of the problem.

One of the difficulties in the matter of growth gradients has been to describe the changes that come from such a differential growth. D'Arcy Thompson, who based his method on that of Albrecht Dürer, evolved the well-known system of cartesian transformations whereby related forms could be compared in a beautiful and simple manner. The process consists merely of drawing rectangular coordinates through the two-dimensional representation of any shape, and then drawing the same coordinate through the homologous points of the related shape (Fig. 50). The modifications of the shapes are entirely reflected by the bending of the coordinates, and at a glance the general distribution of the growth gradients, at least in two dimensions, is apparent. Few attempts have been made to apply this to the growth of any one organism, the work of Richards and Riley (1937) being an exception; but instead it has been used mainly to compare members of related species. As

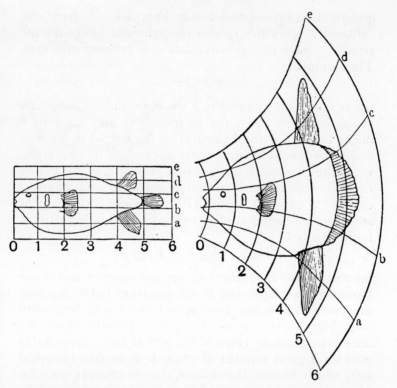

F~IG.~ 50. Cartesian transformation of the outline of the fish *Diodon* (left) to give the outline of the sun-fish *Orthagoriscus* (right). (From Thompson, 1942.)

Huxley (1932) points out, there are problems involved in the handling of these coordinates mathematically, and only in the simplest cases is it possible, for otherwise it becomes hopelessly cumbersome. I do not doubt, though, with the recent interest in applications of mathematics to biology, that there will be some day very elegant methods of describing the transformations of growth.

Just as the method of cartesian transformations are purely descriptive, so is the method of Huxley and Teissier[22] which has been called the formula of heterogonic

[22] See Huxley (1932) for references.

growth, heterauxesis, and now by international agreement, "allometric growth." It also concerns and compares the relative growth of different parts of a growing organism. The formula is

$$y = bx^k$$

where b and k are constants, x the magnitude of some part of the organism and y the magnitude of another part. x might be the length of the arm or the weight of an arm, and y the length of some other appendage or its weight, while the constant k is the actual growth rate. All that is necessary is to compare in similar units two separate structures of a growing body. This equation has the great advantage of being readily convertible to a logarithmic form, that is

$$\log y = \log b + k \log x$$

for then if the logarithms of the quantities y and x are plotted on a graph, and if the equation holds, the line must be a straight one, the slope of which is k, the growth rate (Fig. 51). In this way it has been possible to test the allometric formula empirically, and it holds remarkably well for a great number of cases. It is an odd historical fact, which Evelyn Hutchinson (1948) remarks on, that Huxley was by his own admission greatly influenced by D'Arcy Thompson's cartesian transformations in the conception of allometry, but in his 1942 edition of *Growth and Form*, D'Arcy Thompson barely mentions this whole subject and when he does he rather severely criticizes and dismisses it on the basis that the formula fits too few cases. As much as I admire *Growth and Form*, I do not think this particular point is justified. The astonishing fact is that not only does the allometric formula fit many cases, but it fits a wide diversity of cases. It encompasses weight and length measurements from all the major groups of animals, as well as comparisons of parts of higher plants; it has been used, and J. Needham (1942) gives a plethora of examples, in chemical studies of growth to compare the increase of amount of some particular substance with the

[136]

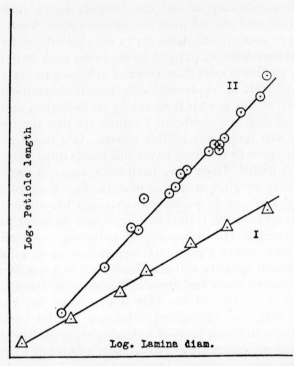

Fig. 51. Graph showing the increase of the logarithm of petiole length plotted against the logarithm of the blade diameter in *Nasturtium* leaves. (From Pearsall, Ann. Bot. *41*, 1927.)

wet or dry weight, or with the amount of another substance. The rule is to find a good fit and a straight line plot, the exception is to have irregular bumps and curves on the graph.

The problem that immediately emerges is that of the meaning of the equation. There are some obvious things such as the fact that all that one is comparing here is the rate of increase in size of two different parts. If the parts grew at precisely the same rate, k would equal 1. It is the size itself that is being compared, not the length of time required to reach a certain size. The problem that is more bothersome, and one which has come up a number of times, is whether or not the formula has a biological meaning, and can we from the formula alone learn something new of growth. It seems to me that all the formula says is that different parts of an organism grow at different rates, and these rates show constant relations to one another, and this is expressed with beautiful mathematical brevity. If this is what is meant by its biological meaning, then all well and good, but I cannot see that the formula alone will reveal any hidden secrets. As a description of relative growth it has no rivals and this is quite enough to keep it useful. There have been some attempts to explain allometry by comparison to models. The work of Robb (1929) is a case in point, and although his suggestion is purely speculative, it does help to obtain a clearer picture of allometry. He makes use of partition coefficients in chemistry, where a substance, depending on its solubility in different solvents, will distribute itself in a specific ratio, say, between water and ether in a separatory funnel. This is only a model and the idea is that some key growth-promoting, growth-limiting substance divides itself unequally in different parts of a developing organism and in this way stimulates growth to occur at a faster rate in some regions than in others. Immediately we are faced with the old problem of how there can be a consistent unequal distribution of chemicals within the body. It may be that the growth-promoting substance is equally distributed, and the affinity of the tissue for this substance varies, and we are back to differences in different parts without beginning to explain whence they came.

Among the most fascinating aspects of allometry are the instances where the formula applies only for the adult animal, and where during regeneration the formula is far askew. In fact, the process of regeneration itself seems to be one in which the stable proportions are sought as rapidly as possible. One of the best instances of this is Huxley's example of the antlers of deer. Antlers are shed annually; and by an elaborate process, which is essentially a regeneration, new antlers are grown. If the logarithm of the body weight of the deer is plotted against the logarithm of the weight of the hard mature antlers, the curve is a good straight one with a constant k (Fig. 52). During the development of the antlers each season, their growth must be extremely fast in order to catch up with the slowly growing body weight. In fact, during one antler-growing season it is possible to follow the changes in k, which first

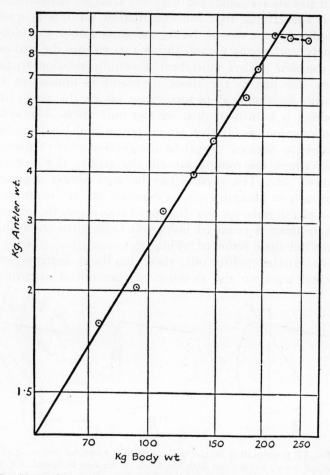

FIG. 52. Mature antler weight plotted against body weight in 527 adult red deer, plotted logarithmically. (From Huxley, Proc. Zool. Soc., 1931.)

are very high when the antler growth is most rapid in the beginning, and then it tapers off to the normal value between mature antlers and body weight. The point is that each year the antler growth stops at just the point where the antler weight is proportional (to the k power) of the body weight. There is then some sort of mechanism whereby the size is limited very accurately so that the final size always comes out with the same allometric ratio. It is conceivable that the explanation for this is quite simple, that the size of the regenerating stump, the blood supply, and all the various things that go into the making of the new antlers must bear a definite relation to the body size just as the shoot in plants is limited in its growth by chemical factors given off in the root. But nothing is known of this; we can only guess. The same phenomenon, as Huxley (1932) points out, has been observed by Abeloos (1932) in the regeneration of planarians, where the more removed, the greater the recovery growth rate. The process can be seen almost diagrammatically in Morgan's (1901) experiments on the amputation of fish tails, for if a diagonal cut is made, the regions where more is removed bulge out faster than those that have but little removed (Fig. 53).

As Huxley points out, there has been some experimental work on the problem of the control of growth

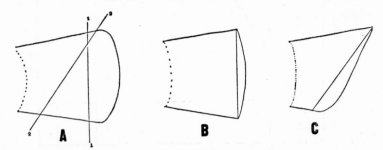

Fig. 53. Regeneration in the tail of the fish, *Fundulus heteroclitus.* A, the tail before amputation with the levels of the cuts indicated. B,C the regeneration after cutting. Note that the fastest regeneration occurs where the greatest amount of material has been removed. (From Morgan, 1901.)

rates, mainly by Twitty and also by Harrison.[23] If the eyes of urodeles of different ages (and therefore of different sizes) were transplanted to hosts of the same species, Twitty found that depending on whether the eyes were too small or too large in relation to the host, their growth speeded up or slowed down so that soon all disparity in size disappeared. He presumes, on the basis of this and some further experiments, that the nutritive capacity of the blood rises with age while the assimilative capacity of a tissue decreases with time. In other experiments of Harrison where two different species of urodeles were used (one fast and the other slow growing) less perfect regulation of the sizes of transplanted eyes was obtained, but instead there were intermediate eye sizes between the tendencies of the host and the donor. It appears in this case that there is a genetically controlled growth rate characteristic of each species, and that even in the new environment this control still exerts some effect.

This brings us quite directly into the final aspect to be considered here concerning the control of growth; that is the control by genes, by the hereditary mechanism. More than with anybody else, this subject has become associated with the name of R. Goldschmidt, for he and his "physiological genetics" are of lasting importance in the field. Goldschmidt conceives of genes as being primarily the controllers of rates of processes; this is the core of his views. It is well known, and thoroughly substantiated in the spectacular advances of the genetics of the bread mold *Neurospora*, that genes are concerned with production of enzymes, although the relation between the genes and the enzymes is still hypothetical. Enzymes are catalysts, and from elementary chemistry we know that their specific function is to control the rate of processes. In his studies on the wing patterns of the butterfly *Lymantria*, Goldschmidt showed that the differences in pattern were directly a result of the differences in rate

[23] See Twitty (1940) for a general review of this subject and for references.

of different reactions involving pigmentation. These, in turn, were gene controlled, and the whole inherited pattern involves a coordinated set of reaction velocities.[24] Such a theory gives considerable insight into the question of why it is that certain tissues or parts of an organism have different growth rates than others, but it does not seem to explain entirely the spatial distribution of these properties. This is no criticism of the theory itself which, like the metabolic gradients of Child, helps to make some aspects of the control of growth understandable, but does not include the whole of it.

There are many examples of genes which control size itself and let us examine a few of these. There are, for instance, the large and small cucurbits of Sinnott (1931, 1935), who showed that there were certain genes concerned with size alone, irrespective of shape. These were most likely a series of multiple factors which are inherited in a blending fashion, and they assorted completely independently from the genes which affect the shape. For that matter it is quite an accepted fact that size is inherited in some way in humans, and we expect tall parents to bear tall children. This is the basis of selection of hogs by husbandrymen, and the reason why farmers in Idaho are so proud of their potatoes. There is also the phenomenon of heterosis or hybrid vigor, where two pure-bred strains, when crossed, will produce offspring of an even greater size than either of the parents, and this is the secret of hybrid corn. The mechanism of this vigor is not at all understood, but somehow the mixture of the foreign genotypes specially favors size in some cases.

There is a newly discovered and most interesting case of the limiting of size by a single gene in *Neurospora*. Ordinarily with the addition of new media this rapidly growing mold will have essentially unlimited growth. The usual method of observing and measuring the growth rate is to place the mold at one end of a long horizontal tube

---

[24] See de Beer (1940) for an excellent short discussion of Goldschmidt's work and the relation of genes to embryology.

containing nutrient agar. The distance covered by the mycelium is then measured at given time intervals, and in this way it may be shown that ordinary *Neurospora* keeps a constant forward rate. There is a certain mutant (called the *nd* mutant) that has been investigated by T. C. Sheng (1951) which has the characteristic of suddenly, at a given moment, stopping its growth in the growth tube. Even in liquid culture of unlimited nutrient the growth will suddenly stop. Without attempting to give all the many details of Sheng's experiments, let us say that he has good evidence that this does not simply involve the depletion of a given substance. It could be that a key substance is destroyed faster than it is synthesized until finally it falls below the threshold concentration, or it could be that there is an inhibitory mechanism initiated by the gene which builds up to a critical concentration. This case differs from others in that it is not a matter of a slower rate of growth, but rather a matter of a sudden stopping, and this stopping is controlled by one gene. There is no way of knowing if the situation in *Neurospora* is at all the same as in other forms, but it is true that some organisms, like normal *Neurospora*, appear to grow indefinitely; lobsters and other crustaceans, fish, turtles, alligators and crocodiles are all supposed to continue growing to some extent throughout their lives, and Went (1942) believes that the giant redwoods and Sequoias of California never cease to grow taller. Most other organisms have, like the *nd* mutant of *Neurospora*, a growth limit, a fixed mature size, and we ourselves are a case in point. Obviously, there are many external factors which may limit and stop growth, such as the exhaustion of food, and these we have already mentioned, but internal factors, specifically genes (in ways unknown) also do the job.

There are some good instances where genes affect the sizes of organisms by affecting the growth hormone. In plants there is the case of tall and dwarf corn studied by van Overbeek (1935). In production of auxin he found no difference between these two genetic varieties of corn;

they both produced an equal amount. But there was a great difference in the oxidative activity of the tissues, and he assumed that the reason for the different sizes is that in the dwarf corn the auxin is destroyed more rapidly, making a lower effective concentration of auxin. This is somewhat similar to the process of etiolation, where if plants are grown in the dark they become extremely long because light destroys the auxin. So again, although both the plant in the light and the plant in the dark produce the same amount of auxin, the latter has more effective auxin and therefore is much greater in size. There are also cases in animals where there are inherited discrepancies in the function of the endocrines. Especially obvious is the case of inherited pituitary dwarfism where there is an inherited paucity of growth hormone. The physical trait that is inherited is a deficiency in the pituitary gland itself, so this case differs from that of auxin dwarfs in plants in that here there is actually less hormone given off rather than a higher oxidative destruction.

One further matter concerning genes that affect increase in size alone is pertinent here. In some experiments on genes which affect the wing shape of the fruit-fly *Drosophila*, Goldschmidt (1938) found that he could get mutants which affected growth by cell division and growth by cell expansion differentially.[25] It will be remembered that in plants there is first a period of growth by cell division, followed by a period of cell expansion. The very same situation occurs in the development of the wing in *Drosophila*. The wing mutant gene *expanded* produces an excess of cell division in a certain direction without affecting the cell expansion, and the result is a broad flat wing. The wing mutant gene *miniature* prevents cell expansion, giving a wing just as its name suggests. It is possible by cross-breeding to obtain flies with both of these genes, and they have small, broad wings. This ex-

[25] Waddington (1940) corroborates Goldschmidt's views on these two effects, although he also finds great significance in the balloon stage and its subsequent contraction in shaping the final wing.

ample shows that the genes come in and control in places
where one would not have suspected them, and it gives
another hint of their rôle as the ultimate controllers.

Of much greater importance to us are the cases when
the genes affect the shape of the living structure by governing the direction of growth. We have already skirted past
some cases of this, the simplest of which is the direction
of the coiling in the snail *Limnaea*.[26] There, a single locus

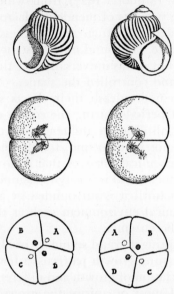

Fig. 54. *Top*: A sinistral and a dextral shell of the snail *Limnaea*. *Center*:
The spindle axes in the two cell stage are oblique, and in the opposite
direction for the sinistral and dextral snails. *Bottom*: Consequently the
cross-furrows and the cell order are also opposed in the sinistral and dextral forms. (From Huxley and de Beer, 1934, after Morgan.)

is involved and, depending on the gene present in the
locus, the coiling will be dextral or sinistral. The effect
of the gene is evident from the very early cleavages of the
egg, for these forms have a spiral cleavage, and the spiral
cleavage reflects the direction of the eventual coiling (Fig.
54).

[26] Boycott et al. (1930).

In cucurbits, Sinnott (1931, 1935) has also found genes which affect shape solely, and as we said before, they segregate independently of the genes which affect size. He found, for instance, that if he crossed a disc-shaped summer squash with one spherical in shape, the F_1 were totally discs, while the F_2 showed 3:1 segregation of discs over spheres (Sinnott, 1922). The flattening factors appeared dominant, and this was borne out in another series of experiments (Sinnott, 1927) from which he assumed that there were two sets of mendelian factors, a dominant one which tended to flatten, and a recessive one which tended to elongate. He found other instances that did not fit this scheme, but it was universally true that in some way genes affected and controlled the shape.

All genes do not unleash their effects simultaneously, but at different periods during the course of the development, and this also has its influence. A reason why this might be so is not hard to find, for there is a succession of events and chemical changes that follow one another during development, and it is easy to assume that a specific gene cannot act until it is surrounded by a desirable and responsive chemical environment such as the proper substrate for specific enzymes.

Before attempting a grand summary of all that has been discussed concerning growth patterns, a few words should be said of the relation of growth and differentiation. In the development of most organisms the growth, the increase in size, occurs simultaneously with the process of differentiation, the appearance of differences in the structure of parts, and to consider one without the other as we have done is somewhat artificial. Growth has been abstracted in this way so that the elements which go to make up development may be clearly delineated. But many of the factors which limit the patterns of growth overlap with those which limit differentiation, and until differentiation has also been discussed it is impossible to enter into the general subject of theories of development.

What we can do, however, is to seek those elements in

the patterning of growth that appear common to all organisms. It has been shown that patterns are delineated in
some of the simpler forms in a superficial way, by some
direct influence of the environment, and this is of importance mainly in that it can be removed and discarded
from the profound problem of growth controls which
seem to be self-contained within the organism. These controls, which we have sometimes called intrinsic pattern
limits, have a variety of ways in which they may mechanically operate—they may result in oriented cleavage planes
which are synonymous with the direction of growth; they
may operate within a uninucleate cell, among cells, within
large multinucleate masses or coenocytes, among loose
masses of filaments, among meristems; they may operate
with the assistance of growth hormones. The evidence is
mounting that for each one of these mechanical means
of expressing growth there is a genetic control. Even though
most of the steps of this control are not known, some
aspects do not seem perplexing; for instance, the theories
of Goldschmidt and Child give a plausible basis for an
understanding of what particular genes do for particular
regions, in the way of affecting the rates of processes, and
what such rates, including, of course, metabolic rates,
might do to affect the pattern of growth. There is a general theory to cover every aspect of the control of growth
save one, and that is the problem of *the configuration
within the whole organism*. In some lower forms the
environment, as Child shows, does the spacing, affects and
determines the configuration of the dominant and domi-
nated regions. In more complex forms this seems to arise
of its own. It is one matter to say that a gene affects the
rate of growth of a part, but it is another to say that all
the different parts of the body, as allometry has shown,
have their specific coordinated growth rates. It may be
that the answer lies simply in the fact that the germ is
so constituted that its internal environment, its internal
configuration, must necessarily, by epigenetic causation,
result in the consistent form of the adult. But it is no

answer to refer the configuration of the adult back to the configuration of the germ. We will not be satisfied until we know the secret of the construction of the germ, how the genes and all the other protoplasm manage to create the perfect pattern of growth.

5. Patterns of Morphogenetic Movements

GROWTH involves an increase of living material, and by adding certain quantities of new material at specific places a new shape is created. To use an old analogy, one in fact which Aristotle made free use of, it is like the art of sculpture, and in this case the sculptor creates his statue solely by adding material, and never by removing it. Sometimes a sculptor starts with a block of soft clay and, by kneading and modeling it, pushes the clay about to form the shape of his desires without ever adding any new material. This is, in effect, morphogenetic movement, the only difference being that in organisms there is no sculptor; the cells themselves do the moving and like Pygmalion they bring their Galatea to life.

There are many instances among living things where masses of protoplasm or groups of cells move from one region to another during the period of development, and in so doing mold the shape of the organism. These morphogenetic movements of cells or of protoplasm differ from any other movements in that they occur during development and that in some way, indirectly or directly, they affect the mature form.

This phenomenon has in the past been almost solely within the province of the animal embryologists (especially vertebrate embryologists) and it was they who made the clear distinction between growth and morphogenetic movements. The reason for this, at least among the higher forms, is that for the most part plant cells are rigid and immobile and animal cells are not. There are some examples of movement in the higher plants, for example the slipping of the cambial initial cells after division, but this probably is not so much an active movement on the part of the cells as it is a passive result of the pressures created within the expanding cambium, and the cells slip just the way a cake of soap will slip as one squeezes it in the hand. There is, however, little reason why the lower plants and animals, the algae, fungi, bacteria, protozoa, and sponges have not been examined for this phenomenon, for, as I shall endeavor to show, they give many beautiful examples.

As in the case of growth, the main concern here is with the mechanisms of control, that is the patterns of morphogenetic movements. The arguments for this are much the same, namely that the integration of the movements, the direction of the movements, reflects the coordination of the developmental process, and this we have surmised to be the core of the problem of development. Again, as in growth, where the mechanism of the synthesis of new protoplasm is far from fully known, the mechanism of the movements of cells (or of protoplasm) is remarkably obscure. This is especially well shown in the vast literature on amoeboid motion, where the actual progress in understanding is very limited. In the nineteenth century Rhumbler[1] imagined the phenomenon of surface tension to account completely for the pseudopods of an amoeba; a localized low tension was supposed to have produced a sudden bulging out of the protoplasm like a balloon under pressure where the weak points blister out. But, as has already been said, the surface tension is now known to be too low to account for any such phenomenon. S. O. Mast and his followers relied on the fact that the cortical layer of the amoeba is a firm gel, while the central layer is fluid and squirts forward like a fountain. This structural difference is undoubtedly important, as Marsland and Brown (1936) and others have shown by subjecting amoebae to high pressures thereby liquefying the gel and preventing motion. It is argued that the gel is contractile and squeezes the fluid forward and while such gel contractility would explain the movement, its existence is purely hypothetical.[2] N. Rashevsky, as has already been said, points out that the forces involved in diffusion would

[1] See L. V. Heilbrunn (1943) for a good general discussion of the older theories of amoeboid motion.

[2] Recently Goldacre and Lorch (1950) have advanced an interesting theory involving the folding and unfolding of protein molecules.

be sufficient to account for the movement, but there is no evidence as yet that diffusion is involved. There are many complications, such as the close similarity between cytoplasmic streaming and amoeboid motion, and while Rashevsky's theory would account for both, others might only account for one. But it is even uncertain whether cyclosis involves the same mechanism as amoeboid motion, or even that the cyclosis of higher plants, say in the leaves of *Elodea*, is the same as the cyclosis found in the filamentous fungi. And there may even be different mechanisms of amoeboid motion, for there is a great difference in the appearance of the movement of small amoebae and the movement of the immense masses of myxomycete plasmodia. In myxomycetes there is also a cortical gel and a central fluid protoplasm, although the gel part is not one large sack, but a ramifying network of canals much like small blood vessels branching out into capillaries (Fig. 67). The internal fluid gushes through these vessels, and just as in the blood of ascidians, it reverses itself after a period, the periods in *Physarum* being quite short, about three minutes apart. But the flow in one direction is longer and harder so that the plasmodium as a whole moves in one direction. This may be beautifully seen in time lapse motion pictures, the first of which were taken by F. Howard, and later by W. Seifriz, for the forward edge seems to scrub back and forth, and like successive waves in an incoming tide, the edge slowly advances. Another curiously different amoeboid motion comes from *Reticulomyxa filosa*, a new species recently discovered and described by R. Nauss (1949). It consists of a large network of fine protoplasmic filapodia which become increasingly dense as they approach the central body. Under the microscope the strands themselves may be seen to move by watching the particles in them which glide along smoothly. In some instances as many as ten such strands will seem to be compacted together in a large bundle, and here is the peculiar aspect, for although these strands appear to be a continuous solid mass, they move independently of one another, some rising and some falling like the many ropes that move when an elevator is in operation. The strands not only appear but actually are continuous, for particles will pass from one strand to another. If there is a unitary principle for all these types of motions, then any explanation must also fit *Reticulomyxa*, but so far there is nothing but speculation.[3]

We should consider other kinds of movements besides amoeboid movement, such as ciliary or flagellar movement, muscular movement, and the gliding motion of diatoms, blue-green algae, and bacteria. In the case of flagella (or cilia) there is believed to be a great affinity between the pseudopod and the thin whip-like flagellum, for certain forms will transform a pseudopod into a flagellum, and the reverse is also found. But whether this close physical bond between the two structures means that their mechanisms are similar is not known. It is believed that the flagella are made up of fibrous proteins which themselves contract, but the evidence for this is still wanting. As for muscular movement, more is known here than of any other. The recent work of Szent-Györgyi (1947, 1948) and his workers has clearly demonstrated contractile proteins, and there is a real beginning of an understanding of the chemical mechanics of muscle. The motion of diatoms is as strange as it is obscure; the tiny shells glide about in the water despite the fact that they have no visible swimming protuberances from the hard silica shell. Somehow currents are set up near the grooves which penetrate the shell and keep its protoplasm in contact with the outside medium, but no one has seen how. Although they have no place in the discussion of morphogenetic movements, the motion of blue-green algae such as *Oscillatoria* is in a similar category with that of the diatoms, and equally enigmatic. The motion of bacteria is at the moment a subject of heated debate. Many firmly believe that in the flagellated forms the flagella are responsible for the locomotion, but Pijper (1948) has some evidence, documented

[3] See Loewy (1949).

with an extraordinary motion picture, that the movement of the bacteria is more likely the result of bending movements and that the flagella are passive, the body-wriggling being the active component. It is conceivable that there are different methods of locomotion among different bacteria, and as a matter of fact there are some bacteria, such as the myxobacteria, which are motile although they lack flagella.

But in all these cases, and this is the reason that I have brushed over them so superficially, we have talked about the mechanism of motion. It would undoubtedly be of great value to have the mechanism of each type completely explained, and this is still one of the pressing and urgent problems of the physiologist. Here we must be content with being aware of the fact that these types of motion exist, and the sorts of problems they present. The reason for this, which has already been said, is that the way in which these motions are guided, controlled, and directed to achieve a pattern is the matter with which we are involved. In discussing the control of growth first came the extrinsic factors of control, those easy to see and explain, and we moved slowly to the more difficult intrinsic factors. The very same plan will be adopted here for morphogenetic movements, and it must always be remembered that growth and morphogenetic movements achieve essentially the same thing: they shape the organism, so any comparison of the mechanism of control will be valuable. Shaping by growth and shaping by morphogenetic movements are without question different methods of shaping, yet the fact that the end result is the same makes one look deep for unifying control mechanisms.

The case of the diatoms may be rather quickly dispensed with since it is even doubtful that its movements are truly morphogenetic in any sense. It is true that the cells of the colonial forms of the diatoms *Navicula* and *Cymbella* (Fig. 31) move about to a limited extent within their mucilaginous housing, and since the cells determine the shape of the sheath, these movements do contribute to the shape somewhat. But much of the distribution is a result of the growth and cell divisions and this example is more curious than helpful to the argument.

A rather simple movement which might be interpreted as morphogenetic is found in the beautiful large water-mold *Achlya*. The first step in the formation of zoospores consists of dense multinucleate protoplasm accumulating at the tip of a hypha, and a crosswall forms to close off this protoplasm in the tip. Progressive cleavage ensues, that is, clefts appear around the many nuclei so that a group of spores becomes delineated. The osmotic pressure increases within the zoosporangium until finally a pore at the apex opens up and in rapid succession the round nonmotile zoospores pop out. As they do, and this is the part that is of interest here, they stick to one another, at the tip of the zoosporangium spout, forming at first a small irregular bunch of cells that soon fills out into a perfect hollow sphere, a perfect blastula (Fig. 55). The whole process is so rapid, being a matter of a few minutes that at first it seems rather extraordinary. I have made re-peated observations, often disrupting the sphere with a fine needle as it is forming, and I believe that the shape is entirely explicable in terms of the gummy adhesive between the cells and the force of the spout of fluid issuing from the zoosporangium which essentially blows the cells out in the form of a sphere. Later the cells sprout two flagella each and swim away, leaving behind a spherical honeycomb of clear intercellular substance that presuma-bly is the hardened cement which accounted for the original adherence of the cells. The only difficulty with this example is that the form produced by this sudden mass movement has no bearing on the mature form of the filamentous fungus. It is a transitory configuration which takes place during the developmental period but is soon completely lost. Other related members of the Saprolegniales lack this process entirely; it is in no way a necessary step, but seems rather to be the result of a set of chance circumstances. Yet the fact that such a

perfectly coordinated shape is produced by such simple mechanical means (if my interpretation of the mechanics is
correct) is a lesson worth knowing.

It leads us, furthermore, quite directly into the case of

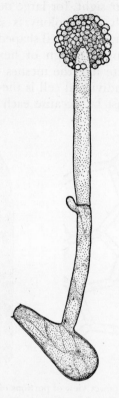

FIG. 55. Zoospore emission in the water mold, *Achlya*. Germination of
a resistant spore forming a typical *Achlya* sporangium. Some of the ad-
herent spores have been washed away showing their arrangement in a
hollow sphere. (From Weston, Amer. J. Bot. *4*, 1917.)

the water net *Hydrodictyon* which R. A. Harper (1908)
and others have so carefully studied and analyzed. In
his *Principles of Biology*, Herbert Spencer says there are
some things which are unknown and some things which
are unknowable, the development of *Hydrodictyon* being

one of the latter. It is unfortunate that he should have chosen this as an example, for at least a good part of its development is now beautifully simple and easy to understand. *Hydrodictyon* is found in fresh water lakes and ponds; it is a familiar sight, for large nets may be as great as a meter in length. The colony is sausage-shaped and hollow in the center, the pencil-shaped cells touching at the ends and making a design of hexagons, pentagons, etc., that appear quite like the meshes of a net (Fig. 56). The shape of each individual cell is the same as the whole colony, and that must be because each cell of the colony

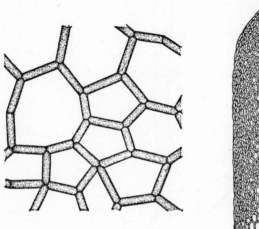
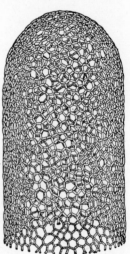

Fig. 56. A low and high power view of portions of a net of *Hydrodictyon*. (From Brown, The Plant Kingdom, Ginn, 1935.)

produces a daughter colony within it and, as we shall see shortly, molds its shape.

In its asexual development, the cells of the mother colony, which are multinucleate, begin with a progressive cleavage, which in this case is a series of radial clefts that cut off the nuclei. In one cell there may be anywhere from 7,000 to 20,000 swarmers produced in this way, and by virtue of being biflagellate they begin a slow writhing movement after the cleavage is well over. A sudden contraction soon brings the swarmers into a dense central column the length of the mother cell, and the real swarming only starts once the swarmers tear loose from the central column and swim freely and rapidly about inside the mother cell. If the cell wall is broken at this stage, the swarmers will escape and swim away, but the fate of such escaped swarmers is not known. The swarmers rapidly buzz about within the mother cell; there is no direction of their movement, it is quite haphazard, the whole of it looking like the movements of shoppers in the bargain basement of a department store. The time comes, after a while, when they seem to tire, the movements slacken their pace and the swarmer cells begin to settle, to plaster themselves against the inside of the mother cell wall. As will soon be evident, these movements, undirected though they may be, are really morphogenetic in character. There is no economy in the movement, for the wild scrambling is not part of the production of the mature shape. The only part of the movement that is constructive is the movement of the cells from their position after progressive cleavage to their final position against the mother cell wall. Although this comes close to being a completely uncontrolled morphogenetic movement, there is one limitation imposed on its freedom that is of great importance to the mature form, and easy to comprehend. It is the physical limit of the mother cell wall, the mold of the mother's womb that governs the future colony, and as was just said, if the swarmers escape by crushing the mother cell walls, their fate is unknown, although most certainly they do not form a new colony.

The round swarmers writhe and slip by each other so that when all their motion ceases they are closely packed along the sausage-shaped wall of the mother cell. There are not enough swarmers to cover the whole surface completely and many holes remain, these holes being the future holes of the meshes in the daughter net. The position then, of the cells after the movement decides the configuration of the future net. The swarmer cells now begin to grow, and here Harper argues strongly for his pressure-contact stimuli, for he says that the axis of growth of the cells (that is they grow mainly in one direction to become sausage-shaped eventually) is in the direction of the greatest resistance. To support this he observed that the parts of the swarmer, the site of the flagella, and other differentiated structures may lie in any orientation with respect to the direction of growth, sometimes the cell will elongate in the same direction as its anterior-posterior (flagellar) axis, and with equal frequency it will elongate at right angles, or any other angle of the original antero-posterior axis. The other evidence for pressure-contact stimuli is that if a swarmer is not squeezed between two or more cells, if it is in a sparse region on the wall, sitting alone, it will not, according to Harper, grow at all. This seems to be another case where the physical tension or compression stimulates growth, which we could add to those given before.

The cells enlarge greatly with growth and in so doing the nuclei divide and keep pace with the increase in protoplasm. The expansion will distend the mother cell wall, until finally the old case will reach its limit, rupture, and free the new colony. From a purely geometric view it may be seen that if the cells push in the direction of greater compression there will be many points where three cells hinge at one point, pushing at 120° from one another, and there are cases of four to two cells meeting at a juncture. A study was made in Harper's laboratory of the frequency of meshes with different cell numbers and, as might have been predicted, in cases where the mother colony was starved and therefore the swarmers few and far between, the meshes were looser, that is more cells per mesh in the daughter colonies. The figures are given below in a table for an average well-fed colony, and it may be seen that the hexagon is the most frequent. There are often irregularities in colonies, such as large holes or a few meshes that seem to project inward, which reflect the

Table[4]

No. of cells in a mesh	Average in per cent
3	1+
4	8+
5	29—
6	43—
7	12—
8	4+
>8	2—

easy pitfalls waiting for this somewhat disorganized morphogenetic movement. Previously we said that the shape of the mother cell and the shape of a whole colony were the same, because the one molded the other, and now this is easy to see. It is a matter of molding in a literal sense, the mold being the cell wall of the mother cell.

Hydrodictyon suits the purposes of this book admirably because in its life cycle it has both a relatively uncoordinated morphogenetic movement, which we have just examined, and one that appears quite highly coordinated, and certainly not at all understood. This coordinated one occurs in the sexual cycle which, to make the story clear, we will follow from the beginning.[5] In certain seasons the cells of a large colony again undergo progressive cleavage, but in this case produce motile flagellated gametes which escape into the surrounding water. After fusion of these isogametes, the zygote loses its motility and becomes encased in a hard spiny shell (Plate V). It is called a polyhedron, which describes it well. This particular stage is a resistant one, the one in fact that carries the species through the rigors of winter. Come spring and gentle weather, it will begin to swell, to grow, and as it does there are many nuclear divisions. When growth ceases the nuclei are cut off with progressive cleavage and the flagellated swarmers, as before, begin to jostle about. The

[4] From Harper (1908, p. 287).
[5] See Pocock (1937) for an excellent description of the sexual cycle.

sharp points of the polyhedra have by now quite disappeared, and the swelling has produced a large round vesicle in which the swarmers have ample room for their mad dance.

And now we come to the part that seems to have a touch of magic in it. From the behavior in the asexual cycle, one would expect the swarmers to plaster themselves on the inside surface of the vesicle, but they do quite the opposite. They form a dense mass in the center of the large spherical vesicle, like a swarm of bees, and as they crowd together the ball of swarmers slowly decreases in one direction and increases in another; slowly the mass of moving cells becomes transformed from a sphere to a disc of cells. The motion of the cells decreases progressively as the disc is formed and it finally stops in a wave that begins at the outside edge and moves inward. Here is then a disc, a flat plate of cells floating freely about in the center of a large vesicle which it does not touch. The morphogenetic movement here has not been molded by any cell or vesicle wall, it has been controlled entirely by the cells themselves which do the moving.

As before, growth now begins and the colony ruptures the vesicle as the cells assume the sausage shape, with the same characteristic meshwork, although the whole net has the shape of a disc (Plate V). Obviously the succeeding asexual generation must again have a sausage-shaped colony, as the cells are sausage-shaped. One peculiar feature is the ring of peripheral cells about the colony which have a projection pointing outward at the ends of each cell. Although the significance of this character is not known, it resembles in a rough way the cells of *Pediastrum*, and for that reason there is thought to be a close phylogenetic affinity between these two organisms.

The morphogenetic movements in *Pediastrum*, which were also studied by Harper (1916, 1918a, 1918b) are quite similar to those found in the sexual phase of *Hydrodictyon*, and since these appear so especially interesting they deserve careful attention. *Pediastrum* is also a fresh water form, although the cells are small, being about 10 to 20μ in diameter, and the colonies are of few cells only, being of 2, 4, 8, 16, 32, and rarely exceeding 64 cells. There are various species of *Pediastrum*, the specific differences based on the shape of the cells themselves. Some have no horns or spikes at all, some have one per cell, some two, and some four. These characteristics are the same irrespective of the size of the colony, which is quite variable for each species, although the cell shape will to some extent affect the general colony shape (Fig. 57). All

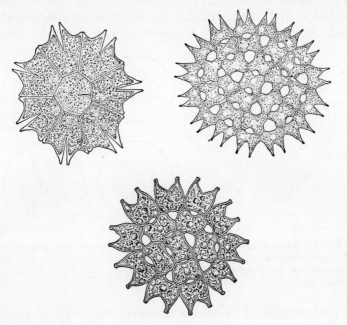

FIG. 57. Three different species of *Pediastrum*. (From Brown, The Plant Kingdom, Ginn, 1935.)

the colonies have one characteristic in common and that is they form flat plates, highly irregular and abnormal colonies being the exception, although even in irregular ones there is a marked tendency toward flatness.

Simply because the method of morphogenetic movement is so similar in the asexual and sexual phases of *Pediastrum*, only the former will be discussed. Here, as in *Hydrodictyon*, each cell of a colony breaks up into swarmers and forms a new colony. However, they differ in many ways and right from the beginning *Pediastrum* shows a different kind of progressive cleavage. Instead of the irregular clefts dividing the nuclei, there are regular furrows that divide the mother cell first into 2 parts, then 4, 8, 16, 32, 64, stopping, as we have said before, at any one of these stages of successive bipartitions (Fig. 58). The mother cell wall, as this division ensues, may be seen to bulge, and finally it splits, with a crescent shaped slit, and the contents, neatly wrapped in a thin vesicle (like

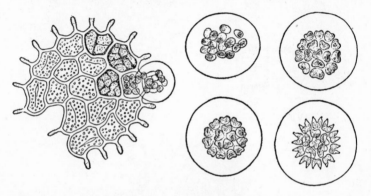

Fig. 58. Asexual development in *Pediastrum* showing the progressive cleavage, emergence of the vesicle, the swarming of the zoospores, and the formation of the daughter colony. (From Brown, The Plant Kingdom, Ginn, 1935.)

a caul) emerge. The spherical vesicle will swell to twice the size of the mother cell, and within it the biflagellate swarmers swim about violently. This particular aspect of the process has been carefully studied by G. M. Smith (1916), who found the swarming to take only three or four minutes. There is then a rather sudden slowing down in which the cells aggregate in the center of the vesicle and begin to show a circular outline still irregular and ill-defined. A period of writhing and struggling follows in which the cells do not move far from their places but seem to be kneading and pushing themselves into a maximally comfortable position. As the movement slows, the prongs or lobes of the cells characteristic of the species begin to appear. The speed of this final fitting together, including the appearance of the lobes is amazing, as can be seen in the camera lucida drawings made by Smith, for the whole process between the beginning and the end takes no longer than ten minutes (Fig. 59).

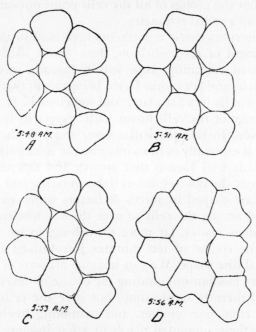

FIG. 59. Colony formation in *Pediastrum*. Outline drawings, made at approximately three minute intervals, of the changes taking place in the first few minutes after the cessation of zoospore movement. In this colony the swarming lasted eight minutes, and the first drawing was made fifteen seconds after the motion ceased. (From G. M. Smith, 1916.)

The cells are packed in the disc in the most efficient way possible. They take the same ring configurations that can be obtained with different numbers of floating corks containing small magnets (with like poles upward) which may be bunched together with a large magnet.[6] They represent the closest crowding configuration. There are, of course, many irregular colonies produced where somehow the cells became stuck and did not slide into their most probable places, but such deviations from the mean are not surprising. What is not at all to be expected is that they assume the shape of a flat disc, for if it were just a matter of crowding, the sphere would be a more likely shape. The other aspect that demands an explanation is that the prongs of all the cells point outward giving the colony a radial symmetry.

The morphogenetic movements here, and in the sexual development of *Hydrodictyon*, show first a wild and uncoordinated swarming, kept within bounds only by the thin vesicle, and later some factor brings them together and makes them lie in a flat plate. And somehow in *Pediastrum* the polarity of the cells forms with respect to the colony as a whole. In this particular case, and this may be its merit, it is especially hard to imagine the underlying mechanism. It is well known that growth and morphogenetic movements do not respect cell boundaries and that organisms are shaped by forces or factors which extend beyond and among the cells to give them a wholeness. But it is another matter, far more disturbing, to see the cells within the course of ten minutes just yanked into this unnatural disc shape. We can imagine all sorts of delicate regulatory mechanisms guiding the course of development, provided there is ample time, but here the cells, widely separate from one another, and swimming freely about, pop into their appointed places in a few instants of time. I have always been struck by the similarity between this process and that of molecules adhering to the face of a growing crystal. I have recently had the good fortune to follow the process through myself, and I should like to do so with the polarizing microscope, for the mature walls are of cellulose and show strong birefringence. But it is hard to believe that even if the birefringence does

[6] See Thompson (1942, pp. 315-317).

suddenly appear in the crucial ten minute period, that it is the crystallization of cellulose on the cell wall that makes this shape, and keeps it flat and disc-like. And even then we must account for the tendency of the cells to aggregate. It is true that there is good reason to suppose that a simple and quite separate mechanism might be involved. To compare this to crystallization seems only to make an analogy, and its merit as an analogy is even difficult to assess.

A big question, that already has come up and will again, is that when the developments of different forms are compared, one of two basic assumptions may be made: that all forms possess the same mechanisms of control of development, just as their metabolic machinery is fundamentally similar, or that there are among organisms many different controlling mechanisms, just as there are many different methods of obtaining energy from the environment. They are both assumptions and we have no way of saying which is true. If it is the latter, then this book is a comparative study of the variety of different control mechanisms during development; if it is the former then we must somehow find a least common denominator in the control of all these forms, and from this book should emerge at least the essentials of a theory to cover the overall mechanism whereby form is guided among organisms. This common denominator will have to include all the odd types of development. It will have to include the development of *Pediastrum* as well as the development of amphibians.

To add to our collection of unusual examples of development, the case of the Myxobacteriales or slime bacteria deserves a prominent place. They were discovered by R. Thaxter (1892, 1897, 1904), the distinguished mycologist who had more success than anyone in recent years in discovering not just new species, but whole new groups of organisms, the myxobacteria being one of them. There has been, since Thaxter, remarkably little work on them; one of the meager handful of exceptions being the large treatise of Jahn (1924), in which he clarifies some points concerning their growth and development and plays havoc with the simple system of classification proposed by Thaxter. But to this day Thaxter's account of the life cycle, which we will follow, neatly includes all the essentials, and his work stands out as an exemplary piece of careful and original observation.

There are a variety of different species of myxobacteria, but for a number of reasons it will be best to limit ourselves to *Chondromyces crocatus*. Its fruiting structure is so large and elaborate, and furthermore I have been observing its development myself recently and have become quite familiar with it.[7] *Chondromyces*, like other myxobacteria, are found in dung of various animals and in soil. The most successful method of isolating them (originally established by Beebe, 1941) is to place pellets of dung over rich soil soaked in water, so the water level rises to the dung. In two weeks time it is not unusual to find an area on one of the pellets covered with a yellow fuzz, which under the microscope appears as glistening stalks with corrugated, round, apical spore masses. These spore masses are clusters of oval shaped cysts, and the stalks often branch and appear like miniature trees (Fig. 60 and Plate VI). By transferring these to a suitable nutrient agar it is possible to observe the whole cycle more closely, and we have found it especially helpful to take time-interval motion pictures of all the stages.

In this motion picture the cysts are seen to germinate in two different ways. The irregular cysts which are crammed full of thousands of rods show, when their movements are speeded up 500 times the normal rate, an internal writhing and boiling, for obviously the rods are already motile within the cyst. The cyst may then suddenly rupture and a great tongue of rods issues forth, or they may trickle out a small hole by twos and threes or tens. In the former case

[7] D. L. Trimble, E. A. Wheaton (in 1950), C. Johnston, and H. C. Urschel (in 1951) have carried on this work as a senior project at Princeton University.

FIG. 60. Culmination in the myxobacterium *Chondromyces crocatus* showing the successive stages of development. The thick fruiting body (5) has been grown in a drier environment than the thinner one (6). (From Thaxter, 1892.)

the emerging rods seem to come out in waves and sometimes, like a pseudopod of an amoeba which changes its
direction, it will pour back into the cyst only to reemerge
again. In the case where the cells stream out in small
numbers it is quite characteristic to see them form a
whirlpool around the point of contact of the cyst and the
agar substratum. This maypole dance may continue for
some time until the rods peel off from the outer edge and
stream off to join some other group of rods.

The small rods, which are from 3 to 8μ long, show a
smooth gliding motion. Occasionally they will bend and
show signs of flexibility, but no such bending movements
appear to be associated with their forward progression.
They also apparently exude some slimy material that
adheres to the substratum, for it is possible to see streaks
on the surface of the agar after some rods have passed
by. These slime tracks play an important part in the guiding of the motion of the other rods, but this matter will
be discussed more fully in a moment. One other important
feature is that it is clearly demonstrated in the movies that
the rods have no "head" or "tail" end, that is, they can
move with equal facility in both directions.

A most striking aspect of these rods is their gregarious
nature. They show a marked tendency to clump, aggregate, and stream together from the very beginning
(Plate VI). Growth and cell division takes place during
these activities, and as a result the aggregates by an in-
cessant process of wandering and fusing become larger
and larger (Fig. 62). It is especially interesting to observe
the motion of the large clumps, for there the great mass
of rods appears to move very rapidly first in one direction
and then another, resembling in some ways the backward
and forward surging of myxomycete plasmodia. When the
clumps have reached a sufficient size they round off into
a knob and begin the final fruiting, the final ascent into
the air.

Thaxter has aptly described this process as being similar
to a funnel, in which the flaring portion of the funnel

continually constricts at its base so that the flaring part as a whole rises, and the thin stem or stalk becomes increasingly longer. Jahn has made some paraffin sections of this stage in *Chondromyces* and shown that the rods themselves are mostly packed in the uppermost advancing edge, and all pointing in their direction of motion, while the remaining stalk is largely a gelatinous mass containing only a few laggard rods that seem to have become trapped in the hardening mucilage. In the final stage of fruiting the cysts become delineated, with the apical glob suddenly showing a lobed formation, and virtually all of these rods themselves become encased in the cysts which soon turn hard and resistant.

In this case there is certainly no doubt at all that these movements are morphogenetic and that they are highly coordinated. The question of what factors guide this movement has received too little attention, although there is one interesting study of R. Stanier (1942) in which some insight into the problem was obtained. He worked with a different species, a species of *Myxococcus* in which he noticed that if the agar was under any strain the aggregation of the rods was oriented in relation to those strains. Ordinarily, the rods will stream into a collection point isodiametrically from all sides, but if the agar is folded slightly the rods will only move along the compression lines so that instead of obtaining a round central collection of rods (which actually in this species is all there is to the fruiting body) he obtained long ones, oriented perpendicularly to the compression lines (Fig. 61). By placing a glass rod under a slip of agar and in this way making it bulge across the middle he obtained fruiting bodies lined up in two directions at right angles to each other showing that the rods would move along either the tension or the compression lines.

Stanier compares this situation (and I think quite rightly) with the contact guidance of nerve cells and fibroblasts shown by Weiss (see p. 66). The difficulty is that there is no evidence that aggregation is always guided in this fashion in nature, although undeniably it is under experimental conditions. It would seem reasonable to postulate that there might be two factors: one (for the sake of argument) a chemotaxis, and the other that lines of tension and compression physically force the elongate

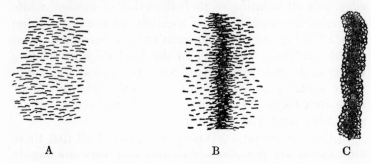

A   B   C

FIG. 61. Diagram illustrating the formation of fruiting bodies in *Myxococcus* as it occurs on an oriented surface. (From Stanier, 1942.)

rods to move in one direction only. There is, of course, no evidence at all for chemotaxis or any other guiding principle other than the one demonstrated by Stanier, but neither is there any evidence that his is the only one and that it is necessary for development.

I have done a few preliminary experiments on the aggregation mechanisms of *Chondromyces*, and the contact guidance of Stanier is fully substantiated. The rods do follow the tracks laid down by the previous rods and it is reasonable to assume that this is a purely mechanical method of orientation. In Figure 62 the details of such an experiment are shown and the motion pictures give many more examples. But it is also possible to demonstrate that the rods will go toward a center even though no tracks are present. This has been done by making a groove in the agar across any possible tracks, and the rods still went around the groove (Fig. 63). In an even better experiment, a center was taken from some distant region and placed near a stream of rods. The original direction of the rods became altered and joined the center across

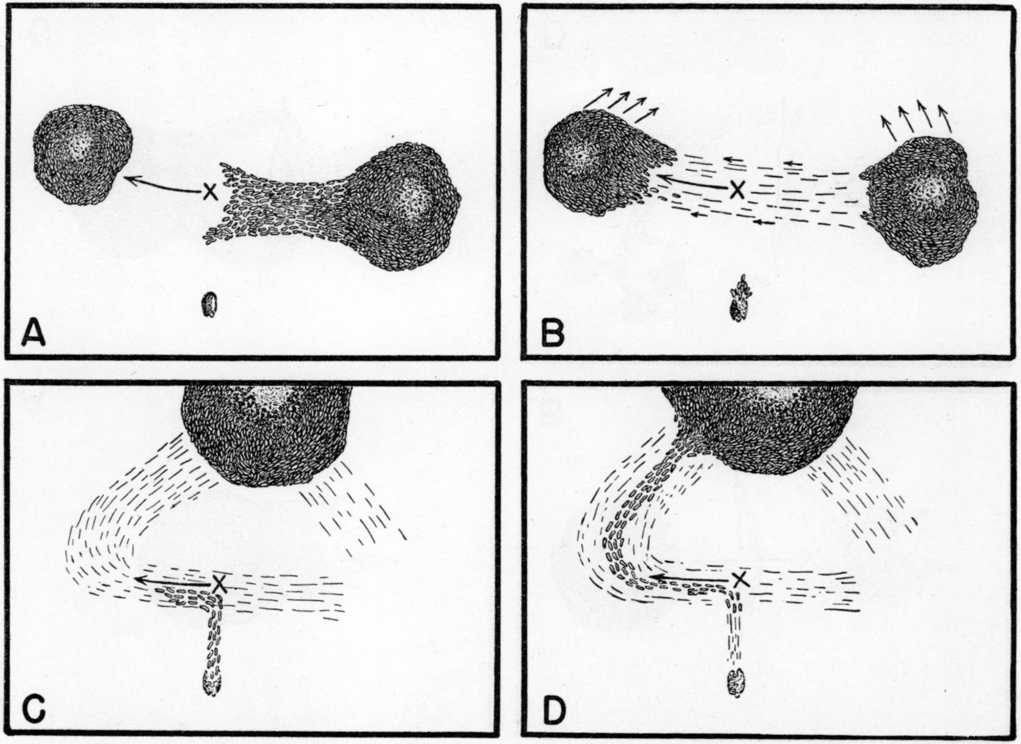

FIG. 62. Diagram of an experiment showing the tendency of rods of *Chondromyces* to follow the tracks laid down by other rods. A, a center is moved from position "X." Note the ungerminated cyst below "X." B, the cells lying between the two centers move principally to the left-hand center and both centers begin to move upward. The cyst has now germinated. C,D, the two centers have now fused into one large center, and the rods from the cyst join it not by the most direct route, but by following the previously laid down tracks. (Original drawing by C. Johnston).

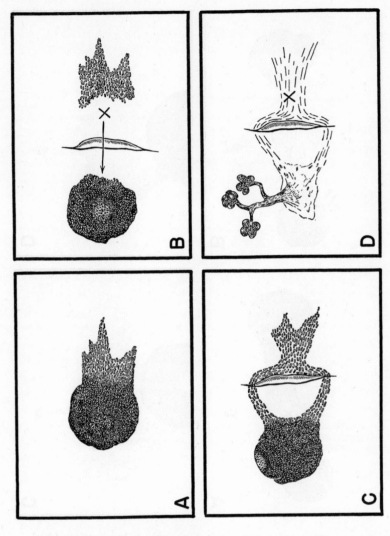

Fig. 63. Diagram to show how the aggregating rods of *Chondromyces* will circumvent an obstacle in order to join a center. A, the original center; B, the center has been moved from "X" to the left and a groove has been cut in the agar; C, the cells join the center by going around the groove; D, the center forms a normal fruiting body (drawn small and out of scale in this picture). (Original drawing by C. Johnston.)

a plain agar gap containing no slime tracks. Thus it would seem that there is some other factor responsible for governing their morphogenetic movement besides contact guidance.

There are also other aspects of the morphogenetic movements in the myxobacteria that need explaining. The whole rising into the air of *Chondromyces*, the control of the branching, the cutting off of the cysts into lobes. Some of these may be accounted for by the method in which the slime is given off, and its behavior upon desiccation. It is possible to affect the thickness of the stalk and the degree of branching by controlling the humidity; the greater humidity favoring a large, more highly branched stalk. But this does not explain the formation of cysts or the mechanism of branching.

More is known of the control of morphogenetic movements in the convergent *Acrasiales* or amoeboid slime molds. This particular group is of special interest to me, for I have been studying them for some years now. Because their nutrient requirements and culture conditions are known, and because their life cycle is so extremely short, lasting only four days, these organisms have been well suited for experimental studies. Especially so is the species *Dictyostelium discoideum*, for its fruiting structure has the most regular and simplest proportions of them all.[8]

The spores of *Dictyostelium* are small and capsule-shaped. Each one, when sown on moist agar, splits and hatches one unicellular amoeba. This amoeba soon begins to feed by engulfing bacteria and divides repeatedly by binary fission. In this vegetative stage of *Dictyostelium* the daughter cells are separate and free-swimming, wandering about quite independently of one another. Their movement is a typical amoeboid or pseudopodial one, and this will be the first case we shall examine of coordinated morphogenetic movements involving amoeboid motion. If the amoebae reach a sufficient number (this critical

[8] For a description of the life cycle see Raper (1935, 1940a), Bonner (1944).

number may be lowered if the food supply is depleted) then the aggregation starts. First a few and then finally all the amoebae start streaming in to central collection points (Fig. 64 and Plate VII). Each amoeba does not make a bee-line to the center, but they come together to form streams, like tributaries collecting to form one large river.

The aggregated cell mass, containing anywhere from a few hundred to 100,000 cells, becomes elongate and will vary in length from 0.1 millimeter to 2 millimeters. Its size is entirely dependent on the number of amoebae that entered into the aggregation circle; there is no evidence of any growth, feeding, or cell division from the moment aggregation starts. This means that there is a fair likelihood that in this case growth and morphogenetic movements are completely separate. The growth is a random undirected process here, and all the molding and sculpturing is done by morphogenetic movements after the growth. The first such movement is that of aggregation, and now the sausage or bullet-shaped cell mass begins a second movement, that of migration. The whole mass glides about the agar at a speed comparable to the speed of an amoeba (roughly 2 mm per hour) giving off from its posterior end a slime streak which is in fact a sausage casing, produced by the sausage of cells, which collapses behind as the cell mass moves (Fig. 65 and Plate VII).[9] With the high powers of the microscope it is possible to see that the amoebae themselves are in active pseudopodial motion and somehow they exude the track and then walk on it, as the carpet of a Persian king is rolled before him. The sheath does not move, the cells move forward from within it, getting their traction on the sheath itself. The length of the migration period is very variable; it may either not exist at all, or it may extend, as we have been

[9] The migrating pseudoplasmodium will move toward light, and it has been shown recently that it is exceptionally sensitive to temperature gradients, migrating toward warmer regions (Bonner, Clarke, Neeley, and Slifkin, 1950).

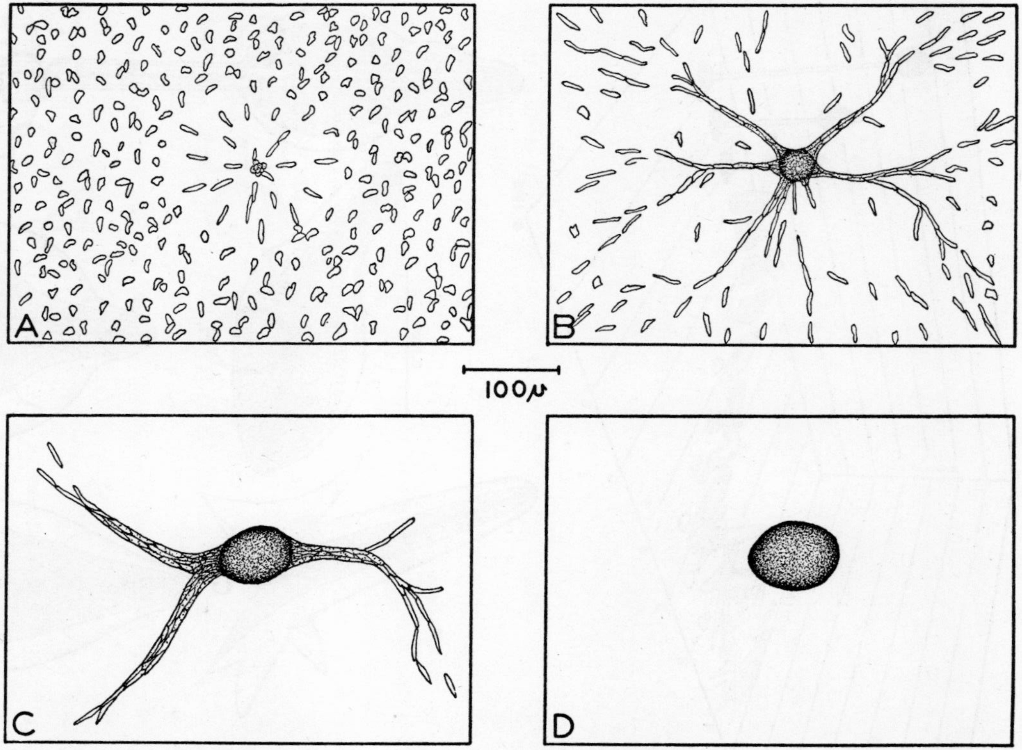

Fig. 64. A semi-diagrammatic representation of 4 stages of the aggregation of *Dictyostelium* taking place under water on the bottom of a glass dish. A, the beginning of aggregation showing the formation of a small center; B, C, successive stages of aggregation showing the thickening of the streams and the enlargement of the center; D, the final cell mass. (From Bonner, 1947.)

100 μ

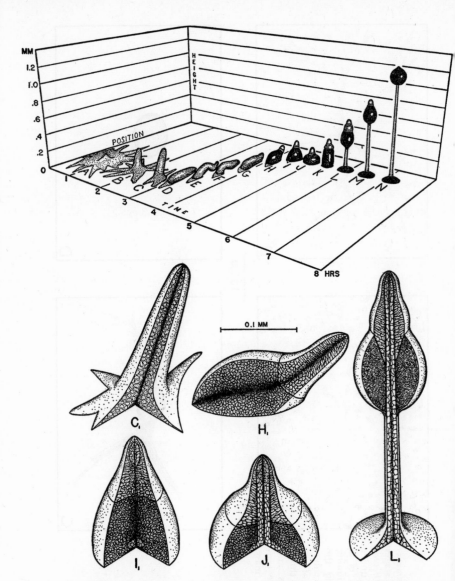

FIG. 65. Development in *Dictyostelium discoideum. Above*: The complete morphogenesis is represented in a three dimensional graph. A-C, aggregation; D-H, migration; I-N, culmination. The presence of prespore cells is indicated by a heavy stippling, H-K; and the presence of true spores by solid black, L-N. *Below*: semi-diagrammatic drawings showing the cell structure at different stages. The letters indicate the corresponding stages given above. (From Bonner, 1944.)

able to show recently, up to two weeks, if the environmental conditions are just right.

The third and last morphogenetic movement is somewhat more involved; it is the final fruiting or culmination where the migrating cell mass rights itself and shoots up into the air to form a delicate stalk supporting at its apex a round smooth spore mass (Fig. 65 and Plate VIII). The anterior cells become the stalk cells, that is, they become large and vacuolated, and encased in a cellulose sheath. First only a few do this and they are driven down like a wedge as more prestalk cells climb to the apex and become stalk cells. The process is the reverse of a fountain; the cells pour up the outside to become trapped and solidified in the central core which is the stalk. In so doing the whole structure rises into the air until all the prestalk cells have been used up. Sometime in the beginning of the rising the prespore cells all became encapsulated into spores, so the final spore mass is resting at the apex.

Some while ago I became interested in the mechanism of the control of the morphogenetic movement of aggregation (Bonner, 1947). The early workers (Olive, 1902; Potts, 1902) had rather tacitly assumed that the process was by chemotaxis, by the orientation of the myxamoebae within a chemical gradient of some active substance, although there was no real evidence that this was so. More recently E. Runyon (1942) showed that if an attracting center was on one side of a semi-permeable cellophane membrane, and the amoebae on the other, the amoebae would orient toward the center even though they were separated by the membrane. Runyon concluded from his ingenious experiment that the incoming amoebae must be guided by chemotaxis, but in fact his evidence was negligible for there are many things which may pass through a cellophane membrane besides chemical substances.

The one mechanism that was certainly impossible was that the amoebae agglutinated, for such forces must operate at close distances, and the thickness of cellophane would be far too great for such forces to be acting across it. A further proof of this came from a technique where the amoebae would aggregate in the bottom of a glass dish filled with water. If in such a preparation a central mass of cells was removed and placed quite a distance from the stream of cells that had been leading to it, three to five minutes afterward each cell in the stream separated from its neighbors and made a bee-line to the central mass at its new location. In this manner one can demonstrate that the amoebae will be attracted to masses that are half a millimeter away, which is equivalent to about sixty amoeba diameters.

In a number of ways, which I shall not enter into here, it was possible to show that any electric or magnetic force was most unlikely. Another possibility was that some sort of ray might guide the amoebae inward, as ships are guided into a harbor by a beacon. It was A. Gurwitsch, with his mitogenetic rays, who imagined that the control of all development was somehow achieved by these rays, although now the evidence of their existence is no longer considered adequate.[10] It was possible to show that no radiation was involved in the aggregation of *Dictyostelium*. This was done by an experiment in which a thin glass shelf was suspended in water. A central mass of cells (i.e. a center) was placed on the upper side and separate amoebae on the underside (Fig. 66,A). After a time the separate amoebae all rounded the edge to the upper side and streamed in to the center. If the center had been a beacon emitting rays, the rays could either have penetrated the glass or not. If they had penetrated one would have expected the same result as with Runyon's cellophane; the amoebae would merely have gathered on the nearest point on the other side of the glass. If the rays had not passed through the glass, one would have expected the individual amoebae to be completely unaffected by the center. Since the amoebae were attracted around a sharp corner, and since no ray can bend around a corner, we can say that

[10] See Hollaender (1936) for a general discussion of the problem.

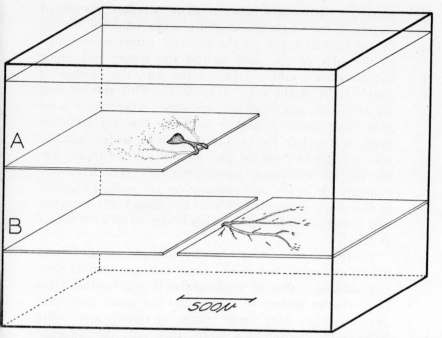

Fig. 66. A semi-diagrammatic representation of two experiments done on aggregation in *Dictyostelium* using coverslip shelves held under water. A, the myxamoebae previously at random under the coverslip are attracted around the edge to the center of the upper surface; B, the myxamoebae previously at random on the right-hand coverslip are attracted to the center on the left-hand coverslip, across the substratum gap. (Bonner, 1947.)

rays, mitogenetic or otherwise, do not play a part in the aggregation of *Dictyostelium*.

Another possibility was that some kind of Langmuirian film might guide the amoebae along the glass-water interface, an idea stimulated by an interesting experiment of Fauré-Fremiet and Wallich (1925) in which they showed, by placing talc on an interface, that there was a visible expanding of materials on the surface before the outward migration of amoebocytes of *Arenicola* (and of various types of cells in tissue culture). To test this hypothesis two submerged glass shelves were placed side by side,

[179]

leaving a narrow gap between them. A center was placed on top of one of the plates and separate amoebae on top of the other. Again all the separate amoebae streamed to the edge of the shelf nearest the center and, since the amoebae could not bridge the gap, they formed a center right at the edge (Fig. 66,B). This proved that the attraction can occur across a region where there is no glass-water interface, and it is known that the amoebae need an interface for locomotion. The amoebae actually appear eager to cross the gap, for one can see them pawing the air with their pseudopods in a very frustrated manner, and if the two glass shelves are pushed together so that the gap is only one amoeba's length, the amoebae will immediately form a hanging bridge to join the center at last.

There are a number of other hypotheses that can be and have been tested, but among those only one showed positive evidence, that of chemotaxis. If aggregation takes place on the bottom of a dish, and the water above the amoebae flows over them gently, as though they were lying at the bottom of a brook, then only the amoebae downstream are oriented toward the center. The amoebae upstream show no interest at all in the center. This must mean that the attracting agent is capable of diffusing, for it can be washed downstream. The only two diffusing agents are heat or chemical substances, and for a number of reasons which I shall not discuss here, heat seems unlikely, leaving a chemical substance as the only possibility.

The center, of course, does not really attract the amoebae in the sense of pulling them in. Presumably the chemical substance that is given off by the center is always more abundant near the center than farther away. Therefore, the front end of the amoebae approaching the center will be surrounded by more of the substance than will the hind end. In other words, all the substance accomplishes is to orient the amoebae by affecting the front end differentially from the hind end, the movement being solely that of the amoebae. The smell of carrion does not pull at the jackal, but it gives him a guide to where he may find the carcass, and the nearer he gets, the stronger the scent. The evidence is thus extremely good for the existence of a chemical influence in the aggregation of *Dictyostelium*. If there were some way of isolating the substance *in vitro* we would have a proof of its existence, but so far all our attempts in this direction have failed.

In Edmund Spenser's *Faerie Queene* there is a witch named Acrasia, and like Circe, she attracts men and transforms them into beasts. It was decided that the chemical substance should be at least tentatively named, and considering its classical reference and the fact that *Dictyostelium* is a member of the *Acrasiales, acrasin* seemed entirely appropriate.

There are many aspects to the development of *Dictyostelium* that are pertinent to the subject matter of this book; in its aggregation we have seen an excellent instance of morphogenetic movement, and furthermore we seem to understand the mechanism whereby it is controlled. But there are other morphogenetic movements besides the aggregation movement, and to what extent may they also be interpreted in terms of gradients of acrasin? The first step was to find if acrasin was produced during the later stages of development, and it was possible not only to demonstrate its presence, but also to show, by two independent means, what was the ability of different parts of the cell mass to emit acrasin.[11]

Despite some earlier evidence to the contrary,[12] it now appears that the tip remains throughout development as the high point of acrasin production, and so from this point of view it is conceivable that acrasin continues to be the guiding principle of movement. However at some stages of migration there are no gradients of acrasin all along the main part of the migrating mass, with the exception of the region adjacent to the tip. Since the movement of the migrating cell mass is the same when there is an even emission along its axis, or when there is a

[11] Bonner (1949).   [12] Bonner and Slifkin (1949).

gradient, it might be assumed that at least an external gradient of acrasin is not necessary for the directed movement of all parts of the cell mass. The same phenomenon is demonstrated in aggregation, where whirlpool aggregation patterns are sometimes obtained;[13] that is, instead of the cells coming in directly to one point they come in at an angle and make a central ring of amoebae with a hollow center. The cells in this ring go round and round following each other like a circle of elephants in the circus, and here again there appears to be directed movement without any overall acrasin gradient.[14]

The argument then is that not all the morphogenetic movements of *Dictyostelium* are controlled by *external* acrasin gradients, gradients in the outside environment, but this does not mean that there might not be *internal* gradients that we cannot see or measure. It is quite conceivable, although treacherously hypothetical, that there may be some sort of gradient within each cell and that these line up with respect to one another much as Rashevsky (1938) imagines might be possible in his purely formal analysis of morphogenetic movements of animals. It is also possible that the contact, the adhesion between the cells works in conjunction with acrasin gradients, so where the cells are not oriented by acrasin, they are guided by the movement tensions of the cells that surround them. The idea here then is that chemotaxis and contact guidance might both be simultaneously operating in *Dictyostelium*.

Even if the movements were entirely coordinated by gradients there would still be the problem (as there was with Child's metabolic gradients) of how the gradient was established in a particular configuration. There is no problem in explaining this for aggregation, because one needs only to postulate that each amoeba produces acrasin; and if more amoebae happen to be in one spot at the onset of aggregation, that spot will become the center, the high point in the acrasin gradient. But the problem

[13] Arndt (1937), Raper (1941).   [14] Bonner (1950).

is greater in migration, for there a uniform external gradient consistently reverts to a high point at the apex and tapers off in the posterior direction. One might argue that there is an invisible external gradient imposed by aggregation that blossoms and becomes evident during the latter part of the migration period. The difficulty is that in one experiment[15] when vegetative amoebae were shaken in water, after a few minutes they stuck together in balls, and with twelve hours of shaking the balls were arrow-shaped, with a head and a tail end, the latter giving off a slime track. These also produced acrasin and somehow despite the shaking and despite the absence of normal aggregation, the cells became coordinated so that they had polarity and their morphogenetic movement (as exhibited by the continued production of slime track) was oriented in one direction only. So we have come back to a familiar barrier in our explanations; we need to know how the spatial configuration of acrasin distribution and of the polarity of movement were determined in the first place.

It is interesting that when one compares *Chondromyces* and *Dictyostelium* that two life cycles could be so similar and yet in one case the fruiting body is constructed by bacterial rods, and in the other by amoebae. There is still another convergent form that builds somewhat similar fruiting bodies, but does so with building material made up of a continuous mass of unconfined multinucleate protoplasm. These are the true slime molds or myxomycetes which are so conspicuous and common in our woods. It is a frequent occurrence to encounter the large slimy plasmodial stage which is usually a yellow (but sometimes white or black) mass covering a damp log, or the fruiting stage which varies tremendously in its shape, there being a large number of different species.

The life cycle of the myxomycetes differs from the previous ones in that Wilson and Cadman (1928) have definitely demonstrated sexuality. The amoeboid swarmers emerge from the spore (the spore shape varies with the

[15] Bonner (1950).

species) and soon sprout a single flagellum. These uninucleate flagellated cells are the gametes, and following fusion the plasmodium begins to grow, for instead of cell division there are nuclear divisions only. I have already described the appearance of the plasmodium and its movement in the beginning of this chapter (Fig. 67). I will only add the fact that when the advancing foraging edge finds food, the majority of the protoplasmic mass will stream toward it to cover and wallow in it. The movements of this plasmodial stage are in no sense morphogenetic, no more

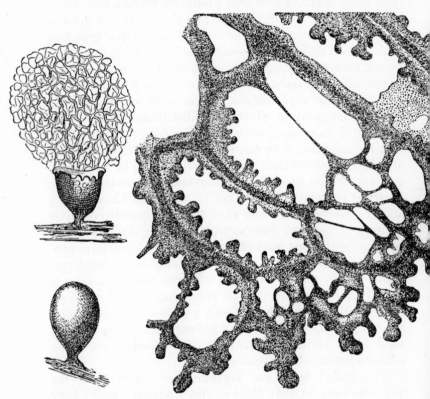

Fig. 67. Myxomycetes. *Right*: the plasmodium of *Didymium*. *Left*: a fruiting body of *Arcyria* before (below) and after (above) spore dispersal. The cottony mass in the upper figure is the capillitium. (From de Bary, Fungi, Mycetozoa and Bacteria, Oxford, 1887.)

so than the random movements of the vegetative amoebae of *Dictyostelium*. It is the period of feeding for the myxomycete, and again this period is completely separate in time from the fruiting or morphogenetic period.

The first sign of fruiting is a condensation of the plasmodium to a confined area and the appearance of a bumpy nodular surface. F. Howard (1931) has examined these stages with paraffin sections in the common *Physarum polycephalum*, and it is possible from his study to follow the morphogenetic movements. The bumps represent the subdivision of the protoplasm which actually becomes isolated by clefts, and each bump develops into a separate fruiting body. The stalk, which is made of noncellular exudate in the myxomycete appears first in the center of the nodule as a deposit, and as the rising starts, the stalk is continuously augmented, mainly at the top to extend it. The protoplasm streams upward on both sides, occasionally in *Physarum* branching (and hence the specific name *polycephalum*) until finally all the protoplasm is at the tip, upheld by the internally deposited stalk (Fig. 68). Progressive cleavage sets in (and reduction division) so finally the haploid spores are delineated, and in the clefts of the progressive cleavage, more exudate or deposit accumulates to form the capillitium. The shapes of the fruiting structure vary greatly with the species, often with a tree-like capillitium as in *Stemonitis* (Fig. 69), and sometimes, as for instance in *Dictydium*, there is a perfectly amazing structure, like a spherical bird cage suspended from a stand.

These morphogenetic movements of myxomycetes which involve the mass transference of large quantities of continuous protoplasm are especially hard to comprehend; for even the mechanics seem nearly impossible. Considering the high degree of precision in the structure of the fruiting body itself there is no question that there is an extensive control of the movements, but how this is achieved seems impossible to see at the moment. It does resemble, as was pointed out before, the growth of mush-

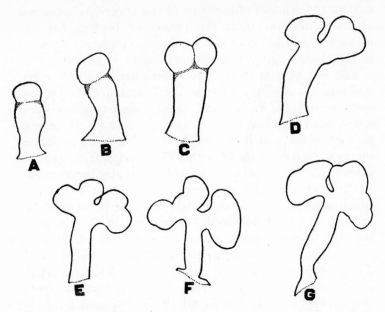

Fig. 68. Development of the fruiting body of the myxomycete *Physarum polycephalum* showing the formation of successive dichotomous lobes. (From Howard, 1931.)

rooms where the protoplasm from the underground vegetative mycelium seemed to surge to a point and push out a mushroom. If the cell walls of the mushroom hyphae may be compared to the stalk and the capillitium of the myxomycete, there may be considerable similarity. There is also another curious parallel among animals. With the coelenterate *Gonionemus*, Perkins (1902) managed to obtain syncitial masses of protoplasm that would rise very much like fruiting in myxomycetes, only to fall and rise again elsewhere. This case has no real bearing on any argument here; it is merely an anomaly so peculiar that, like an archivist, I must include it in our collection.

It is now time to turn to the types of morphogenetic movements characteristic of animals, but in order to keep a direct thread of continuity with what has just been said, the movements of the cytoplasm seen in the eggs of so

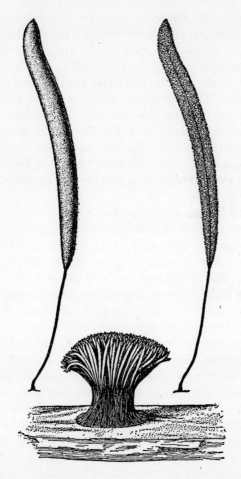

Fig. 69. Fruiting bodies of the myxomycete *Stemonitis*. *Center*, a group of fruiting bodies; *left*, a fruiting body before spore discharge; and *right*, after spore discharge showing the lace-like capillitium. (From Brown, The Plant Kingdom, Ginn, 1935.)

many animals might be briefly mentioned. It is another case of movements which do not involve the motion of cells, but instead the movement of protoplasm alone, as in the myxomycetes. But in the case of eggs the overall form is not directly affected, that is the egg retains its external

[187]

shape while the contents may go through a series of dramatic changes, such as Conklin (1905a) described for the ascidian *Styela*. For this reason these movements are not truly morphogenetic, but instead, as we shall mention later, are more closely involved in the process of differentiation. This process, which is sometimes called oöplasmic segregation, has received considerable attention among embryologists, and D. P. Costello (1948) has even attempted to interpret the movements on the basis of diffusion gradients resulting from differential permeability, even though this attempt is admittedly highly speculative.

The best-known morphogenetic movement among animals is the process of gastrulation, and although the inversion found in the colonies of *Volvox* most likely has no phylogenetic relation to gastrulation proper, some of the mechanical problems are similar, and of interest in their own right. The configuration of the movements of gastrulation and inversion are quite different from those that have already been discussed such as aggregation, and the various types of movements during the fruiting of the slime organisms. A long while ago C. B. Davenport (1895) classified all the various movements (which he had not distinguished from those changes in shape resulting from growth), but we no longer derive so much pleasure from classifying processes as we do trying to reveal their nature, and in this particular instance, clarifying the method in which they are controlled and coordinated.

We have already discussed some aspects of the growth of *Volvox* and now let me say some general things about it.[16] It is a green, slightly elongated sphere made up of a single layer of biflagellate cells, each separated by considerable quantities of jelly. The flagella protrude from the colony and beat in an organized way to give the whole colony a beautiful spinning motion. It spins like a top around the vertical axis, which is slightly longer than the horizontal

[16] The bulk of the material on *Volvox* was obtained from the beautiful paper of M. A. Pocock (1933).

axis. Periodically the ball reverses its spin and whirls in the opposite direction. As it spins the colony also glides slowly through the water. It is quite a sight to see a group of these colonies through the low power of a microscope; they are like a whole planetary system in the small universe of a drop of water, with each spinning green planet gliding through its orbit. Each colony has a rather rudimentary differentiation into front and hind ends, or rather north and south poles. It never turns head over heels but always keeps right side up. The cells in the northern hemisphere differ slightly from those in the southern hemisphere: they are a little larger and have fuller, more intensely green chloroplasts. Furthermore the reproductive cells are only found in the southern hemisphere.

Volvox has both a sexual and an asexual reproduction. In the asexual process certain large cells (gonidia) in this southern hemisphere begin to divide. The daughter cells resulting from division all lie in a plane and would form a sheet of cells if it were flattened out, but they are held together like the mouth of a purse with the strings pulled tight. As the cells continue to divide, they bulge inward to form a pocket, the daughter colony (Fig. 28). The total number of cells in each daughter colony varies, depending on the species, from around 500 to 50,000 cells. Apparently during this dividing process very little if any growth of the total colony takes place, so the dividing cells become progressively smaller and are closely packed in the daughter sphere.

Now this process places the daughter colony in an awkward position. The flagellar ends of the cells—those from which the flagella are destined to come—are turned inward, which means that the future flagella would sprout on the inside of the daughter colony. Such an arrangement would hardly be satisfactory for the locomotion of the colony; it would be like having the propeller of an aeroplane madly churning the air inside the cabin. Nature deals with this problem in a simple, straightforward manner: it turns the spherical daughter colonies inside out

(Fig. 70). The sphere has a hole called the phialopore at the point where it touches the mother colony. If you had a tennis ball with a round hole the size of a nickel cut somewhere in it, you would have a fair model of the colony. Now take the ball and push in the wall opposite the hole; with a little struggling you may be able to turn the tennis ball inside out by pushing it through the hole. This is precisely what the daughter colony does, that is in the course of an hour it turns itself inside out. First one can see a preparatory crinkling of the walls, and then it suddenly inverts. In doing so it frees itself from the mother wall, its phialopore end becomes the south pole, it sprouts flagella that point outward, and the colony begins to swim about merrily inside the mother. Eventually the aged mother, no longer capable of holding her kicking brood, splits open to die and gives birth to the young colonies which rush out into the world.

Sexual reproduction in *Volvox* follows after a period of asexual division, the latter occurring at the beginning of the warm weather in the spring and lasting for some time. Often, as van Leeuwenhoek[17] saw when he first described it in 1700, there will be daughter colonies within daughter colonies—three generations not yet separated. Then suddenly sexual colonies begin to appear and in some forms of *Volvox* separate male and female colonies develop, while in others the colonies are hermaphroditic. In the genesis of a male colony the cell that is to form the sperm, like the cell that forms the daughter colony in asexual reproduction, appears larger than its neighbors. It divides into an inward bulge of many small cells. Also (and this is quite remarkable) this sphere of future sperm cells undergoes inversion exactly as the asexual colonies do. By the time inversion is complete, each cell has sprouted two very long flagella, and the sperm ball begins to move. After some time it pushes its way gently through the wall of the "father" colony and liberates itself. The sperm then separate from one another and swim about freely.

[17] See Dobell (1932).

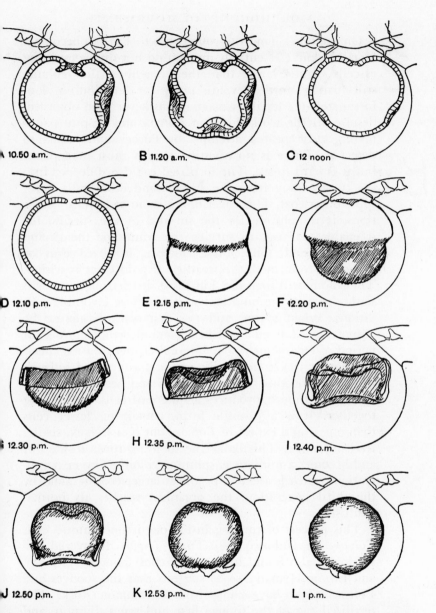

FIG. 70. Inversion of a daughter colony in *Volvox*. A, lip or phialopore depressed, denting beginning; B, denting more extensive; C, dents smoothing out, lip straightening; D, lip straight, colony rounded out again; E, equatorial constriction forming ("hour-glass" stage); F, contraction spread over posterior half; G, folding of posterior half beginning; H, infolding complete; I, posterior half beginning to emerge through a much enlarged phialopore ("hat" stage); J, "flask" stage beginning; K, "flask" stage ending; L, inversion complete, lobes of phialopore closing. (From Pocock, 1933.)

On the other hand the young cells that are to become a female colony (essentially an egg) do not divide; starting as cells slightly larger than their neighbors they enlarge still further until they are ready for fertilization. Unfortunately the fertilization itself has never been observed, despite all the work done on *Volvox* and despite painstaking and repeated attempts by Pocock and others to detect it. There is no question that it must take place, but it is hard to see. The fertilized egg drops deeper into the colony away from the surface and develops a hard, spiny outer coat. This covering, resistant to adverse conditions, is responsible for the survival of the species, for it enables the egg to survive the winter or the drying up of a pond. Once these resistant fertilized eggs or oöspores are formed, the weather may do what it wishes. The colony will soon die, but these little strongboxes will settle down in the mud and wait for more favorable conditions. When spring and the first warmth come, the oöspores split open and their contents emerge. After a period of enlargement and internal changes the egg peels off another jacket and finally emerges as a naked biflagellate cell. Soon this cell settles down and begins to divide. In a short time it produces a sphere of cells, all sticking together. It is a juvenile form, containing fewer cells than one would expect of *Volvox*, but it is *Volvox*, sitting free and alone. This ball, true to form, turns inside out and becomes a miniature, spinning colony. The next generation, which is asexual, produces larger colonies, and by the third generation, the organism reaches its normal adult size.

This process of turning inside out is not unique with *Volvox*. As Duboscq and Tuzet (1937) discovered, inversion is also found in the calcareous sponges (Fig. 71), and Libbie Hyman (1942) suggests that the sponges and *Volvox* might have come from a common stock. The fertilized egg of the sponge first undergoes division, and once a "blastula" of cells is formed it turns inside out much as *Volvox*. It is again a case where the flagellar ends of the cells point in the proper direction as a result of an inversion, for the mobile larva, covered over half its surface with flagella, is the result. This larva will settle on the bottom, its flagellar end will again invaginate in a true gastrulation, and the nonflagellated cells which will constitute the epidermis cover the whole of the sponge.

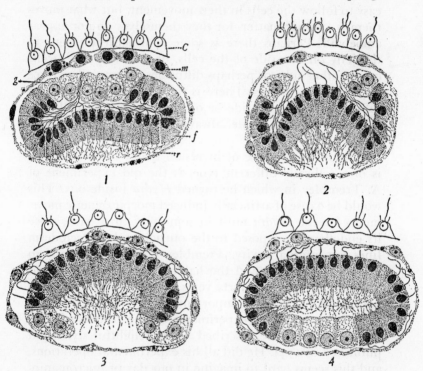

FIG. 71. Four successive stages of the inversion process in the calcareous sponge *Grantia*. c, a choanocyte of the radial canal; m, the placental membrane; g, a nonflagellated, presumptive dermal cell; f, a presumptive collar cell; r, basal filaments. (From Duboscq and Tuzet, C. R. Ac. Sc. *200*, 1935.)

Apparently, then, in sponges there is both an inversion and a gastrulation movement.

The inversion morphogenetic movement of *Volvox* and sponges is a highly coordinated activity, and yet the mechanics of it, the control mechanisms, are unknown and difficult even to imagine. In the case of *Volvox*, as one sees the cells at the edge of the fold (those that are actually turning) in longitudinal section, they appear to be spindle-shaped and as though in turning they all rock back so that their pointed ends on one side are nearly touching, and those on the other side are widely separated. It is easy to follow the cells in their movement, but what moves them is another matter, for they themselves do not appear amoeboid. Perhaps there is some contractile element in the jelly on one side of the cells, or that the jelly swells on the other side, or perhaps diffusion or some other force may account for this. There is no question in *Volvox* of different pressures inside or outside the ball of cells, for the phialopore, the hole, always connects the inside with the outside.

The only other case of inversion that I know, and this is of a radically different type, is the old experiment of A. Trembley in which he turned *Hydra* inside out. This would be a case of artificially induced morphogenetic movement, for the *Hydra* must in some way turn back, since its endoderm is exposed to the outside and the ectoderm lines the internal cavity. Trembley was the first really to learn the structure and the habits of *Hydra*, which had been discovered some forty years earlier by van Leeuwenhoek, and even more important he was the first to do really comprehensive experiments on the regeneration of any form, which he described (in a delightful style) and published in 1744. He did all his experimental operations, and this seems hard to imagine in our day of micromanipulators, by holding the organism in a drop of water in the palm of his left hand, while operating with the other. He inverted the *Hydra* by pushing it onto the end of a bristle and then withdrawing the bristle much as one might turn a sock about by putting one's hand in the end and pushing through. In these instances, it was only a matter of a few hours before the *Hydra* had, of its own accord, turned itself back. The movement here is clearly a muscular, contractile movement. To prevent this from occurring Trembley would pierce the inverted *Hydra* with another bristle transversely through the mouth region to bar any reversal movement. Such *Hydra* he found would live and after a period feed, so he kept them alive for many months, and they would bud and give rise to normal young *Hydra*. Recently Roudabusch (1933) has been able to show that in these instances there is a cellular movement and the ectoderm cells slip and infiltrate past the endoderm cells so that in a while each layer will again occupy its proper position. Presumably this morphogenetic movement is by amoeboid motion, but what guides the inside cells out and vice versa is an unsolved riddle.

To return to gastrulation, many experiments have been done on these movements in echinoderms and I should particularly like to consider briefly the work of A. R. Moore.[18] By altering the osmotic pressure within the blastula, he found what pressure was sufficient to prevent gastrulation and in this way was able to calculate the force necessary for invagination.[19] This information has not yet been too valuable in elucidating any theory of the movements. There is also, along this line, the work of A. Tyler[20] on the energetics of sea urchin development, where he showed that more energy per quantity of tissue was required for gastrulation in half or dwarf embryos than in normal ones, and normal ones required more than giant embryos consisting of two embryos artificially fused. As an explanation of this he suggests that since the wall thickness of the blastula stays the same for all three size embryos, the work per mass of tissue is greater in the smaller embryos and therefore more energy is required.[21]

[18] See Moore (1945) for a general review of his work.

[19] This was also done by Waddington (see Waddington, 1940, for the reference) for the amphibian using magnets and steel balls. Moore obtained a force of 3.9-7.8 gms/mm^2 and Waddington obtained 0.00034 gms/mm^2.

[20] Reviewed in Tyler (1942).

[21] A study of the morphogenetic movements in the amoeboid slime molds was also made, and it was also found to be possible to interpret it with essentially the same hypothesis (Bonner and Eldredge, 1945).

Of even greater interest to us is the experiment in which Moore cut the blastula so that the vegetal plate, that part which invaginates, is isolated. The invagination then occurs in the isolated piece, showing little concern with the fact that it has been cut off from the rest of the embryo. At the time of this discovery it was thought that gastrulation might involve differences in pressure between the inside and outside, much as one might collapse a tennis ball by sucking the air out from within it, but Moore definitely showed this was not so. It had long been thought that the explanation of gastrulation involved some such simple mechanism, and even D'Arcy Thompson has an illustration of a gelatin capsule collapsed on one side by differential dehydration, which was supposed to be a good model of gastrulation.[22] But now it is known that the cells themselves, which in echinoderms are compacted close together like wedges, must move and alter their shape. In his *Mathematical Biophysics* Rashevsky has considered this special case and believes that it too can be interpreted in terms of chemical gradients within the cells and that diffusion forces could conceivably be sufficient to accomplish the task. It could also be that there is contractility here, as there is in the case of *Hydra*, but no such force has been demonstrated. It is a frustrating fact that the mechanics of gastrulation in echinoderms, so easy and beautiful to watch under the microscope, is so obstinate in concealing its mechanism, but then it is somewhat consoling to remember that mitosis, which is even more common and easier to see in living organisms, is equally refractory.

The work of Vogt[23] stands out as the classic work on the definite demonstration and clear description of morphogenetic movements in animals. He worked with amphibians (although his technique has been used for a great multitude of forms), and by marking certain regions with vital dyes it was possible to follow the motions of

[22] Thompson (1942, pp. 561-562, Fig. 216).
[23] See Huxley and de Beer (1934).

those cells through gastrulation. Little blocks of agar containing different colored dyes were placed on specific areas of the amphibian blastula, and kept there long enough to spot the embryo. Then simply by making camera lucida drawings and noting the passage of time, Vogt was able to plot the course of the movements, and was able to show what regions of the blastula were to become what regions of the embryo and adult. Such "fate maps," as they are called, have now been made not only for amphibians of different kinds, but also of every group of vertebrates. It is possible, as J. Pasteels (1940) has shown, to have a comparative anatomy of gastrulation morphogenetic movements.

The movements of the different vertebrates do in fact differ greatly in their manner, and they all differ greatly from the simple gastrulation of echinoderms. The reasons appear to be largely connected with the yolk distribution: in sea urchins or star fish the yolk is relatively evenly distributed throughout the egg, while in frogs and salamanders there is a large concentration at one end of the egg. The invagination is therefore vastly modified so that instead of a whole side of the blastula pushing inward, there is a small opening or blastopore and (as Vogt showed) the whole outside surface moves toward the blastopore, passing through it much like a napkin being pulled through a napkin ring. Once inside the narrow blastopore the cells again spread out but this time on the inside of the embryo, forming the gastrula (Fig. 72). In fish and birds the process becomes so highly modified by the relatively immense quantity of yolk that the invagination practically takes place on a plane, since the embryo is really sitting like a covering on top of the great yolk mass.

In all of these cases the early morphogenetic movements play a vital and indispensable role in the development. It is primarily by this means, rather than by differential growth or oriented mitotic activity, that the animal embryo distributes its material at least in the early stages of development. But there are other movements

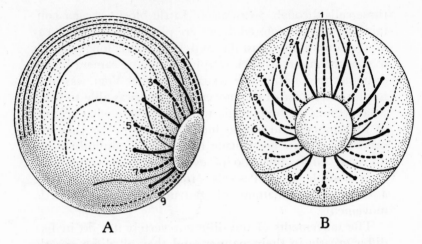

A   B

FIG. 72. Diagrams to show the direction of movement of the parts of the blastula during gastrulation in amphibia. A, lateral view, B, dorsal view. The thick lines indicate the direction of movement on the surface; the thin lines show the movement beneath the surface after invagination at the blastopore rim. (From Vogt, Roux. Arch. Entwickl. *120*, 1929.)

besides gastrulation which appear later, such as the closing of the neural folds to form the nerve tube and even in the formation of appendages. It is a process which exists in all the phases of animal development, although never so strikingly as in the early development.

It might be wrong to devote so little time to the description of morphogenetic movements of animals, but my reason for doing this is that this is the province of the animal embryologists, and there have been so many books that have done justice to this aspect. Our concern here is more with the control of these movements, and as an introduction to this, I should like to say something of the recent work of J. Holtfreter (1943a, 1943b, 1944).

Although the gastrulation movements of amphibians had been known and described for some time, Holtfreter increased our knowledge of them many times, and oddly enough mainly by just describing them again. By painstaking and keen observation he saw things in the same movements that had not been seen before. From this came the fact that the noncellular material or exudate which covers the egg plays an important role, one that had not been suspected. The superficial cells seem to be intimately connected to this covering material, which Holtfreter calls the *surface coat,* and he considers this coat to be the principle that unifies the cells and makes their movements coordinated. As he himself points out, one of the problems had been that it was thought impossible for cells to move by amoeboid motion, and yet they do so in a body in such a coordinated way that it appears as one mass movement. Holtfreter (1943b, p. 262) quotes Vogt as saying "it does not appear at all as if cells were working in the sense that single part-movements were combining to form the movements of masses; for even the most natural and plausible explanation by means of amoeboid motion of single cells fails utterly." The surface coat itself may be shown in eggs that have been kept from being fertilized to exhibit contractions and movements that closely resemble those found on the surface during gastrulation. The movements themselves, in normal gastrulation, originate from the amoeboid embryonic cells, but the surface coat guides these movements, according to Holtfreter's theory, and heads the cells towards the blastopore.

Since the coat remains on the surface it will not account for the invagination movement proper. In carefully examining the cells about the blastopore region Holtfreter noticed that as invagination starts, even those cells which have penetrated deeply into the interior are for the most part connected by fine strands to the surface coat at the blastopore lip, and give the cells a flask or bottle shape (Fig. 73). These strings of coat material presumably help to unify the inrolling over the blastopore lip, but there must be a reason why the cells should move inward at all. From other experiments he showed that the cells themselves have this tendency; it is not pressure exerted at the surface which propels them inward. At this juncture Holtfreter made a rather specific suggestion: that there was a gradient of hydrogen ion concentration that affected the surface tension of the cells so that they are pushed inward. It would seem, although this is admittedly a small point of criticism in so admirable a work, that it is unnecessary to be so specific as to how the cells are attracted inward, other than suggesting that it is by a chemical gradient. As a working hypothesis the idea of surface tension and pH gradients is certainly reasonable, but pH

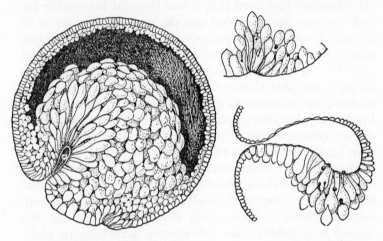

FIG. 73. Somewhat schematic sections through an advanced gastrula stage of an amphibian. *Left*: the whole embryo. *Upper right*: ingression of cells at the ventral blastopore lip. *Lower right*: the endoderm cells lining the archenteron. (From Holtfreter, 1943b.)

gradients appear unlikely in view of the fact that recently Stableford (1949) has shown, by artificially changing the pH in the blastula cavity, that invagination will occur with virtually any internal pH. There are many good cases where amoeboid cells become oriented in a chemical gradient, but in no case is it known how the chemical acts.

Another most important point made by Holtfreter is that the cells in different regions soon take on special properties with respect to their movement—properties which involve their tendency to stick to other cells, spread over surfaces, ball up, etc. These properties, which give the specific patterns of movements to cells in specific regions, he considers to be already determined in the egg. He says "the pattern of the movements is predetermined through the organization of the egg substances. How the latter comes into being remains to be answered."[24]

It may not be an odd coincidence that the problem of the patterns of growth and that of the patterns produced by morphogenetic movements should both be ultimately pushed back to a single problem: that of the localization of differences in different parts of the egg or germ. In the case of growth it was shown that these differences (which were bound up with the genetic constitution of the germ) ultimately controlled the growth either by affecting the rate of production or rate of destruction of growth hormones, or by affecting the reactivity of regions to such hormones, or by other means less easy to see. But in any event a certain structural pattern of the germ was thought to be a necessary basis for the pattern of the future development. With morphogenetic movements the situation appears much the same, although far less is known about it. As Holtfreter has suggested, the original control of the movements can be referred back to the pattern of the germ, but the intermediary steps are not so clear. Gradients of chemical substances sometimes seem to play a part; oriented ultrastructures may guide the movement of cells; adhesive, contractile exudates may be important. All these may be involved, for different movements, but the connection between these controls and the germ configuration is obscure.

One of the reasons for this is that so very little is known of the genetic control of morphogenetic movements. A difficulty is that the morphogenetic movements occur so early in the development that any mutant gene which affected them would undoubtedly be classed as lethal in that the embryo would not even survive gastrulation. There are, of course, many such lethal mutants that act before gastrulation and kill the embryo, but how can we ever know whether it was because the control mechanism

[24] Holtfreter (1944, p. 209).

of the morphogenetic movement was destroyed and not some other totally unrelated process necessary for life. There are so many ways of killing living organisms, and the less differentiation there is, as is the case in early embryos, the harder it is to analyze the cause of death.

There are some morphogenetic movements in the later embryonic life, and in one specific instance we have some knowledge of the effect of the genetic constitution of the cells on morphogenetic movements. In a series of interesting experiments Twitty[25] has studied the characteristics of chromatophore migration in two different species of salamander, *Triturus rivularis* and *Triturus torosus*. The chromatophores arise from the neural crest and migrate downward on the flanks of the embryo. The distribution of the chromatophores is characteristic of the species, for in *T. rivularis* they are quite evenly distributed all over

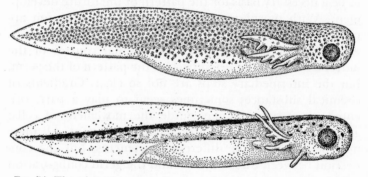

FIG. 74. The pigment pattern in young larvae of two species of salamander. *Above: Triturus rivularis* with a dispersed pattern. *Below: Triturus torosus* with a condensed streak of chromatophores. (From Twitty, 1949.)

the body wall, and in *T. torosus* they are densely congregated in a streak along the region of the lateral line (Fig. 74). In experiments on the dispersed type (*T. rivularis*) Twitty found that they tended to spread in all directions to wherever there was an absence of chromatophores, and if he removed the neural crest from its dorsal

[25] Reviewed in Twitty (1949).

position and grafted it onto the flank, the chromatophores would leave it and migrate up over the back onto the other flank as well as coming there from down under the belly. The chromatophores would exhibit this same migratory tendency in tissue culture, and here he was able to show good evidence that the cells gave off some substance, a gradient of which would orient the cells away from the source of production or high concentration point. By this means their movement is controlled, for they attempted to spread as far away as possible from one another. This phenomenon was supported by an experiment in which the spreading cells had to pass under a piece of glass coverslip. The cells under the coverslip were more widely separated from one another than the uncovered ones, presumably because the substance was trapped under the glass and rose to a higher concentration.

When the chromatophores of *T. torosus*, which shows the condensed streak pattern in the living animal, were grown in tissue culture, then the cells showed a quite different behavior. They did migrate for short periods, but then exhibited a marked tendency to clump. In fact the *in vitro* behavior of the cells not only reflects the chromatophore pattern of the embryo but also explains the difference in pattern. In this rather neat way, Twitty has shown that the pattern may be entirely a result of the migratory tendencies of the cells, which behave the same in tissue culture as in the embryos. But most important to us is the fact that the tendency to migrate, which is the basis of the pattern, is consistently different for the two species. Even though we do not know the genes involved, we may call this an inherited and therefore a genetic difference, and so here is a good case of the control of morphogenetic movements by genes. The factor that is inherited is the tendency to migrate and respond to the substances given off by the other cells; the rest, that is the whole chromatophore pattern, follows from this.[26]

[26] H. C. Dalton (1950) has shown that the axolotl behaves quite differently, for there the tendency to migrate is limited by the genetic con-

There are theoretically many ways in which movement could be controlled, and we have eliminated none of them. The ability of the cells to move may be controlled directly by genes or the local environmental conditions. The local environmental conditions must be consistently spaced, and this we have referred back to the configuration of the germ. The cells may respond to chemical gradients or oriented ultrastructures which, as we have already said, P. Weiss has shown to be so important in the orientation of movements. The chemical gradients may arise in many cases simply as a result of the distribution of cells, and the cell distribution may be happenstance. But no doubt there are cases where the distribution of the gradients may again be directly referred back to the germ. As for ultrastructures (which we shall speak of again), it is hard to imagine that any elaborate molecular orientation within the organism is not predetermined by the orientation within the egg. There appear to be many possible ways in which the pattern of morphogenetic movements could be controlled, some of which we have mentioned and most likely there are more. There is every reason to believe that organisms make use of many of them, not just one, and perhaps even many in the development of one organism. Admittedly much of this is speculation, but I have purposely kept it on a general level so as to increase its chances of being reasonable.

---

stitution of the epidermis rather than that of the pigment cells. The pigment cells spread readily under the epidermis of black axolotls, but fail to do so under the epidermis of white axolotls.

6. Polarity and Symmetry

THERE is one characteristic of developing organisms which has been briefly touched upon many times in the past discussion and which now deserves our full attention. This is polarity or, more generally, the symmetry of living forms. It shows itself by the fact that organisms have heads and tails, or roots and shoots, or various kinds of symmetry, radial and bilateral. It is the sign, the mark of organization within the organism, and in the beginning of development it is the first recognizable indication of the order that is to follow. Polarity is then a descriptive term referring to the geometry of the pattern, and for this reason it is especially hard to imagine that there is only one mechanism responsible for it. If one examines the shape of inanimate objects, they, too, often have a polarity, a symmetry, and one does not expect that they have all achieved their polarity in the same way: the symmetry of a crystal is of a different nature from that of a droplet of water. We have seen instances when growth has been directed in a polarized fashion, and also instances of morphogenetic movements. Soon, when we enter into the matter of differentiation, we shall see that the appearance of new structures is oriented and polarized. The one aspect of biological polarity, however, that does unify the concept and make us seek the underlying cause or causes, is the fact that it is the original indication of all the complex processes of development that are to come.

In most forms it is difficult to observe the laying down of the main axis of the embryo, for it is already present in the egg. In some way, during the formation of the egg in the ovary, its polarity or polar axis is established. There are forms in which the bilateral symmetry is also established in the beginning, while in others it may arise later. In amphibians the sperm entrance point and the trajectory of the sperm nucleus through the cytoplasm to the female nucleus apparently in some way affects the direction of the first cleavage plane and hence the secondary polar axis.

There is, fortunately, a case of an egg shed which appears to be completely devoid of any polar axis, and it acquires one after some time. This occurs in the brown alga *Fucus*, or rockweed, and the problem has been intensively studied by Whitaker and a number of others.[1]

As the egg first floats free in the sea water it is completely spherical, with the nucleus at the very center. The egg is soft and pliable until well after fertilization, when it becomes rigid. There are two signs of polarity which follow one another in succession. The first is the protuberance sticking out on one side of the egg, giving it a tear drop shape (Fig. 75). This protuberance, which

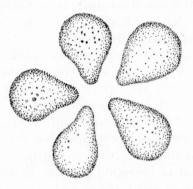

Fig. 75. Developing *Fucus* eggs showing the "group effect" in which the rhizoids point away from the center of the group. (Drawn from photograph by Whitaker, 1940.)

appears in *Fucus* about 17 or 18 hours after fertilization, is to become the rhizoid. The next sign, which appears in about 25 hours after fertilization, is the first cleavage plane, and it is always at right angles to the recently acquired long axis of the cell (as would be expected from Sachs' rule).

Of all the ways in which the polarity is established, the entrance point of the sperm is the most obvious. But it

[1] Reviewed in Whitaker (1940).

has not been possible to demonstrate clearly its influence in *Fucus*, although in a related form, *Cystosira barbata*, if it is kept in the dark, the rhizoid will definitely form at the sperm entrance point. The reason for doing the experiment in the dark is that light will, if it falls on the egg at a critical period, affect the polarity so that the rhizoids grow away from the light, in the direction of minimum light intensity. In *Cystosira* this critical period is at about 4 hours after fertilization, and in *Fucus* it is about 12 to 13 hours after fertilization. Another polarity-inducing factor is seen if the eggs are reared in numbers in the dark; under these conditions the rhizoids will turn toward each other, toward the center of the group, and Whitaker has called this the "group effect" (Fig. 75). On the basis of this experiment Whitaker suggested that carbon dioxide might be a potent factor in that it would tend to accumulate in the regions where the cells were thickest. It was also found that the group effect was altered by the pH of the medium, for at low pH's the effect was marked, but at high pH's the effect was reversed so that the rhizoids pointed away from the center. The carbon dioxide hypothesis does not completely account for the reverse group effect, and furthermore pH gradients in themselves are active (although the pH gradients are accompanied by gradients of carbon dioxide). Whitaker believes that the temperature effect might also be explained in a similar way, for Lowrance (1937) showed that if the eggs are placed in a temperature gradient of as little as $5.3°$ C/cm the rhizoids appear on the warmer side. It is assumed that the greater warmth results in higher metabolic activity and a greater production of carbon dioxide. It is also possible to affect the polarity by subjecting the eggs in their critical period to centrifugal force. But here again Whitaker found a marked pH effect, for at high pH's the rhizoids were centrifugal, and at low pH's they were centripetal. Alteration of the egg shape was also found to be a potent factor; for if the eggs, which are soft during the critical period, are sucked into a pipette so that they become molded into an elongate shape, then the rhizoid will invariably grow out from one of the pointed ends. If the eggs are placed in an electrical field, Lund found that the rhizoids will always form on the positive side, but the matter of electrical fields and polarity will be reserved for discussion later. Another quite different factor that has been studied is the effect of the plant growth hormone, auxin, on polarity in *Fucus*. By mashing the eggs and testing the contents on *Avena* coleoptiles, it has been shown that the eggs contain auxin. Auxin has been introduced to one side of the egg, and it was found that the rhizoid develops on the auxin side; the experiment was carefully done in a buffered medium to prevent any pH effect.[2] On the basis of this experiment it is conceivable that the polarity here involves a differential concentration of auxin, which in turn affects the growth differentially.

As R. Bloch (1943) points out in his comprehensive review on polarity in plants, there is another case when the polarity is extremely pliable, and that is the work of Fitting on the establishment of dorso-ventrality in the liverwort *Marchantia*. To put the matter briefly, it is affected by light, by gravity, by contact with the substrate, and by temperature gradients; it is in fact a situation basically similar to that of *Fucus*.

In both these cases there is no specificity as to the agent involved in establishing the direction of polarity; it resembles the case of activation of the egg in parthenogenesis, where almost any shock provides sufficient energy of activation to initiate the process. The response involves the laying down of a nonuniform pattern, a high point and a low point, a rhizoidal and a thallus end in the case of *Fucus*. It does not seem as though the exact nature of the stimulus will tell us much, it being so unspecific, for the problem that is of real importance is what is the physical basis of the polarity itself. Is it merely a con-

[2] This is the work of DuBuy and Olson. See Whitaker (1940) for reference.

centration gradient of substances, as Child would have it, or is there an elaborate crystalline lattice as others would have it? There is no reason that both should not exist simultaneously, and there is no reason why some other quite different mechanism should not be responsible. Before discussing these theories any further it is best to examine other properties associated with polarity, for they may help to clarify its nature.

There is a large number of organisms which can be shown to have a plastic, regulatory type of development, that is, in these organisms the tissue from various parts of the embryo is at an early stage quite totipotent, capable of becoming virtually any other tissue if it is transferred to another location. This is really a matter which concerns differentiation, but these regulative developing organisms possess polarity, and it exhibits itself in a striking way. As an example (from the many to choose from), take the case of the planula larva of hydroids studied by G. Teissier (1931) in which he managed to fuse the larvae, to graft them together. If they were lined up so that their antero-posterior axes were parallel and the heads pointing the same way, then when they were fused they formed one large larva (Fig. 76). If, however, they were put together

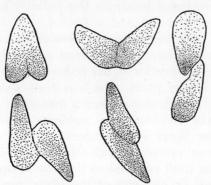

FIG. 76. Experimental fusion of the planula larvae of a hydroid (*Amphisbetia operculata*). Only the type of fusion in which the axes are aligned (upper left) gives normal giant embryos; the others give double monsters. (From Teissier, 1931.)

[209]

at any other orientation, then a double embryo was formed. The same was found to be true of sea-urchin embryos many years ago by Driesch (1907), and even in *Dictyostelium*, the amoeboid slime mold, it is possible to fuse the migrating pseudoplasmodia to form one by first carefully lining them up. One is reminded of the liquid crystals of ammonium oleate that Lehmann showed would fuse if they lie beside each other (Fig. 11), but the crystals do not have a head and a tail, and can fuse provided only that they are parallel. This superficial similarity is hardly to be considered evidence that liquid crystals are or are not involved in polarity. There are cases, for instance the sea urchin, where the gradient hypothesis is somewhat favored, for Runnström, Hörstadius, and others[3] have shown that the sea urchin is controlled in its early development by a double gradient, one from each pole, and it is obvious that unless the fusion is made so that these poles are lined up, there will be four poles instead of just two, and therefore two embryos instead of one. There is no doubt that in this case the gradients exist, but there also might be other physico-chemical factors which are simultaneously oriented and polar.

Perhaps of even greater interest and importance here are the experiments in which the polarity has been reversed in its direction and a few of such cases among plants and animals may be considered. The green coenocytic alga, *Bryopsis*, has been especially useful in experimental studies for it has remarkable powers of regeneration. If the plant, which is feather-shaped (Fig. 35) is turned upside down, then a new shoot will appear at the holdfast end, and new holdfasts or rhizoids will appear at the lower end. Steinecke (1925) stained the apical and basal cytoplasm with vital dyes, and found that the cytoplasm itself reversed so that the cytoplasm which was previously at one end of the plant, now moved to the other, this being possible since there are no internal cell walls. By further experiments, involving illumina-

[3] See Huxley and de Beer (1934) or Needham (1942) for references.

tion from below, and blocking out certain regions, Steinecke showed that it was apparently not gravity, but
light, which stimulated the movement of the cell contents. There is a considerable amount of cyclosis in the
organism normally, and it is easy to observe that the
chloroplasts will move towards the lighter side. Possibly
through the photosynthesis occurring in specific regions,
gradients are set up which are responsible for the cyclosis,
but as we have already said, the nature of cyclosis is not
certain. In this example it seems as though the reversal of
polarity is easy to understand. It involves simply a transference of the protoplasm, a slipping about of the protoplasm, so that shoot-forming protoplasm again reappears
on the light side, and rhizoid forming protoplasm on
the dark side.[4] This hypothesis may serve well for *Bryopsis*,
but there are other cases in which the organism is divided
into cellular compartments, and these require a different
interpretation. This does not weaken the case for *Bryopsis*;
there is no reason, as we have already said, to expect only
one physical basis for polarity.

The colonial hydroid *Antennularia* is a good example to
contrast with *Bryopsis* in that the general appearance is
remarkably similar in a superficial way, but the internal
structure is radically different. The body of *Antennularia*
is made up of a layer of uninucleate ectoderm cells, a
thin mesoglea, and an internal cylinder of endoderm
cells. There is no direct protoplasmic connection between
the cells in the feather-shaped colony, although the central
gastrovascular canal is continuous up and down the colony,
connecting all the hydranths. As J. Loeb (1894) showed,
in this case also if the animal is turned upside down the
polarity is reversed and new hydranths begin to appear at
the old basal end of the colony, and vice-versa (Fig. 77).
The reason for such reversal is not at all known, in this
case, and much more is known in the case of the related
hydroid, *Tubularia*.

[4] Recently W. P. Jacobs (1951) has obtained evidence of rhizoid induction in *Bryopsis* by indole acetic acid.

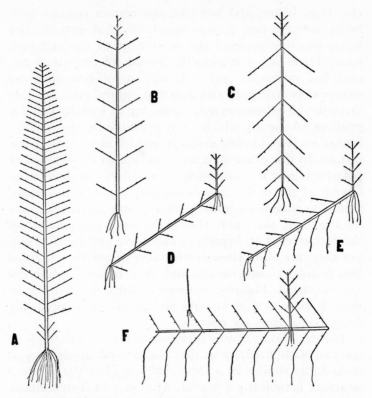

FIG. 77. Regeneration in the colonial hydroid, *Antennularia antennina.*
A, a normal stalk. B, a piece regenerating in the normal vertical position.
C-F, pieces regenerating in various positions. (From Morgan, 1901, after
Loeb.)

In 1903 T. H. Morgan published a paper amplifying a
previous observation of Loeb, and showed that if small
sections of the stalk of *Tubularia* (without any hydranths)
were implanted into sand, the end sticking out would always become the hydranth end despite the original polarity.
In a series of excellent papers, L. G. Barth[5] showed that
a key factor responsible for the reversal of polarity was
the oxygen concentration. He fitted glass tubes over the
stalks, and again found that the hydranth always appeared

[5] Reviewed in Barth (1940).

at the other end. He then measured the rate of hydranth formation in various concentrations of oxygen, and found that there was a good correlation. He also found that in the normal polarized stalk there is a gradient of oxygen consumption, highest at the tip and tapering off at the base, and that this gradient coincided with the rate of regeneration of pieces cut from these different regions. S. M. and F. C. Rose (1941) discovered that there was also an inhibitor involved, for they found that "stem water," water in which pieces of stalk had been kept for some time, would inhibit all regeneration even if its oxygen concentration was high. Regeneration is limited then by the oxygen tension and the toxic inhibiting substance, and these will both alter the polarity. The evidence here therefore strongly supports a gradient hypothesis of polarity, one which involves merely the proper concentration of critical substances. In view of the fact that the gastrovascular canal is continuous through the length of all these pieces of stem, there is every reason that the movement of any substance within the canal might be facilitated. In fact, Barth has shown that by occluding the internal canal in various ways, the apical end regenerates less quickly than in the controls, and the basal end more quickly. In a hypothetical scheme, Barth suggests that there is a free circulation in the canal and that there are substrates for critical enzymes passing about in it. There being a greater concentration of the enzymes in the apical end (as is reflected by its higher metabolism), the apical end obtains most of the substrates within the canal, in that way dominating the basal end. If the ligature occludes the canal, the apical end has less substrate and therefore is smaller, and the basal end has more and therefore is larger. It should also be mentioned that because gradients and chemical differences appear important here, it does not mean at all that polarity is entirely explained by gradients, and other factors, such as molecular orientation, may well be closely linked to the gradients; there is no evidence for or against such a possibility.

In passing I should say that these experiments on *Tubularia* suggest that perhaps the oxygen tension is important also in *Bryopsis*, for there, since the plant is photosynthetic, the oxygen tension would be highest in those regions which are most illuminated. This speculation is somewhat supported by work of C. M. Child (1917) on the red alga *Griffithsia* in which he confined pieces of the thallus in small quantities of water for a few days, or placed them in water of a low oxygen tension, and all signs of the original polarity became obliterated. By returning the pieces to favorable conditions, a new polarity appeared depending on the environmental conditions.

There are a number of cases where the polarity of a piece has been reversed by transplantation, simply by inverting a section of an organism and reattaching it. F. Peebles (1900) has done this with *Hydra* and other hydroids by cutting out a middle section of the body, reversing it, and replacing the anterior and the posterior portions on the cut ends. An even more remarkable case is that recently discovered by E. G. Butler (1949), in which he amputated a hand and inserted the distal end of the limb into a slit cut in the flank of a salamander, *Amblystoma*. After the wound had healed and the limb was permanently stuck in the pocket, he cut the forearm in two, across the humerus. The loose piece of arm, held only by the embedded tip, then became transformed so that it produced a new hand at its new distal end. Neither of these cases helps in revealing physical bases of polarity, but they are curious and interesting.

There are many examples of naturally occurring polarity reversals in regeneration which labor under the cumbersome term "heteromorphosis." For instance, in the case of *Planaria*, the flat worm, if a transverse cut is made too close to the head, then instead of a whole body being regenerated, as would be the case if the cut were further back, another head is produced with its axis in the reverse direction from the original head. The new head is a mirror image of the older one; were they crystals we would

call this a case of twinning. *Tubularia* may be made to do
the same thing by cutting close to the hydranth, so that
a double hydranth is formed (Fig. 78). The common earth-
worm will also do it, and as V. Tartar (1941) tells us,
ciliate protozoa such as *Bursaria* often do it after being cut
in two. But in *Bursaria* the situation may even be more
complex, for sometimes the orientation of the two pieces
are mirror images, but the direction of the ciliary beat will
reverse in one of the halves so that the cilia are beating

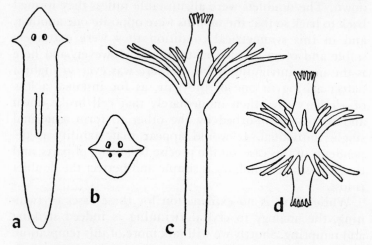

Fig. 78. Heteromorphosis in the flatworm *Planaria* and in the coelenterate *Tubularia*. a, normal *Planaria*; b, a double head resulting from
cutting off a small piece of the head region; c, the end of a stalk of
Tubularia showing a normal hydranth; d, a double hydranth resulting
from the regeneration of a small piece of stem. (After Child, 1941.)

harmoniously over the whole organism. Not only will
the anterior portions twin, but also the posterior portions,
and finally in some instances not only will the anterior-
posterior axis be reversed, but also the dorso-ventral, giving a completely twisted-about twin.

Fauré-Fremiet has recently (1945) described an especially interesting observation in connection with twinning
in the ciliate *Urostyla*. Here, by the addition of small
amounts of formaldehyde to the medium it is possible to

prevent the separation of the daughter cells after division, and in this way he obtained twins, triplets, and even quadruplets (Fig. 79). These different combined forms possessed different degrees of stability, that is different abilities to persist in their multiple state. The quadruplets were extremely unstable, and soon one of the four individuals was lost, this being the source of triplets. The triplets were somewhat more stable and would even persist through a few divisions, although they finally would break down. The doublets were all unstable unless they formed back to back so that the mouths were opposite one another, and in this symmetrical condition they were extremely stable and often divided many times. However, and here is the most intriguing point, if there was ever so slight a defect arising in one of the pair, as for instance a loss of a ciliary row, then immediately that cell broke down and become reabsorbed by the other to form a normal single individual. It would appear that stability is dependent, in this case, on the precise balancing of parts, and that unless the symmetry is simple and perfect the doublet is lost.

While there is no explanation for these cases of twinning, the analogy to crystal twinning is indeed striking and tempting. Shortly we will talk more of this temptation, but here let us examine a case of twinning in plants where the explanation, although purely hypothetical, is quite different. If a fair size section of stem is cut, it will, as every gardener who propagates plants by stem cuttings knows, regenerate new shoots at the apical end and new roots at the basal end. It has already been shown that auxin applied for a limited time on the basal region will stimulate the initiation of roots. It is well known that if the stem section is made very small then no roots will appear at the basal end, but shoots appear at both ends; a case of heteromorphosis. Auxin moves, as we shall soon discuss in detail, from the apex to the base, and on the basis of this the plant physiologist explains the fact that roots are ordinarily initiated in a stem cutting because the auxin

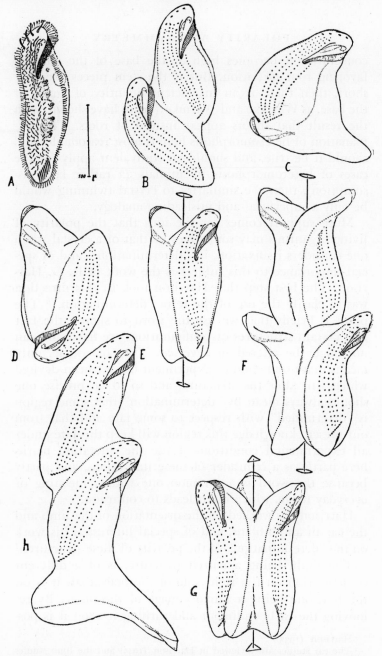

FIG. 79. Double and multiple monsters experimentally induced in *Urostyla*. A, a normal individual; B, C, D, unstable doublets; E, a stable, symmetrical twin; F, a stable twin resulting in a chain as a result of cell division; G, a triplet formed as a result of the elimination of one of the cells in F; H, the disintegration process of the unstable triplet. (From Fauré-Fremiet, 1945.)

concentration becomes high at the base of the cutting, favoring root initiation. But if the stem pieces are very short, then there is an insufficient quantity of auxin at the base, as Warmke and Warmke (1950) have shown, with the result that shoots appear instead of roots. This explanation of heteromorphosis here is most reasonable; and should it be true, and should an equivalent apply for the cases of heteromorphosis in animals (a rather large assumption), then the similarity to crystal twinning would be only a superficial and misleading analogy.

More support comes for the idea that the polarity of living organisms may sometimes be that of a crystal when one considers its fixation, its "determination," and of special importance to this subject is the work of R. G. Harrison. The first step that Harrison took in this direction was to clarify the use of the term "determination."[6] The point is briefly that we use the word to signify the fact that certain structures or configurations are fixed and can no longer be altered or reversed. This, of course, only means that no method or experiment has yet been devised which will alter the structure, and so to be precise one should always mean by "determination" that some region is "determined" with respect to some fate and that from our present knowledge this region will keep this fate under all experimental conditions. I use the quotation marks here partly as a reminder of these limitations, and partly because the word is a common one with a meaning of everyday usage, which often leads to confusion.

Harrison has worked on the orientation of the limb and the ear in amphibians, and of special interest is his work on the "determination" of the polarity of these structures.[7]

The limb, being a paired structure, is of a different configuration on the right side of the body than it is on the left, one being a mirror image of the other. By removing the early rudiment and turning it 180° it is pos-

[6] Harrison (1933).
[7] The ear studies are reviewed in Harrison (1945) and the limb studies by Swett (1937), who did much of the original work himself.

sible to reverse the antero-posterior axis; in fact by the proper rotations, and using limbs from both sides of the body, it is also possible to reverse the dorso-ventral and medio-lateral, or inside-out axis. If these operations were made early enough in the development, it was found that the polarity would in every case become reversed, but if they were done in late embryos, the adult limbs were abnormal in orientation. The polar axes had become "determined" and moreover it was possible to find at what stage during the development this had occurred. The development of *Amblystoma*, the newt which was used for these experiments, has been subdivided by Harrison into stages marked by their morphology rather than size or time; the stage numbers start with one and work up. Using this index it was found that all the axes were not determined at once, but first the antero-posterior axis at a very early stage, certainly not later than stage 20, next the dorso-ventral axis at about stages 33-35, and finally the medio-lateral axis at about stages 35-37.

These beautiful and meticulous experiments have been discussed by Harrison (1945) for the ear, which behaves in essentially a similar manner, and he suggests that this fixation of the three main axes in succession might be a transition from the isotropic condition of a liquid to the successive mesoforms found in crystallization (from a melt); first molecular orientation in one axis, then two, and finally three to form a crystalline space lattice. To support this hypothesis he further found that if the operation was made during the critical periods then there was an extremely high incidence of twinning of the ear structure, a phenomenon so characteristic of crystals. In an attempt to find actual physical support for this idea, Harrison made some X-ray diffraction studies of the ear with the crystallographers Astbury and Rudall,[8] but it was not possible to detect any space lattice. As they point out, this does not mean there might not be one there, but simply that it was impossible to reveal it with existing techniques.

[8] Harrison, Astbury, and Rudall (1940).

From his crystallographic concept of polarity, Harrison has built up a whole theory of development based on the space lattice of protein molecules. As an hypothesis he presents it in a convincing and compelling way, not completely excluding the idea of chemical gradients, but suggesting that they are a result of the space lattice. He considers the proteins with their frequent dipole character to account directly for the differences in direction, in polarity, and the fact that one end of the molecule differs from the other means that in a crystal the properties in one direction will differ from those of another, a phenomenon we have already seen to be true. These differences give rise to differences in concentrations of specific substances which in turn give rise to differentiations, a matter which will be considered in the next chapter. This theory of Harrison has the great merit that it completely accounts for the spacing of the structures in the embryo and does not refer the problem back another step.

In the egg of *Fucus*, it is also possible, as Child[9] has shown, to obtain twinning, but in this case affecting the egg with two different stimuli, as for instance light from one side for a period, and then by turning the egg, illuminating the other side (Fig. 80). Here the twinning seems to be produced by gradients, although as has already been said, a space lattice might also be involved. The matter would be quite simplified if a gradient could determine the orientation of a space lattice and a space lattice could determine the orientation of a gradient. If this were so then all these diverse examples would be unified.

Before leaving the subject of "determination," there is another point of considerable interest. In animals Harrison has postulated that "determination" of the polarity involves an internal crystallization, and now we may ask what is there in plants which "determines" the polarity of cells. *Fucus* would offer a perfect example, and there also the process of "determination" is a crystallization, al-

[9] See Child (1941).

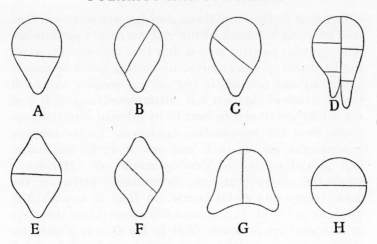

Fig. 80. Experimental alteration of polarity in *Fucus*. A, normal development with the plane of cell division at right angle to the axis indicated by rhizoid growth. B-D, altered relations of rhizoid outgrowth and division plane resulting from a change of direction of illumination. E-H, twins resulting from periodic changes of 180° of the direction of light. (From Child, 1941.)

though in this case it is not internal, but the laying down of the rigid crystalline cellulose cell wall. The very same is true of higher plants, for once the walls have "crystallized" the shape and polarity are beyond altering. There is no doubt but that the "determination" here is only in the wall, for in tyloses of woody plants, where the cell contents burst through one of the bordered pits of a rigid cell, the escaped protoplasm will, in its new confines, divide and change as though it had been delivered from its prison. If Astbury (1945) is correct, it is the nucleoproteins within the cell which orient the direction of cellulose deposition, and perhaps the nucleoproteins among the cells are somehow loosely coordinated together, so that the overall plant has its polarity.

There is another interesting experiment on the "determination" of polarity done by V. Twitty (1928) in which he studied the effect of temperature on the stage of development at which "determination" of the direction of the ciliary beat in the amphibian *Amblystoma* occurred. The cilia covering the flank of the embryo have a definite antero-posterior polarity, that is they beat backwards towards the hind end of the embryo. By cutting out a square of epidermis and rotating it 180° it was possible to find if the direction of the beat was "determined," for if it was, the square continued to beat in its original direction, opposite from the surrounding epidermis. Twitty ran two experiments, one at 15°C and one at 25°C, and found that at the equivalent developmental (or "Harrison") stages the ciliary beat was "determined" earlier at the colder temperature. Of course, in *time* it was actually much longer at 15°C, and what this shows is that the effect of increased temperature (that is, the Q_{10}) is greater for development as a whole than it is for "determination." It is also true that low temperatures favor crystallization, but this fact can hardly be taken too seriously here, for all it really shows is that the idea of crystallization is not completely incompatible with "determination."

At first it seems as though nerve impulses are polarized and go in one direction only, for we think of one part of the body as informing another part, but in fact an impulse will pass either way on a nerve. The reason that impulses ordinarily go one way along a nerve is that one end of the neuron is stimulated and the impulse passes to the other end, but should the nerve be stimulated in the middle, which is easy to do experimentally, the impulse will pass both ways. This principle is best illustrated in an old experiment of Mayer (1906) on the jelly fish *Cassiopea* which, if cut into a ring and stimulated, will give a wave of contraction that passes around the bell. If one stimulates at one point, the impulse starts in both directions, meeting finally at a point opposite the starting point, each having traveled half way round the circumference. When the impulses meet they extinguish one another, but if by applying ice on one side of the region stimulated, the impulse on that side is diminished, the other will make the complete circle and continue to do so for many hours.

There are two main reasons why a higher animal does not remain in such a chaotic state. In the first place there are the synapses, the connections between one neuron and the next, where the fibers do not actually touch but lie in close proximity to one another. It is thought (with considerable evidence) that in some way neurohumors (mainly acetylcholine) are produced at one ending and stimulate the other. It is quite easy to see that if only one end is capable of producing sufficient acetylcholine to cross the gap the synapses will give a polarity to the whole nervous system and control the direction of the impulse. The situation is even more complicated, for the neurons are frequently connected in such a way that a number of them come together in one synapse, and the impulse will selectively go through certain pathways. An animal injected with strychnine will undergo the most violent and gruesome spasms, because the drug eliminates the selection among pathways, and all the nerves at each junction become stimulated. The other reason that the nervous system retains order is that the configuration of the nerves themselves is orderly. They connect the receptors, the eye, ear, nose, etc., with the effectors, mainly the various muscles, and they are connected in an intricate pattern in the spinal chord, most especially in the brain. Thus we see that the polarity of the nerves themselves is not seen in the direction of the impulse, but in the direction of the whole fiber, the placement of its dendrite and axon ends with respect to the whole organism, and the laying down of the whole intricate pattern of all the nerves. The polarity of the nervous system is no superficial physiological property, but a deep-seated property related to the whole pattern in which the nerves are arranged during development.

The situation in plants is radically different. There, not only does the mature organism perform its living functions with no nervous system, but also development is unassisted by any dominant brain region. Instead the dominant region emits auxin and in some ways the transport of auxin serves an analogous function to the transmission of nerve impulses; they both are correlation mechanisms. The biggest difference, however, is that auxin is transported in a strictly polarized fashion, it moves, at least in the shoot of the plant, in one way only.

This phenomenon, as Went[10] has shown, is an easy one to demonstrate. If a section of a shoot is placed right side up between two agar blocks, the upper one containing auxin, then in a matter of hours the auxin will have become reduced in the upper block and accumulated in considerable quantity in the lower block. (The auxin content of the blocks is measured by the *Avena* test.) If the same experiment is performed with the piece of stem reversed, basal end upwards, then the auxin in the upper block remains there—none enters the lower block. It may be easily shown, by doing the whole experiment upside down, that gravity has no effect. Even more remarkable, and especially disturbing to the physical chemists, is the experiment in which auxin is placed in the blocks both at the apex and the base of the stem cutting. Then the apical one again becomes depleted, and the basal one increases its concentration. This means that there has been an accumulation of auxin against a concentration gradient, which for one completely excludes the idea of diffusion as the responsible mechanism.

There are other reasons also (if such be needed) for discarding diffusion. The rate of this polar transport is in the neighborhood of 10-15 mm/hour,[11] which is many times greater than what one would expect of diffusion of auxin. This is a simple enough fact to record, but very hard to explain. It was thought that it might be connected in some way with cyclosis within the cells, but the polar transport rate exceeds even the rate of cyclosis. The only reasonable explanation suggested thus far is one demonstrated by van Honert (1932) using a model. A long horizontal tube was half-filled with water and half with ether, an ether-water interface ran the length of the tube,

---

[10] See Went and Thimann (1937).   [11] In *Avena* sections at 25°C.

entering into a large reservoir at each end. If then certain substances were poured in one end, they moved along the interface at rates equivalent to polar transport and accumulated in the other reservoir provided there was a chemical system in the other reservoir that would effectively remove the substance. Potassium oleate was poured in one end and it was combined with hydrochloric acid in the reservoir. It is conceivable that an interface between cells, or between protoplasm and cell membrane, might be capable of supporting such rapid movement along it, but certain problems remain unanswered: for instance, why will the auxin accumulate against a concentration gradient, and why will the auxin move in one direction only? These two problems are undoubtedly one; it is likely that a single physico-chemical process will account for both, but the nature of the process is completely mystifying.[12] Many times before the study of plants has enlarged our knowledge of physical chemistry, as for instance the discovery by Brown of the motion named after him, or even better the discovery by Pfeffer of osmosis, and it may well be that plants are again about to teach us a new principle, although it is equally likely that it is a well-known one to which we are for the moment blind.

The fact that auxin moves against a concentration gradient suggests that in some way the metabolism is involved, for work is being done and energy is required. We have already shown that a diffusion gradient will not do, and it is also hard to imagine how the crystalline structure of the cell wall (or of the protoplasm if such exists) could in any way completely account for polar transport. W. P. Jacobs (1950) has shown that polar transport does not exist in a very young seedling, but appears only after the first few days of growth. Whatever it is, it apparently may arise gradually during the early development. For a brief moment it was thought that the answer might be found in

[12] One odd fact, that may be of great significance in the elucidation of polar transport, is Clark's (1938) discovery that it is specifically abolished by sodium glycocholate.

electricity, for it was known that the plant stem had a potential difference between the apical and basal ends. But Clark (1937, 1938) found that no matter what was the sign of the potential difference, the polar transport was unaffected.

The idea that polarity, in fact that all of development, is governed by electrical fields is one that has had a number of adherents, and especially ardent among these are Burr and Lund. By means of beautiful techniques and very delicate instruments it has been shown that in all organisms there are potential differences, and it is possible to draw out a sort of a rudimentary electrical field for the organism that reflects its actual shape.

There is no quarrel with the reality of these electrical potentials or the excellence of their experimental measurements; the argument comes in interpreting their role in development. Are they, as most people assume, passive byproducts of all the chemical and physical activities within the cell, or are they responsible for controlling and governing all the activities during development. There are two matters—the morphological shape with all the chemical and physical differences of parts, and the electric field—and the question is which controls which. There is no doubt (for they can be measured both in the living system and in models) that electrical potentials accompany the various chemical and physical changes of development. This is expected from the very nature of electricity itself. Concerning the reverse, there is no theoretical reason why potential differences could not do much to guide the course of certain processes.

Perhaps the most thoughtful and soundest presentation of the case to support this latter view is that of Lund (1947) in his recent book. He shows that not only does the electrical polarity correlate with the morphological polarity, but also it is possible to control the direction of polarity by electrical current. To take examples familiar to us, it is possible to control the direction of polarity in *Fucus*, where the rhizoid will grow toward the anode, and in pieces of *Tubularia* stem the site of formation of the new hydranth will be affected by the direction of the current irrespective of the direction of the previous polarity.[13] I cannot here do justice to Lund's hypothesis, but must express my opinion that I do not find much strength in these arguments. There are no doubt cases where the potential will have a marked effect on some reaction which will ultimately have its effect on the shape, and that therefore electricity is an active force in the epigenetic course of development, but this does not mean that it need control the whole course of development. The evidence that electricity plays this part is in the final analysis negligible and moreover, were it so, man's supremacy on the earth would be quite lost to the electric eel.

In the beginning of this chapter there was a warning that most likely polarity in living organisms is not the symmetry of just one physico-chemical phenomenon, but of many, and thus far we have suggested instances where it might be interpreted in terms of gradients of chemical substances, and others in which there is a hint that some type of crystalline network, and still others such as polar transport in plants were a good explanation is still completely wanting. It is commonly imagined that perhaps the polarity that first appears in the developing embryo, which is, as we said before, the first sign of organization, might be fundamentally the same for all forms, but this is no more than pure conjecture. The special case of polar transport seems to serve a different function, and there is no rational reason why it should be the same problem.

It is somewhat helpful to examine primitive colonial forms to see how the individual polarities of the cells have become fused into one overall polarity. There is one especially curious case in the colonial diatoms described by Wagner (1934). In *Nitschia putrida* the boat-shaped cells sometimes form loose colonies, and since the cells move, the whole colony will move, and the astounding aspect is that the swarm which makes up the colony moves as an or-

[13] See Barth (1934).

ganized body (Fig. 81). The cells form two zones in the meteor-shaped mass: an outer zone in which the cells lie parallel to the surface, and an inner zone in which they lie straight in the direction of the movement. This gives the swarm a morphological polarity, a rounded head and a trailing tail, and the movement is consistently head first. The swarm moves evenly, and should an obstacle be in its way it will either surround it and close the ranks

Fig. 81. Organized swarms of the diatom *Nitschia putrida*. (From Wagner, 1934.)

again as it passes, or if the obstacle is larger, then the mass will split in two to form two separate normal colonies. Occasionally two colonies going in approximately the same direction will veer into one another, and they then fuse to form one large colony. The behavior in the amoeboid slime mold *Dictyostelium* is remarkably similar, not only in its general characteristics but also in the fact that any good explanation is wanting.

In *Dictyostelium* it is impossible to interpret the polarity of the migrating sausage in terms of those of the individual cells, for the long axes of the cells may be oriented at right angles to the direction of movement.[14] Instead the polarity

[14] Bonner (1950).

seems to have transcended the individual cells, and appears in the cell mass as a whole. This fact is important, for in the multicellular phase of this slime mold the cell boundaries seem to have lost their importance for polarity, and all the protoplasm works together. For this reason explanations which involve chemical gradients or crystal lattices which extend through the individual cells and ignore the compartments are useful, even though they both are to varying degrees hypothetical.

But still there is no reason why *Nitschia* and *Dictyostelium* should be explained the same way, and to drive this point home one need only examine the herding and schooling of some of the higher animals where the mass of animals has a polarity of its own. There are some extraordinary cases that defy explanation such as the "snake worms" of the larvae of *Sciara* flies. According to Imms (1934) it has been frequently reported in Europe and this country that a large number of larvae will come together, all lined up in the same direction, and form a moving mass that often is 12 to 15 feet long, 2 to 3 inches broad, and about ½ inch thick, and which moves at about a rate of an inch an hour. This strange phenomenon occurs shortly before pupation, but its significance is not known. In ants there are many fairly precise orientations of masses of individuals, and of special note is the marching and foraging formations of army ants. There something of the coordinating mechanism is known, and Schneirla (1933, 1940) tells us that the blind ants tend to follow tracks where ants have been previously. It is a follow-the-leader instinct affected by a chemical sense and also strongly affected by the physical structure of the terrain. The only ants, then, that have any special problem are those in front of the column and they appear somewhat bewildered and groping, but the back pressure of the guided, marching ants is great and keeps pushing onward the confused, irresolute, and constantly changing leaders. This instinct to follow is so clear-cut that if they are placed on a large flat area and they start to move in a circle, they will follow one another round and round the circle for many hours until they die (Fig. 82). No single ant has the unhappiness to be a leader and be pushed into the unknown, but this ideal equality leads to their destruction.

Flocks of birds in flight also may show a beautiful polarity and symmetry and we have all marvelled at a "V" of wild geese flying high in a cold autumn sky. There is no doubt the actual positions are achieved by eyesight,

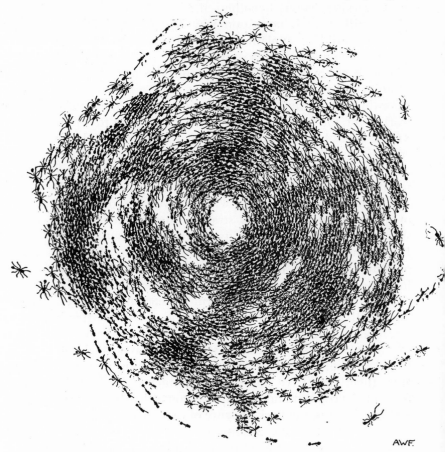

AWF.

Fig. 82. Army ants following one another in a circle. (Drawing of a photograph. From Schneirla and Piel, Scientific American, *179*, June, 1948.)

just as a pilot flying formation in an aeroplane must watch his neighbor every instant and keep his plane in the correct position. But there is another reason for the "V" shape, and this is an aerodynamic one, for the air disturbances created by a goose are such that another goose flying slightly behind and to one side will be in a zone devoid of turbulence, and may even be benefited by some upwash. Thus, if all the birds in a gaggle of geese attempt to fly as close as possible, the "V" formation is the best one to avoid turbulences. Here the mechanism of the oriented alignments differs from those of army ants and involves a combination of eyesight and a muscle sensitivity to air turbulence during flight.

The schooling of fish has been studied carefully by Parr (1927) who has shown that the perfect form of the school is the result of receptors of the fish, most especially vision, and that the fish align themselves by looking at their neighbors and gauging their position accordingly.[15] Although there is no doubt of this explanation, there are still some unsettling facts, such as the case Gudger (1929) shows us where the fish are lined up in perfect rows like the beginning of a crystal lattice (Plate IX) for again we are not so sure all is understood.

So we see that in aggregates of animals complex matters involving sensory perception enter into the mechanism of the polarity of the aggregate; sometimes a chemical sense, sometimes visual, and sometimes a mechanical or pressure sense as in the flight of geese. The moral from this should be that symmetry, or polarity, is merely a geometrical configuration, and there is nothing to exclude the idea that the basis of this polarity during development might be vastly different in different forms—just as the blind army ant differs from the fish that needs its eyesight for schooling.

[15] See review on the schooling of fish by Morrow (1948).

7. Patterns of Differentiation

WE HAVE at last come to the matter of differentiation, an aspect of development which not only is vastly important but which may also tell us more of the overall mechanism of development. The growth of organisms was compared to the work of a sculptor who continually adds clay to make a shape, and morphogenetic movements involve the pushing and the molding of the clay. But differentiation is another matter, for the various regions of the statue would become transformed from clay into other materials of different chemical composition. One might say that a child's doll in which the body is china, the hair, wool, and the eyes glass shows a certain degree of differentiation, but I fear the analogy is wearing thin.

In living organisms, during development, the various parts take on, by synthesis, differences in chemical composition so that the protoplasm is changed in some constitutional manner; for instance, an amoeboid embryonic cell may differentiate into a nerve cell. This may be and often is accompanied by a change in the shape or size of the structure, making it sometimes difficult to separate morphogenetic movements and growth from differentiation. The word "differentiation" is used here in a very general sense without any specific reference to the structures involved. The structure that becomes altered in its chemical constitution might be a cell, a multinucleate mass, a tissue, an organ, an organ system, or a whole organism. If at any point the structure involved is pertinent, then expressions such as "cellular" or "tissue" differentiation will be used.

As before, the concern here is mainly with the pattern of differentiation rather than with the process itself. Differentiation might be pictured as a series of chemical reactions in which the end products are different from the primary reactants. To take an easy example, amphibian melanophores are said to have become differentiated when they turn black, and this is thought to be a simple series of chemical reactions involving melanin formation with the enzyme tyrosinase. Although it is true that few cases are so obvious as this, it is assumed (for there is really no other alternative) that differentiation involves a series of chemical reactions seeking an equilibrium during development. The condition required, then, for this chemical process is that the initial reactants are together in a specified region. Since it is rare that the whole organism differentiates into one structure, but different parts go different ways, the major problem of the pattern of differentiation resolves itself as to how these specific substances are distributed in space in the beginning, and the reader may remember that the control of growth and morphogenetic movements presented the very same problem. There are cases where the differentiation might be considered relatively uncontrolled and uncoordinated. For instance, in the case of bacteria certain cells become condensed into spore cells, but there does not appear to be any order which determines which cells are to become spores. The result is quite haphazard and there is no spore-bearing zone in a bacteria colony.

It is perhaps misleading to talk of the differentiation of a cell, such as the nerve cell, for parts of the cell itself may differentiate. In elaborate protozoa, as for instance ciliates, there are many structures and organelles, the gullet, the trichocysts, the cilia, the neuromotor net, the contractile vacuole, to mention a few, and all of these are part of a single cell.[1] Multinucleate organisms, where the cell wall boundaries are lost, also have differentiations of parts. And even more interesting is the differentiation of groups of cells to form tissues, such as nerve bundles, or the phloem, the bast of plants. On a still higher level the differentiation is with respect to organs such as the

[1] I say "single cell" in full cognizance of C. Dobell's (1911) frantic plea for calling the protozoa "acellular" organisms. For a number of reasons I do not think his point is well taken, and I would prefer to use other means of clarifying concepts than by coining new words.

kidney, or the leaf. Further up the scale there are organ systems, for example the vascular system of animals, or the vascular system of plants. And finally all these are brought together harmoniously to give organisms.

Our task is to examine this elaborate wholeness of organisms, to find how the intricate individual arises in development. It is helpful to recall again what we said previously of the relation of differentiation and size; that the division of labor which arises from differentiation is required if the organism is to achieve any size. The differentiation involves differences in structure, and these structures are all associated with specific functions; this is as true of the organelles of protozoa as it is in our own vast and complex organs. The reason for pointing out the connection between differentiation, structure, and function is that if in abstraction we consider function alone, then the problem of the *wholeness* of organisms becomes much easier to grasp. If we are asked to describe, or characterize living things, the simplest and most generally accepted way is to say that living things are those that are capable of metabolism, coordination, locomotion, development, and reproduction. Living organisms possess all these functions, and this is what distinguishes them from the nonliving. These five major groups of functions furthermore, are necessary for life, and without one of them there would be no living world. It is true that an individual organism may live for a period without development or reproduction, and in this case only metabolism, coordination, and some degree of locomotion would be required. But the point is that an organism is alive because it can of its own accord perform these basic functions: it is therefore a package of functions. There may be secondary functions which are not vital, and a blind man may live a happy life, although if we do not look at one individual, but at the species and its place in evolution, then each minor function is vital to the survival of the species. For life, then, the functions must be parcelled together into a unity, and the suitability of such "functional wholes" is not hard to see.

But if we again shift back to the structures associated with the functions, and ask how it is that they arose to produce a "structural whole," then the going becomes more difficult, and we are back to our old problem. There is a harmonious community of activities within the organism, and these come from differentiated structures which arose in development. If one says that all that need be done is to know the organization of the germ, and from it arises the differentiated adult, then one is faced with the problem of the germ. One could avoid the problem, I suppose, by saying that nothing caused the configuration of the germ and that it came directly from the parent. This would chase any possible solution way out of sight into the remote beginnings of life on earth. It would seem that there are a number of reasons why this is a false position, the variety of plants and animals that have arisen in the course of evolution being one.

There are many cases where it can be inferred from the evidence that the egg itself has its materials so distributed that the subsequent development involves merely the partitioning of these materials into small cell compartments, each of which in different regions of the embryo will contain different substances and therefore differentiate into different structures. This is assumed to be the mechanism of what embryologists call mosaic development, a type of development which may be observed in many of the phyla in the animal kingdom.

The study of mosaic development, which is the classical work of experimental embryology, has been reviewed and discussed in detail in so many places that I shall not enter in upon it here in any detail. Among the many organisms that have this type of development, there are great variations in details of the process, and here we shall consider only one example. The ascidian *Styela* (which used to bear the equally beautiful generic name of *Cynthia*) was first described by E. G. Conklin (1905a), who then later did so much to investigate the details and reveal by experiment the nature of mosaicism. The unfertilized egg of *Styela* is evenly spotted with yellowish pigment granules, but immediately following fertilization these yellow granules seem to drain down to the vegetal pole of the egg, leaving the animal pole filled with yolk except for a small apical cap of clear protoplasm (Fig. 83). The sperm which lies in the vegative portion will then move towards the center of the egg, and since it follows a consistent path every time, presumably there is already a plane of bilateral symmetry within the egg. The male nucleus pulls the yellow material inward as it moves so that finally there is a yellow crescent of material which extends half way around the egg, and is in fact the presumptive mesoderm. Immediately above this yellow crescent there is a clear crescent, and before the first cleavage is completed the clear portion spreads out over the whole animal sphere of the embryo to become the presumptive epidermis. After the first cleavage three regions become distinguishable in the vegetative half: the yellow crescent which will become mesoderm, a clear grey crescent on the opposite side of the egg from the yellow crescent which will become the neural tube and the notochord, and finally the vegetative pole region which is rich in yolk and is the presumptive endoderm. There may be some variations in the timing of the processes, but always there are these protoplasmic movements which precede the localization of the material, and of special interest is the fact that all the localization of material does not take place at one time, but in a series of steps. Most of the movements of material take place within ten minutes after fertilization, and following this very fluid period, the protoplasm suddenly becomes highly viscous, as though to gel the position of the substances once they have reached their proper places.

Of special interest is Conklin's experimental analysis. He was able, by killing various cells after the first and second division, to show that there was absolutely no

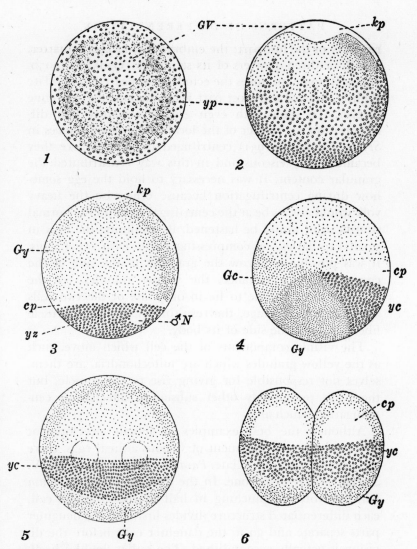

FIG. 83. Localization of substances in *Styela*. Yellow spongioplasm (yp) containing mitochondria represented by small circles; gray yolk (Gy) by close stippling; clear protoplasm (cp) unshaded. 1, before fertilization, showing the germinal vesicle area (GV) and the yellow cytoplasm evenly distributed over the surface. 2, immediately after entrance of the sperm, showing a clear region (kp) derived from the germinal vesicle at the animal pole, and the yellow cytoplasm is streaming down to the vegetative pole. 3, the yellow cytoplasm forms a cap at the vegetative pole (yz) containing the male pronucleus. The clear cytoplasm (cp) forms a layer just above it. 4, left side view of the egg just before cleavage, showing the yellow crescent (yc) and the clear crescent (cp) posterior, and the gray crescent (Gc) anterior. 5, Egg similar to the preceding, viewed from the posterior pole. 6, two-cell stage viewed from the posterior pole. (From Conklin, Chap. IX of Cowdry, General Cytology, Chicago, 1924.)

recovery of the lost part; the embryo just lacked a quarter, a half, or three quarters of its structure (Conklin, 1905b, 1906). In some instances the ectoderm appeared to regulate slightly, but for the most part what was missing was gone forever. To show with even greater certainty that differentiation is a matter of the localization of substances in *Styela*, Conklin (1931) centrifuged the eggs before they became overly viscous and in this way redistributed the granular content. It was necessary to hold the egg somehow during centrifugation because otherwise the heavy yolk would always be at the centrifugal end and the normal stratification would be hastened. By confining the eggs in small capillaries, or compressing them with other eggs, it was possible to throw the granules to the side of the egg, and if, for instance, the yellow granules (of the yellow crescent) came to lie in only one of the two cells after the first cleavage, the resulting embryo had muscle fibers on only one side of its body.

The visible components of the cell which move, such as the yellow granules which are mitochondria, are themselves not responsible for giving rise to the muscle, but there are presumably other substances affected by centrifugation which are.

Although the best examples of mosaic development come from the development of various animal eggs, there are other cases, the ciliate *Paramecium* according to V. Tartar (1941) being one. In the division of *Paramecium* which involves a pinching in half of the elliptical cell, each differentiated structure divides first, and the daughter parts separate and go to the daughter cells before the division is actually accomplished. The gullet doubles itself, as do the contractile vacuoles, and even the kinetosomes at the base of the cilia divide, so that all the preparations have been made well before the fission. If *Paramecium* is cut in two, it will not, like *Stentor* and so many other protozoa, recover and regenerate the lost part. It will remain deficient, and if the structure lost is of vital importance, such as the gullet, the *Paramecium* will die, in this case from starvation.[2]

Even though the ciliate *Stentor* regenerates well, recently P. B. Weisz (1949) has shown that, contrary to earlier work, certain parts of the long annulate nucleus will favor the regeneration of certain specific structures. According to Weisz during some phases of the division cycle all parts of the nucleus are equally effective in causing the regeneration of the whole of the lost part, but in other phases, there are some nodes of the long nucleus that fail to induce the regeneration of certain structures.

If development in all organisms were mosaic, I think we would feel that it was an easy problem and we might be well on our way of knowing the chemistry of these organ forming substances that become localized. As was said before, there would be the matter of how these substances became arranged the way they do, and in both *Styela* and *Paramecium* there are apparently morphogenetic movements intimately connected with the localization. These movements, though they might be mediated by diffusion or by some other means, must in turn be the result of the original localization of materials, which reminds us again of the importance of the configuration of the germ, and so the problem may still not be as easy as one might imagine. But there is another kind of development—regulative development—which requires an entirely different view from mosaic development, and in fact at first seems quite opposite to it.

It used to be thought that there are two separate kinds of development, mosaic and regulative, but now the two are interpreted on a common ground. The basis of mutual understanding emerged when "determination" in embryos

[2] Diatoms also exhibit mosaicism of an interesting sort. Upon cell division the valves separate and each half forms a new valve within the parent valve. Thus, the average valve size of a clone will become progressively smaller. The spacings of the sculpturings on the valves remain the same, resulting in a loss in the number of the pits. However, upon auxospore formation, when a totally new large individual is formed, the original number of markings is restored.

became better known, for it is now believed that regulative development is the development occurring before "determination" can be demonstrated (and for that reason is sometimes called "undeterminative" development), while mosaic development takes place after "determination" (and therefore is sometimes called "determinative" development). So in this scheme the only difference between the development of *Styela* and that of a hydroid is that in *Styela* the "determination" can be demonstrated very early (about ten minutes after fertilization)[3] and in the hydroids it would be quite the other extreme, for at least in some regions it can never be demonstrated at all. But even in ascidians the mosaic character goes, and the mature ascidian is capable of regeneration, of regulative development. In the asexual budding process it has been shown that apparently all the cells, that is ectoderm, mesoderm, or endoderm cells, retain the ability to produce whole new adult forms.[4]

In the particular case of *Styela* there is an interesting new facet of "determination." We talked before of "determination" involving a crystallization process, and talked of Harrison's evidence for the ear of the amphibian, and the crystallization of the cell wall in plants. In *Styela* the "determination" is correlated with a sudden great increase in viscosity, giving rise to the intriguing possibility that all the organ-forming substances are fixed in a particular place. In all these cases "determination" seems to consist of a physical restraint on the protoplasm so that it becomes locked into position, and this now gives us a reasonable general statement of the nature of "determination." Exactly how the restraint is achieved from a physico-chemical point of view is not always clear: in plants it is the crystallization of the cellulose wall; in animals it might either be

---

[3] The ascidian has considerable regulative powers at very early stages (see Dalcq, 1941).

[4] Rose (1939) has also demonstrated that the degree of mosaicism in ascidians is not quite as extensive as previously thought, for he gives evidence of the anterior regions inducing the differentiation of the posterior regions.

by crystallization, and we would then assume that the increased viscosity of *Styela* represents an internal crystallization, or it might be that there are other non-crystalline solidifications such as gelation which would account for some or all of the cases of "determination" in animals.[5]

It is my feeling that the most difficult aspect of development to comprehend is regulation, which exists before it is possible to demonstrate "determination." Once an embryo is "determined" we think of all the parts, with their different chemical composition as simply following out a series of chemical reactions to become differentiated, but we have no simple scheme, even a hypothetical one, which can account for the mysteries of regulation. It was this very thought that made Driesch (1907), who did so much to reveal the nature of regulation in the embryos of echinoderms, turn to entelechies, for he could not bring himself to imagine any part of physics or chemistry accounting for so beautiful and so adaptable a process as regulation.

Regulation, as we shall soon see in detail, involves the whole organism, so that if it is cut in two, for instance, each half is perfectly formed although only half the size. More than anything else, this sensing of the whole, this making of a perfect whole from a small bit of a previous whole, is what seems marvelous to us, so much so that we become, I think, psychologically affected and troubled, and cannot believe that a solution to such a problem would be anything but difficult, if not impossible. I cannot assess why this thought of wholeness and regulation should affect us so, but there are many evidences of it: from Hans Driesch, from Lloyd Morgan and his concept of emergence, from Jan Christian Smuts and his holism.[6] But perhaps the closest tie is with the Gestalt psychologists, W. Köhler (1929) in particular, who have so successfully shown that

[5] Needham (1936) expresses a similar view when he says "The distinction between mosaic and regulation eggs, therefore, can partly be defined in terms of internal friction." (p. 72)

[6] See Wheeler (1928) for a delightful essay on this general subject, with a good list of references.

we tend to think in wholes, that is take auditory and visual sensations and group them together in our minds. An old and familiar example is the case of music which is but a sequence of notes, although to us it becomes a melody, a theme, a unit, and the individual tones are lost in our minds to the impression of the whole melody. Perhaps, then, because our minds are forever grouping stimuli from the outside, it is a severe subconscious shock to find that developing organisms also have their Gestalt.

It is helpful and steadying to the mind to look in the physical world for analogies to regulation in organisms; and there are many, all easy to understand. A frequently used example is that of the magnet whose properties are observed so well with iron filings; no matter how a magnet is fragmented, each part has a north and a south pole, each part regains its wholeness. I am not suggesting for a minute that magnetism is involved in development of organisms, for there is every evidence that no living process is much affected by reasonable magnetic forces.[7] Another analogy might be partition coefficients where a substance has a different solubility in two imiscible solvents that are in contact. The ratio of the solute will adjust its distribution, will regulate itself according to any changes in the relative quantity of the solvents. An even better example, and one which has been discussed at some length, is regulation during crystal growth, where no matter what part of the crystal is removed, the new growth will repair the damage to form a new and perfect crystal. This does not involve, as does biological regulation, the redistribution of the old parts, but merely the correct placement of new materials; but in liquid crystals even the old parts, which are loosely held together, will rearrange to form a perfect new crystal. There is no evidence that organisms are large liquid crystals (a matter which we will discuss later), but I mention it here only because it is a good analogy, and it shows, along with the other analogies, that regulation

[7] See Heilbrunn (1943, pp. 498-499).

is not so peculiar to the living as it would seem at first glance.

Let us now devote some attention to regulation in organisms, and see, by examining a number of different forms, what its particular properties are. Because the animal kingdom is so much richer in its variety of different kinds of differentiations, and because of the elaborateness of animal structure, it provides especially good examples.

We have seen a case of mosaic development among protozoa, and have mentioned that in many phases of its division cycle *Stentor* shows admirable regulation and will produce, if it is bisected, two perfectly formed smaller *Stentors*. The deficient pieces become modified so that lost parts are restored by the transformation of already differentiated parts. V. Tartar (1941) tells of a curious aspect of these operations which I have observed a number of times. If *Stentor* is almost cut in two, the pieces hanging together only by a small thread, the two halves first appear crimped at the edges, much as one imagines a tube of toothpaste might look after it has been cut in two with a pair of scissors. The halves will slowly come together so that they are again opposite one another, and the crimped edges will open up and fuse so smoothly and suddenly that it becomes hard to believe that the animal was ever cut. Tartar has repeated this cutting in the same place up to twenty times, and then finally the organism gives up and bursts. There seems to be a closer affinity between the parts that were together before; one is reminded of the forming of the plates of cells in *Pediastrum* where the cells seemed to snap into their assigned places in a very short time.

Another protozoan, *Stylonchia*, shows (according to Tartar) an ability to regulate even without any cutting. If the organism is starved, then it will become smaller and smaller, and as it does it continually reorganizes itself so that its proportions remain the same.

In all these cases of regeneration and regulation of protozoa it is necessary to have some part of the nucleus in the fragment, for without it the piece will live for a short

[243]

while, but will never show any signs of reconstitution. It is often assumed that the nucleus contains the necessary factors which govern the reformation of lost parts, and although the evidence from the protozoa supports this point, we must turn to other forms for more striking evidence.

Largely because of the great advances of the study of genetics many differentiations are known, and many assumed to be determined ultimately by the genes in the chromosomes. This does not exclude the idea that some differentiations might be effected solely by factors in the cytoplasm, but in most cases the nucleus undoubtedly plays a major role. Aside from the genetic evidence, the most direct information on the role of the nucleus comes from the work of Hämmerling[8] on *Acetabularia,* the coenocytic green alga that lives in the sea. Hämmerling worked with two species, each of which has the general appearance of a mushroom about five centimeters high (Fig. 84). They have a rhizoidal base, a straight stalk, and an umbrella-like hat, differing in its pattern in the two species. Since it is a member of the Siphonales, there are no internal cross-walls; and, what is especially unique, one large nucleus is located at the base of the stalk in the rhizoid. Should there be any other nuclear material located in other parts of the plant, all the implications of these experiments would be invalidated, and this criticism has been raised, but Hämmerling assures us that there is only one nucleus. It is possible to graft these algae, and by placing a stalk of one species over the rhizoid (and nucleus) of another, a new hat will be regenerated. This hat will be characteristic of the nucleus, not of the stalk which contained the bulk of the cytoplasm (Fig. 84). It is true that in the first months of regeneration the hat first resembles the stalk, and then later becomes entirely characteristic of the species belonging to the nucleus. Hämmerling explains this by assuming that the stalk is still full of substances produced by the old nucleus, which have

---

[8] See Hämmerling (1946) for references.

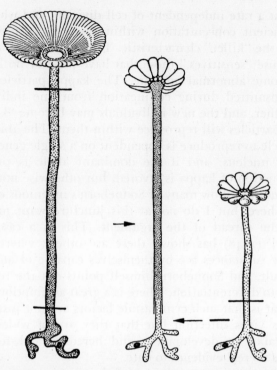

FIG. 84. Regeneration in *Acetabularia. Left: A. mediterranea. Right: A. Wettsteinii. Middle*: a graft in which the stalk of *A. mediterranea* is grafted onto the nuclear portion of *A. Wettsteinii*, and the new hat formed at the tip is characteristic of the nucleated portion. Note the single nucleus in the rhizoidal base. (From Hämmerling, 1946.)

to be used up before those of the new nucleus can reach the regenerating hat. The evidence would seem excellent in this case that the nucleus directs the pattern of differentiation.

There are a few cases where factors associated mainly with the cytoplasm seem to affect the differentiation, and I should like to make a brief mention of T. Sonneborn's work on cytoplasmic inheritance in *Paramecium*.[9] There are cytoplasmic particles (the kappa particles) which dup-

[9] See his general review (Sonneborn, 1949) for references and a clear discussion of this work.

licate at a rate independent of cell division, and which, if in sufficient concentration within the *Paramecium* will give it the "killer" characteristic. That is, these *Paramecia* will cause "sensitives," those that have little or no kappa, to become abnormal and die. The kappa particles may be transmitted during conjugation from one individual to another, and the new individuals may become "killers" if the particles will reproduce within them. The ability of a particle to reproduce is dependent on a single gene locus in the nucleus; and if the dominant allele is present, reproduction of kappa is favored, but otherwise not. It is a pity not to follow many of Sonneborn's ingenious experiments here, but I do not at this juncture want to stray from the thread of the argument. This is a case, and Caspari (1948) has shown there are others, where cytoplasmic substances are by themselves capable of affecting the adult, and Sonneborn himself points out the relation of this to differentiation. There is a great assumption here, and that is that such cytoplasmic factors are not just some curious virus infection but that they are of widespread importance in development and heredity, and for this there is no real evidence to date.

There are two general types of theories concerning how these nuclear and cytoplasmic particles ultimately affect differentiations, and I should like to show that they are not antithetic. One is that differentiation results in the differences of material, both nuclear and/or cytoplasmic becoming localized in different parts of the embryo, and the other is that at least for a period the nuclei and the cytoplasm of all the different parts of an organism *may* be (that is they do not necessarily *have* to be) the same. So that we may easily refer to these two theories, as examples are discussed, let us call the first the "difference" theory, and the second the "equivalence" theory. From the onset I shall state my view to show the tenor of the way, and that is that the "difference" theory applies to those cases where "determination" can be demonstrated, and the "equivalence" theory applies to cases of regulation; and just as it is possible to show degrees of "determination," so there are many intergrades between complete "equivalence" and complete "differences."

In the case of the segregation of cytoplasmic materials, we have already amply covered this subject in showing examples of mosaic development. In most cases there is no evidence whether the cytoplasmic materials have been produced by the nucleus originally or not, and there is no reason not to assume that some have and perhaps some have not. It is usually the accepted view that the nuclei of all the cells are the same, and this is based on the fact that nuclei appear generally fairly uniform throughout a mature organism. On the basis of cytological studies in plants Huskins (1947) differs sharply from this traditional view, for he finds that different plant tissues have different numbers of chromosomes—different degress of polyploidy —and says that the nuclei are not at all equivalent throughout an organism. It would be quite impossible to explain all differences arising in differentiation on the basis of this regional polyploidy (and Huskins does not attempt this), especially, as will be shown, in regulative organisms. Even in polyploids the gene contents are assumed to have the same properties, being merely duplicated, and polyploid animals and plants differ little from diploid ones, except for differences in size, especially cell size. G. Fankhauser (1945a, 1945b) has made it clear that in the differentiation of certain tissues, such as the tubule walls in the kidney, the wall thickness is the same even though the cells are larger (being polyploid), showing that, if anything, the size effect of the polyploidy is being suppressed or compensated for. There is a classic case of chromosome difference arising in development, and that is in the round worm *Ascaris* where Boveri showed that in the early cleavages the germ line became quite distinct from the soma and had a different nuclear behavior.[10] But for the most part the weight of the evidence supports the view that the genes and the chromosomes do not segregate or differ

[10] See Wilson (1925).

radically during development, and they are at least similar in structure throughout the body of all organisms.

In instances of regulatory development not only is there an equivalence of the nuclei, but also in the beginning there is evidence of an equivalence in the whole protoplasm, as Driesch (1907) showed so well; and let us now look at a series of cases of regulatory development to support such a contention. The ideal circumstance would be cases in which one could take an organism apart, separate its cells and rearrange them together to see if it is possible to make a new organism with differentiated parts. If the different cells of an organism show differentiations before they are separated, obviously there must have been chemical differences among the parts. The point here is not that there might be differences, but that also there is something basically similar in all the cells, for otherwise it would be difficult to account for their ability to become different structures with new locations in respect to the whole. Admittedly such experiments would hardly prove that there is a basic uniform set of factors within each cell, but it would strongly indicate that such is the case.

The best known and earliest authenticated instance is that of H. V. Wilson (1907, 1911a) in which he dissociated sponge cells by pushing a sponge through fine bolting cloth. The cells will settle to the bottom and soon clump, almost undoubtedly by agglutination. Galtsoff (1923, 1925) studied this process and found that the amoeboid cells moved about at random, and as they collided with another cell they would stick until larger and larger balls of cells were formed.[11] It is necessary apparently to achieve a certain size clump in order that development may proceed, and if this threshold is reached then in about four days flagellated chambers will begin to appear and function, and the canals will begin to riddle the mass. It

[11] There is not complete agreement on this point, and de Laubenfels (1932) favors the view that at least in some species there is a contractile jelly which pulls the cells together. Fauré-Fremiet (1932) makes the most reasonable suggestion that a simple agglutination phenomenon is involved.

turns out, however, that the sponge has its limitations as an example, because, as Brien (1937) and others point out, different kinds of cells go through the bolting cloth, the small amoebae (pinacocytes) which produce epithelial and canal lining cells, the collar cells of the flagellated chambers (choanocytes), and the large amoebae (archeocytes) which produce the remaining cell types, such as the wandering amoeboid cells, and the spicule-forming cells. It is difficult to separate these cells, and determine whether one type can be transformed into another (although there are some reports in the literature (see Brien, 1937), and also the preliminary work of C. K. Liu (1948) indicates that amoebocytes may becomes choanocytes). Nevertheless it is assumed that the different cell types pass through the bolting cloth without becoming modified, and simply start their old activity again. The problem of how they achieve the pattern in the new sponge is hard to see. It is possible that there are aggregations of certain cell types, for although Galtsoff did not observe this, it might possibly occur within the cell mass, because the cells certainly move about.[12] In any event the pattern of the sponges is a complex problem of which we know little. In part its shape appears strictly governed by hydraulic forces such as those Bidder (1923, 1936-37) discusses, but then there must be inherited shape factors for the sponge as a whole, and somehow they operate in this loose and complex mass of cells.

The only instance in the sponge where a group of cells appear equivalent comes from those sponges that form gemmules. For in the gemmule there is only one cell type, archeocytes, and these amoeboid cells give rise to all the different cells of the sponge. At first it would seem an odd paradox that in the case of gemmule reproduction the ultimate fate of a cell would appear to be the result of its

---

[12] This would be akin to the specific clumping of bacteria discovered by Topley et al. (1935). They found that if two species of bacteria and their respective antisera were mixed, the resulting clumps were homogeneous; that is, they were composed entirely of one or the other species.

position within the whole organism according to the principle advanced by Driesch (1907), while in the case of the dissociation experiments their position appears to be the result of their predetermined function. Perhaps the mechanism is the same in both cases, and in the gemmule first the cells become partly differentiated, and then they find their position according to the function they are capable of performing. But all these matters are entirely speculative and it might be more profitable to turn to other forms to pursue our problem of establishing the equivalence of parts of a developing organism.

The amoeboid slime mold *Dictyostelium* is almost an ideal example, for any modification after cutting away part of the sausage-shaped migrating cell mass must consist entirely of regulation, of the redistribution of the parts, for there is no intake of energy from the moment the independent cells stream in and aggregate. The cell mass is then entirely a result of the streaming together of the cells, and their ultimate fate in differentiation depends on when they entered the aggregation stage, for if they are early they become large vacuolated stalk cells, and if they are late they become small encapsulated spore cells.

The immediate problem here is whether or not it is possible to make potential spore cells become stalk cells, and potential stalk cells become spore cells. If so, the conditions set up would be satisfied, and we would have evidence that the cells in the different parts of *Dictyostelium* were initially the same, and that they became modified only by virtue of their position in the whole. As Raper (1940b) showed, if a posterior half, or for that matter practically any fraction of the whole, is cut off from the rest of the migrating cell mass, it will produce a normal fruiting body. That is, it will have a stalk, while previously it was to give spores only. If an anterior tip of a migrating cell mass is isolated it will give a fruiting body,[13] and thus potential stalk cells have become converted to spore cells. The only

[13] The proportions of this fruiting body may be abnormal. See Raper (1940b), Bonner and Slifkin (1949).

cells whose fate cannot be altered in such a way are the cells at the very tip itself, for they always must be stalk cells. The only way they can conceivably be altered (and this is somewhat hypothetical) is by separating the tip cells by disrupting them with a glass rod as Raper (1940b) has done. Then they will aggregate for a second time and it is possible that at least some of the tip cells which have become widely scattered will enter into the aggregations late and become spore cells. From these various experiments there seems to be excellent evidence that differentiation is not controlled in this case by the localization of specific differentiation determinants, but that all the cells possess all the determinants, and that their expression is dependent upon their position within the whole cell mass.[14]

A short while ago I became interested in the specific problem of the control of differentiation in *Dictyostelium*.[15] I had found previously that already in the migration stage it was possible to see a sharp line of demarcation between the anterior stalk cells which were larger and the posterior spore cells which were smaller. In measuring a whole series of fruiting bodies of different sizes (not forgetting that the size is dependent here on the number of amoebae which aggregate to a center) it was found that the per cent of the volume of the cell mass to become the stalk and the dry weight were the same irrespective of the total size. The proportions, then, are perfectly accommodated to differences in size.

The process of aggregation is effected by chemotaxis toward a substance acrasin, which continues to be emitted by the cell mass. Recently we have made attempts to correlate the acrasin distribution with the appearance of the division line that separates the presumptive spore cells and the presumptive stalk cells, but there seems to be no

[14] We were able to grow a colony from a single spore and to do so for a number of successive generations. Sussman (in press) has further shown that it is possible to obtain normal fruiting bodies from single amoebae from any stage of development.

[15] Bonner and Slifkin (1949), Bonner (in press).

correlation between the two phenomena. It is possible to reveal the division line by staining the separate cells before aggregation with a vital dye, and then after aggregation, with the beginning of differentiation, the evenly stained migrating mass will suddenly have a dark tip (presumptive stalk) sharply separated from a lightly stained posterior end (presumptive spore). This striking color change no doubt reflects differences in the chemical constitution of the anterior stalk region and the posterior spore region, for they do differentiate into different tissues, but how do these differences arise with a consistent antero-posterior polarity, and how do they regulate the division line between stalk and spore cells so accurately? One feels that one is close to the real problem here—the problem of the control of the proportions of the cell types in differentiation. It brings us back to the problem of a basic configuration in the cell mass, but one cannot even discriminate here between a theory involving diffusion gradients or some sort of ultrastructure. There is a crystalline deposition of the cellulose sheath about the stalk cells, and the slime sheath itself covering the whole cell mass shows birefringence, but this tells us nothing of how the organism consistently marks off a certain per cent of its cells for stalk cells. But at least we have, in this example, dissected and exposed the enigma of regulation in organisms and shown what manner of problem faces us.

The oldest and still one of the best examples of regulation is the fresh water polyp or *Hydra* which Trembley (1744) studied so carefully. If the *Hydra* is cut in almost any way, the pieces will rebuild the lost parts. They will do so without feeding or the intake of new energy, but entirely by the rearrangement of the existing parts, entirely by regulation. If for instance the *Hydra* is cut transversely, the basal portion will regenerate a new mouth, and new tentacles, and the apical portion will regenerate a new foot. Cells which previously performed one function and had one place in the body, now, after the operation, become modified and assume new functions. In all cases, a perfect, although immature *Hydra* is the result. The only parts that cannot do this are the tentacles, which for some reason are incapable, without the mouth region, of regenerating a new body.

Some years ago H. V. Wilson (1911b) showed that not only sponges but certain hydroids could be pressed through bolting cloth and the dissociated cells reunited and rebuilt a new organism. More recently Papenfuss (1934) in *Hydra* and Beadle and Booth (1938) in *Cordylophora* have studied the process in detail and found that in order to obtain reorganization it is necessary to have both endoderm and ectoderm together in the mass. Isolated endoderm cells are incapable of holding together and soon disintegrate, while pure ectoderm masses round up rapidly, but form mere hollow balls without any further differentiation. Thus in hydroids there is a mixed situation, for it is impossible to make mature ectoderm become endoderm and vice versa, but all the cells possess in a broad way the ability to become parts of different structures; that is, for instance, a body-wall cell may become a tentacle cell. The experiments on inversion of *Hydra* where the ectoderm slips past the endoderm gives further evidence that these cell types are "determined," but in a general way the cells of certain regions may regulate to become part of another region, and this regulation always takes cognizance of the whole organism.

In 1909 E. Browne (now E. B. Harvey) found that there was a specific region of *Hydra* that could induce the formation of a new *Hydra*.[16] This region was that immediately surrounding the mouth (the hypostome), and if a piece of tissue from this region was grafted to the flank of another *Hydra*, invariably a new *Hydra*, a bud, would arise at that point. There apparently was some property associated with the hypostome region which could cause indifferent tissue to develop into a whole *Hydra*. This region seemed to be a center of organization, and some-

---

[16] This has been fully substantiated in other hydroids. See Beadle and Booth (1938).

what later Spemann began to see the same phenomenon in amphibian development, with his discovery of what he called the organizer.

This is now a familiar story, told many times and in many places, and even Spemann (1938) himself has described it in summary in his book. The principal point is that there are certain regions in the developing amphibian embryo which are capable of inducing differentiated structures, much as the hypostome does in *Hydra*. Of first importance is the region of the dorsal lip of the blastopore, the primary organizer, which is responsible for inducing the whole primary axis of the embryo. Spemann demonstrated this phenomenon in a number of ways, all basically similar, involving the transplantation of dorsal lip material to other regions and thereby inducing a second embryo. The whole development did not resolve itself, according to Spemann's findings, to this one primary organizer, but there were secondary organizers involved in the formation of various structures, such as the lens, the ear, the limbs, the tail, and many others. Even the primary organizer, as it became spread out under the ectoderm as a result of gastrulation showed some degree of specificity, and he demonstrated that there were differences between the head organizer and the trunk organizer.

Concerning the nature of the organizer, Spemann himself was rather cautious, and it has often been felt that his word "organizer" was too grand and ascribes too much power to the region which stimulated the surrounding tissues into morphogenetic activity. For this reason the term "inductor" is now preferred by most embryologists, although of course the process is the important thing and not its name. But the first blow to the initial concept of organizer action was the experiment of Holtfreter[17] in which he found that dead blastopore lip material would also induce a new embryo, and this began a long series of experimental activity which still continues today to find

[17] See Spemann (1938), or Needham (1942).

the inductor substance or evocator as Waddington (1940) has called it. The difficulty with the experiments was not to find a substance which would induce, but that so many different substances when implanted into embryos would give a second embryonic axis. There are those who favored some sterol compounds related to oestrogens and carcinogens, some favored glycogen, some favored nucleic acid derivatives, and there are still others.[18] Holtfreter suggested that the reason that so many things are successful is that when they are introduced into the embryo they kill or partially cytolize the surrounding cells, and that these damaged cells give off unknown substances which are the real agents responsible for induction.[19] If this hypothesis is correct it does make the chemical problem most difficult and frustrating, for it would seem to be almost an impossible task to study an experiment on induction without somehow damaging the cells.

We may feel certain that some chemical substance is involved and that there undoubtedly are different substances (or groups of substances) or different amounts of substances associated with the different activity of different inductors. There are no known cases in developing embryos where the inductor does not lie in direct contact with the affected tissues, so that it is assumed that it is a simple case of the substances passing directly from the inductor to the reacting region. It is no longer imagined that the inductor actually organizes the adjacent tissues, but that the process must be thought of more in terms of a stimulus and response, that is the inductor activates the tissues to develop, and their pattern of development is largely a product of their own. The way in which the tissue reacts has often been referred to as the biological or morphogenetic field, and this name is no more than another word for the pattern laid down in the course of development. But again the problem here is not one of finding a name, but as everyone will admit, it is finding an explanation of the process.

[18] See Needham (1942), Brachet (1944).   [19] See Holtfreter (1948).

A clear conception of amphibian development may be obtained if it is compared to the growth of plants where the main inductor substance auxin is well known. There the shape of the plant is dependent on the distribution of the sites of auxin production and the reaction of the various parts of the plant to auxin. (There is, in addition, the polar transport of auxin, which has no known analogue in amphibians.) There are also in plants other inductors, such as the flowering hormones, which have their specific effect on differentiation, and this hormone might be compared to the secondary inductors of amphibians. In amphibians the shape is dependent on a number of inductors, primary and secondary, the distribution of these inductor regions in the embryo, and the reactivity of the various parts to the evocators. The distribution of the evocators is partly affected by growth, but mainly by morphogenetic movement, but this still requires some initial configuration. It does seem, then, that in this elaborate and complex case of development as though there had been a separation of many processes, some stimulating and some responding, and from all this arises a very perfect kind of order. But each element, if it is analyzed, comes down to one thing, and that is an initial spatial configuration. It must be in the egg, but then it must also be in all the cells of, for instance, the blastula, for it is possible, by adding an extra dorsal lip of the blastopore to make two embryos from one. The primary induction and response set up the secondary ones, so that by a series of steps a mature organism comes forth, all because the gun was loaded just right and only one thing could happen when the trigger was pulled. There is no one element in amphibian development which controls everything, for the inductors and the reacting regions are mutually dependent; the only necessary requirement for both is that the initial protoplasm be of just one critical construction. After a period of cell division the mass cell movements bring the inductor region to its correct position, and it then liberates inductors which make the cells lying near somehow regulate into a patterned whole much the way the dissociated cells of *Hydra* formed such a whole. From this pattern arise new, lesser inductors which bring forth the limbs, the ears, and so forth. Each time there is a particular kind of stimulus (presumably a special chemical substance) at a particular place, which makes the cells, in a patterned manner take one of the many courses of differentiation of which they are capable. The pattern is in a small way contributed to by the nature and the location of the inductor, but it is largely produced by the many cells which respond to it, each essentially similar in the beginning of induction, for there is no evidence of localization or "determination" at this stage.

There are some old experiments of Herbst[20] which show in a striking way, how, during regeneration, different inductors may affect the nature of the regeneration. It involves the process of heteromorphosis, that is, when the lost part is not regenerated, but some different structure appears in its place. If the eye of the shrimp *Palaemon* is amputated above the nerve ganglion in its stalk, a new eye is regenerated, but if the level of amputation is below and the ganglion is removed, an antenna grows out in the place of the eye (Fig. 85). Another example is the case of mantids, where if the antenna is cut off two segments above the head, a new antenna is regenerated, but if only one segment is left a leg crops out from the head in its place. It might be assumed that there are substances which are given off by the remaining stump and that the nature of these substances differs depending on the level of amputation. The cells have the potentiality to produce either of the two structures involved, and the inductor decides which of the two it will be.

We have said that embryonic inductors must act at close range, but there are also hormones which circulate freely in the blood stream that affect differentiation in much the same way. Especially pertinent in this regard is the question of sex determination in which it has been shown

[20] See Morgan (1901), and Huxley and de Beer (1934).

that animals such as amphibians are potentially bisexual, and that the actual characters which are evoked are called forth by the sex hormones.[21] Of course the sex of an amphibian is determined ultimately by the nucleus containing the sex chromosomes, which are different for the

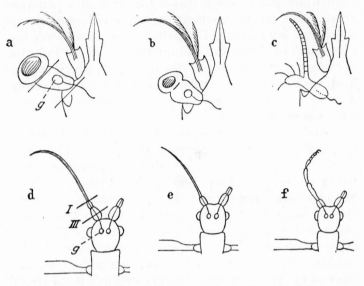

FIG. 85. Diagram to illustrate heteromorphosis. *Above*: In *Palaemon* removal of the eye without removal of its ganglion (a, distal cut) leads to regeneration of an eye (b); with removal of the ganglion (a, proximal cut), to that of an antenna-like organ (c). *Below*: In *mantids* amputation of the antenna in the region of the flagellum (d, I) leads to regeneration of a fresh flagellum (e); in a basal joint (d, III), to that of a leg (f). (From Huxley and de Beer, 1934, after Przibram.)

male and the female, but in some animals these do not act, so to speak, directly on the cells, but through the medium of hormones. In discussing growth much was said on the nature of hormone control of development,

[21] See the review by Witschi (1932). There are some beautiful examples of hormonal induction in the fungi. Especially notable is the work of J. Raper (1951) on the induction of sexual structures in the water mold *Achlya* by a series of hormones. Also it is known that in fungi that possess hyphal fusion, the tip of one hypha will induce a corresponding bud on the side of another hypha.

and now I wish only to emphasize the close relation between hormones and inductors.

Since all the cells, and most especially all the nuclei, have fundamental similarities in regulative organisms, it becomes increasingly important to examine the role of the gene during development, for each nucleus contains a complete gene complement. It is imagined that not all genes have their effect at the same time during development, but that some act early, and some late. Those last to exert themselves are the easiest to study, for the characters they affect are the most superficial and therefore the least lethal. It is for this reason that genes controlling color or bristle number or wing shape are commonly used by the geneticist, but any genes affecting the primary organizer would be harder to uproot.

A particular instance of the relation between induction and genetic constitution comes from some well-known experiments[22] on intergeneric transplantation between frogs and salamanders. Frog tadpoles have paired structures known as suckers located near the gill arches which serve to anchor them to submerged objects. The larva of a salamander has in the same regions straight peg-like protuberances, known as balancers, whose function is not entirely clear but is thought to be related to steadying and supporting the resting animal. Each of these structures has an underlying secondary inductor involved in its formation, and the location of this inductor is in the same spot for both embryos. If the ectoderm of any part of the flank of a tadpole was placed over the salamander organizer, Schotté found that it induced a tadpole sucker, and in the reverse experiment the induced structure was again characteristic of the ectoderm. The inductor is unspecific and will cause any ectoderm lying over it (whether it be the normal ectoderm or some foreign ectoderm) to produce either a sucker or a balancer. Which of these two courses is taken depends solely on the ectoderm and its genetic constitution.

[22] Work of Spemann, Schotté, Rotmann. See Needham (1942).

Another case where the superficial genetic characters seem to take their own course, and do not completely fit in with the overall development plan, is the case of mosaics in insects. It is possible to get gynandromorphs where one side of the body is male and the other female, yet the whole insect has developed harmoniously from the egg (Fig. 86). The sex characters, which are determined by the chromosomes, have expressed themselves late so as not to interfere with development, and in any event a gene which might be involved directly with development should be the same for both sexes. Mosaic characters involve other factors than sex, such as color, and the mosaic pattern on the body may have varied distributions. However, in each case they must necessarily be superficial characters not directly involved with the major steps of development.

Evidence on the nature of genes involved with the early developmental process is negligible because of the obvious deadliness of such defects.[23] And it is hard, when development stops at the beginning, to be quite certain just why it stopped. The riddle is too obscure to solve. There are gene mutants which stop development at almost any stage, but this does not clarify the relation of genes to inductors, or to the basic reactions which have been induced.

As one examines the separate processes involved in differentiation it is easy to forget the most important fact that the organism always differentiates as a whole, and that the particular course of the differentiation of a part is determined by its position with respect to the whole. There are many ways in which this whole may be constructed, not only in a variety of shapes, but with quite different building materials, and now I propose to survey a wide variety of ways in which this has been done, always with the hope

[23] For instance Poulson (1940) has shown that in the absence of all or part of a chromosome the embryos of *Drosophila* never go far in their development.

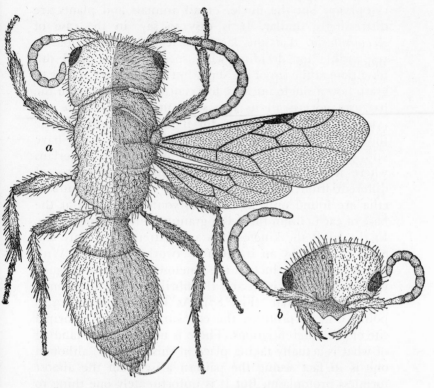

FIG. 86. A gynandromorphous insect, *Pseudomethoca canadensis*. The black right half is that of the winged male, while the red left half is of the wingless female. (From Wheeler, Psyche, *17*, 1910.)

that such a survey will help to clarify the kind of explanation that is needed.

The simplest and in some respects the most puzzling kind of building block to understand is the case of an isolated single cell with one nucleus, for there the single nucleus and the cytoplasm appear to be responsible for carving out all sorts of elaborate and consistent differentiations which have been lost by amputation. If the nucleus were identical in shape to the whole cell, a sort of a homunculus, we would feel more comfortable, but instead it not only is different from the shape of the

[261]

cytoplasm, but the nuclei of all animals and plants are distressingly similar. It is easy to say, in the case of *Acetabularia*, that the large nucleus in the rhizoid is responsible for deciding what species of hat shall differentiate at the tip of the stalk, but it is another matter to grasp how a single nucleus, five centimeters away from the hat, can govern all its fine sculpturings. Of course the cytoplasm is involved also, for it must not only execute the orders dictated by the nucleus, but may, as we have said, give some of its own. There is a case in suctorians where it was possible to actually follow the course of differentiation from the beginning.[24] In these organisms cilia are found only in the embryonic stage, and at the base of each cilium there is a granule called a kinetosome. In the adult the kinetosomes are scattered unevenly and are connected by an irregular network of fibrilles. With the onset of reproduction the kinetosomes become aligned with military precision and the fibrillar network becomes beautifully regular (Fig. 87). As Fauré-Fremiet (1948) points out, in protozoa the cell surface is the principal site of the differentiations. There is no real understanding of what is actually taking place in this example, although one is in fact seeing the pattern arise from the almost formless protoplasm. But it is unfortunately one thing to see a process occur and another to explain it. It does not seem possible to explain this kind of order on the basis of diffusion gradients; it seems more likely that this involves the formation of some kind of a rigid ultrastructure, but its exact nature is totally unknown.

Differentiation may occur with an orderly pattern in cases where the organism has no internal cell walls, and is multinucleate. The coenocytic algae, many fungi, and the true slime molds or myxomycetes show this well. In the myxomycetes the final differentiation is accompanied by the progressive cleavage where the nuclei again become delineated by cell walls. In his celebrated experiment on the annelid worm *Chaetopterus*, F. R. Lillie (1902) found

[24] See Lwoff (1950, p. 65).

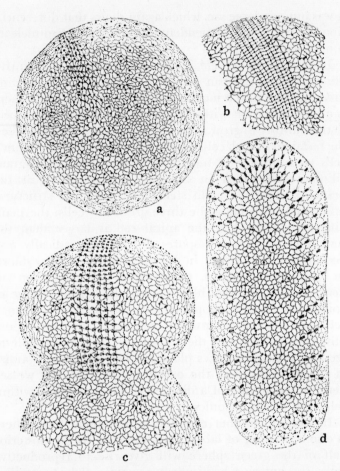

FIG. 87. The formation of regular ciliary rows in the suctorian, *Podophrya fixa*. a, adult showing an irregular network and the beginning of the alignment of the kinetosomes; b, c, progressive stages of alignment; d, the embryo. (From Chatton, E., Lwoff, A., Lwoff, M., Tellier, L., C. R. Soc. Biol., *100*, 1929 in Lwoff, 1950.)

that by placing them in sea water containing potassium chloride, the egg would not cleave, although there were many nuclear divisions. He was able, in this way, to get a kind of rudimentary differentiation without cleavage where the beginnings of the larva were visible even though it was but one large sac, which again shows that differentiation is in no way dependent on the small uninucleate compartments.

In the colonial ciliate *Zoothamnion* we saw a primitive multicellular organism in which, besides each cell being differentiated into a mouth and a stalk and so forth, there is a differentiation within the colony largely with respect to their ability to grow. The apical cell produced branches, the terminal branch cells produced branch cells, the branch cells were ordinarily incapable of division, and migrant ciliospores occurred in the first cells of some of the branches, near the main stem. There is little structural differentiation among the three groups of cells, the main difference being that the apical cell is larger than the rest. The migrant ciliospores differ more radically and become quite altered in their appearance. As shown in Summer's (1938b) experiments on regulation in *Zoothamnion*, it is possible for any of the cells to become an apical cell upon appropriate amputation, and a branch cell may become a terminal branch cell or a ciliospore (the regular origin of the ciliospores). It is impossible to see how regulation takes place and how one part is aware of the deficiencies of the other; but nevertheless we see here the beginning of a division of labor not just within cells, but within colonies.

In *Volvox*, another example of a colonial form, there is also a division of labor: only the cells in the posterior half of the green sphere will give rise to reproductive cells; the anterior hemisphere remains solely vegetative. In sponges the differentiation becomes far more marked and there are not only many cell types but also organized flagellated chambers, canals, and an epithelial outer coating surrounding the sponge. There are in the sponge, besides an elaboration of the different cell types, symmetrical patterns made up of these cells. But their symmetry, their cohesiveness, seems pale in comparison to the coelenterates where the organization is so closely integrated. From the coelenterates upward, the differentiation becomes progressively more elaborate, with increasing grouping of functions, so that tissues and organs and organ systems arise, each closely integrated with one another.

Of particular interest are the colonial coelenterates in which the different polyps or attached medusae, which are connected together through their gastro-intestinal canals, become modified for specific functions. This is known as polymorphism, and it differs from division of labor arising in tissues or organs in that whole organisms are grouped together and the different organisms become specialized in different functions. *Zoothamnion* is an example of this in that the different cells, each of which is in a sense an independent organism, become modified in the division of labor of the colony.

A primitive case of polymorphism is that of *Hydractinia*, the colonial hydroid that forms a mat on the mollusc shells inhabited by hermit crabs. From the mat, which is largely a tangle of stolons, arise zooids or individual persons and these vary in their structure (Fig. 88). There are those which closely resemble *Hydra* which are the feeding polyps; there are protective polyps which have no mouth or tentacles but instead have mace-like knobs which stud their tips; another type of protective polyp which lacks the apical knobs will often be found specifically along the edge of a colony; and finally there are the male polyps and the female polyps which carry the sperm and the eggs.

While *Hydractinia* is a good example of a lowly polymorphic coelenterate, the Siphonophores give beautiful examples of really elaborate polymorphism. A familiar example is *Physalia*, the Portuguese-man-of-war, which has its blue floats resting on the surface of the sea. But because the parts of *Agalma* are a bit more strung out they are easier to see (Fig. 89). In *Agalma* there are even more different types of zooids than in *Hydractinia* and they are grouped together in a systematic symmetrical way. At the top there is a medusa which has become modified into a float, and below this there is a group of medusae which

[265]

have become swimming bells and are capable of squirting out water. Below this there is a mixture of the remaining polymorphic types: there are the feeding polyps whose tentacles have become quite changed from what is seen in

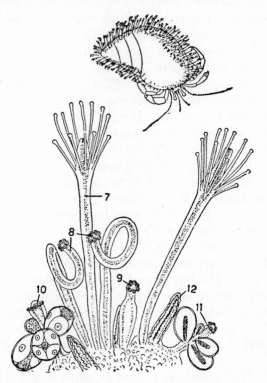

Fig. 88. *Hydractinia*, a polymorphic coelenterate. *Above*: Its appearance on a snail shell inhabited by a hermit crab. *Below*: A cluster of polyps showing the different types; 7, a feeding polyp; 8, protective polyps; 9, 10, 11, undifferentiated, male, and female reproductive polyps respectively; 12, spines. (From Hyman, 1940.)

Hydra, there are bottle-shaped "feelers" which also have long tentacles, there are the large fleshy protective bracts whose medusoid ancestry is hard to see, which form a sort of covering, and finally the male persons and the female persons. All these organisms live harmoniously to-

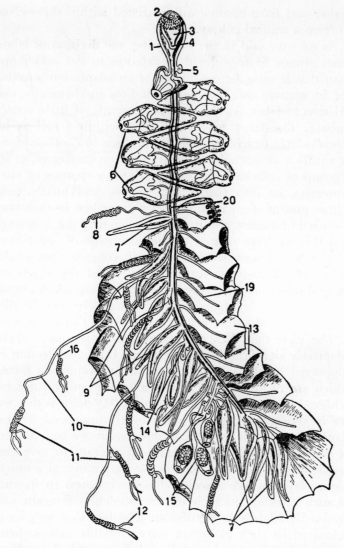

FIG. 89. The siphonophore, *Agalma*. 1, the float; 2, pigment in the float; 3, air sac; 4, funnel; 5, the budding zone of the swimming bells; 6, swimming bells; 7, the "feeler" polyps; 8, their tentacles; 9, the feeding polyps; 10, their tentacles; 11, area of stinging cells; 12, end filaments; 13, bracts; 14, sperm-bearing male polyps; 15, egg-bearing female polyps; 16, lateral contractile branches of the tentacles. (From Hyman, 1940, after Mayer.)

[267]

gether and have become differentiated within themselves to form a unified colony.

As we have said in the beginning, the division of labor must always be considered in relation to size and more than that it must be considered as an adaptation selected for in nature, and the matter of how mechanically the division of labor is achieved is apparently of little consequence. The labor may be divided within a cell as in *Acetabularia*, or within a colony of cells as in *Zoothamnion*, or within a multinucleate sac as in the myxomycetes, or in a group of cells such as *Dictyostelium* or sponges or coelenterates, or into tissues and organs, and finally now within groups of organisms adhering together. In each case there is a wholeness, a unity which comes with the structure, and this we have related to the advantage of functional wholes, for without being functionally cohesive they would either not live, or at least not withstand the rigors of natural selection. The very fact that they are wholes must be adaptively advantageous, and natural selection, by differential reproduction, would tend to keep them that way.

The view that these structural wholes are most likely adaptively significant and have arisen through selection is supported by the fact that there are polymorphic forms which are of an entirely different nature and cannot be achieved by a comparable mechanism. My point is that we are in constant danger of being overly impressed by the significance of this wholeness, and already we have talked of physical models of regulation to attempt to give the problem some perspective. Now we have a case at a much higher level, where a society has a wholeness to it, and in such cases as ant societies the wholeness is again undoubtedly adaptively significant. The fact that ants have colonized in such elaborate ways probably makes them better suited to survive and reproduce, and the colony has a unity that in many ways equals the unity of an organism, differing mainly in that the parts are not physically attached as they are in the colonies we have discussed thus far.

This matter has already been well considered by W. M. Wheeler in his delightful essay "The ant-colony as an organism," in which he draws the many parallels between the two levels of organization.[25] The fertile queen is the germ plasm and the eggs she lays become the soma (and in some cases more germ plasm when she produces new queens). The soma are largely the sterile workers which in the first broods of a young queen starting a colony are small and uniform, but with successive broods they become, in many species of ants, highly polymorphic. There are those whose duties may involve the care of the young and gathering food (and these may be of more than one size) and then finally the largest become the soldiers who confine their activities to protecting the colony.

The basis of polymorphism is not completely clear, and Light (1942-1943) has pointed out that it varies with different groups of social insects. The only positively established inheritance difference is that which distinguishes the sexes and gives sexual dimorphism. In the bees the female castes (queen and worker) are apparently determined on the basis of the quantity and especially the quality of the food received during larval growth. The rich "royal jelly" is only fitting for a queen. In the ants and termites the situation is extremely uncertain, although apparently the presence of members of certain castes somehow inhibits further development of those castes. This may possibly be by the passing of inhibiting substances from one individual to another, but, as Light points out, there is no firmly established evidence for such "social hormones" as they have been called.

Of special interest here is the ability of a colony to regulate in the event of losses of some of its members. For instance, in an ant colony, if all the workers are removed, the queen will start a new brood again to "regenerate" the lost "soma." Another way in which regulation is shown is in cases where all the food is removed from the colony, and there is a regular sequence of disappearance of the

[25] See also Emerson (1939).

different forms obviously related to the survival of the colony as a whole: first the larvae, next the soldiers, then the males, the large workers, the small workers, and lastly the queen. If the queen is removed the colony regulates by one or several of the large workers' becoming fertile and beginning to lay eggs. And finally they show a kind of regulation by rebuilding the form of a partially destroyed nest.

In many respects the ant colony may resemble an organism, and it does afford a splendid analogy, but it is out of the question that the mechanism whereby the division of labor and its wholeness is achieved is the same in both cases, even if "social hormones" were firmly established. In ants there are complex matters of instincts and of senses such as chemical senses and sight which obviously are not equivalent to anything in development. Just as we see perfect orientation in the schooling of fish, this does not mean that they are governed by the same means as the orientation and polarity of cells. Parr (1927) has shown that fish use their eyesight, and we do not expect cells to do the same thing in the same way.

The moral then is that differentiation and the wholeness which characterizes developing organisms is not unique to them, but must instead be thought of as a condition which can be achieved in a number of ways, and has been achieved because both the division of labor and its unity are of great adaptive significance, and are selected for in evolution. There is no certainty that even the way in which differentiations arise in development is the same for all organisms. If there is a different method of regulation for crystals and for ant colonies, why could there not be many different mechanical means in which regulation exerts itself within developing organisms, for after all each one would be equally adaptive. And moreover, there are different levels of differentiation within developing organisms, if one compares differentiation within a cell, or within an organ or within a colony of polymorphic polyps. Each one may be achieved in an independent fashion; but not necessarily so.

8. An Analysis of Development

IN THE beginning of this book I dissected the whole matter of development into a number of arbitrary processes, and during the course of the book I have given scattered examples of the various ways in which these processes have been carried out by a wide variety of living forms. The examples represent a mere fraction of all those that exist, but it is hoped that the major and most diverse cases have been touched upon. In this final chapter I wish to bring together the elements common to all developments so that not only should it be possible to summarize and crystallize the major analytical ideas of the book, but also to construct a generalized statement of development of all living forms.

There are, it seems to me, three major constructive processes, that is, processes which involve a progressive change in the life histories of organisms. These are growth, morphogenetic movements, and differentiation. The pattern of a developing organism is achieved, as we have said so many times, by the limiting of these three constructive processes in various ways so that the pattern attained by development may be thought of as a result of the relation between the constructive processes and their limiting processes.

The three constructive processes sometimes work together and sometimes work independently in time. Some organisms lack one type almost entirely (such as higher plants which lack morphogenetic movements). To illustrate the possible combinations of these processes, which may vary from point to point in time during the course of development, it is helpful to place the three types at the poles of a triangular coordinate system so frequently used by the physical chemist (Fig. 90). Then any point within the graph will indicate varying degrees of the three types, and a point directly in the middle indicates a stage of development exhibiting all three processes equally. Likewise points lying midway at the sides of the triangle repre-

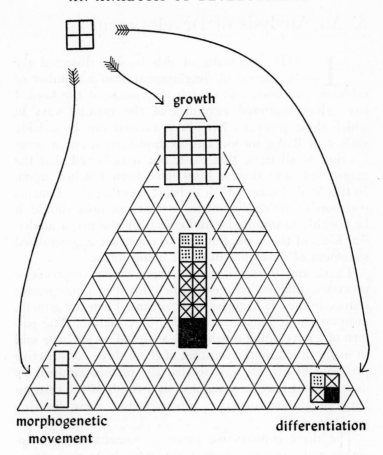

growth

morphogenetic
movement

differentiation

FIG. 90. Diagram to illustrate the possible interrelations between growth, morphogenetic movement, and differentiation.

sent development in which two processes contribute equally, but the third not at all. Were this graph extended through space to give a third dimension, the changes of these relations during the course of development of one organism could be plotted.

The limiting factors are harder to classify, although they may be roughly separated into external and internal. Of the external limiting factors we have considered food supply, size, mechanical forces, and allied factors all of which are involved in the relation of the organism to its environment. Of the internal limits we talked of molecular orientation, hormones, inductors, and gene products. In the case of limiting chemical substances it was pointed out that the spatial and temporal distribution of the substances and the distribution of the specific reactivities to the substances were an integral part of such internal limits, and we referred them back to the configuration of the germ, a matter which we will now consider in more detail.

It would perhaps be best first to point out that it is to some extent an abstraction to separate the progressive processes from their limits, for the two will in many instances be bound together so that any physical separation is likely to be impossible. We have then these two factors which are interdependent and lying together in space and time in the germ. In order to satisfy the conditions found in the development of different organisms it is possible to sort out certain common properties of the configuration of these two factors in the germ:

1. The configuration must be of such a nature that it may be inherited, that is passed on from generation to generation. Ample evidence has been given to show that most characters involving form and pattern are genetic, and that therefore the basis of the configuration of the germ must be directly related to the genes on the chromosomes. This does not exclude the possibility that cytoplasmic factors might also independently play a role, nor does it specify the nature of the relation between genic and cytoplasmic factors.

2. The configuration is such that during development both the amount of progressive change and the direction of change are accounted for. This was shown especially clearly in considering growth, where the pattern was the result of both the amount of growth and its direction.

3. In organisms which are capable of any degree of regulation, it is necessary that the configuration be of a

structure which involves the repetition of parts in three dimensions, as Driesch (1907) understood so well when he postulated his "equipotential system." How else would it be possible to understand regulation where, for instance, two blastomeres may produce perfect dwarf embryos, for all substances must exist and be arranged in an orderly fashion in both blastomeres. This requirement would presumably not be true for organisms during a strictly mosaic stage of development, but regulation is so widespread a phenomenon that the requirement may still be considered general. It should be added that the repeating configuration must also be capable of accounting for the cases where two whole embryos are lined up and fused into one giant whole embryo.

The repetitive units in the configuration are certainly not necessarily those of a cell, but may exist within one cell as in regenerating protozoa. (It is conceivable that in protozoa the units are repeated in different parts of the nucleus.)

This last statement brings home a point that I have mentioned already many times in this book: it is that the physical bases of many developmental processes may or may not be the same for all organisms. There are many reasons to believe that polarity, which merely refers to the geometric configuration of an organism, has different physical bases in different instances. In the discussion of the organized control of differentiation, where single cells, groups of cells, and groups of organisms had in each case a wholeness to them, it was again argued that the mechanism involved might or might not be different in each case, and that the only factor that they surely had in common was the selective advantage of wholeness, of cohesive unity. So there is no *a priori* reason to expect the repetitive units found in regulatory organisms exhibiting equivalence of parts to be the same for all organisms. It is true that all organisms have a gene mechanism and the factors which are equivalent are inherited, which suggests a common mechanism, but it would still not be surprising if the repetitive units of single-celled organisms differ greatly from multicellular ones.

As a final matter we might reflect for a moment upon the physical nature of these repetitive units for any organism or group of organisms. Were this known, then, as we said in the introductory chapter, we would have an explanation which would give great satisfaction—it would be an explanation expressed in terms of relatively smaller units and give a micro-structure theory. It would perhaps not be profitable, since the facts are so few, to make conjectures concerning the nature of a micro-theory in cases of development, but instead we might examine an analogy which does fit many of the facts and which illustrates how such a theory could give a desirable explanation.

The analogy is the crystal analogy, for there the growth, the form, the properties of the crystal are entirely understood on the basis of equivalent repetitive units, the molecules, giving a most helpful micro-structure theory. The molecules in a crystal are arranged in an orderly fashion to give a space-lattice. The external shape of the crystal will be a direct result of the shapes of the molecules and of their space-lattice; there is a low and finite number of symmetries possible. Thus the polarity of the crystal is interpretable in terms of its repetitive units. Because of the shape of the molecules not only will the relative amount and direction of growth be predictable, but the crystal will have different properties in different directions. It is well known that crystals dissolve more readily in some directions than others, their magnetic susceptibility differs with direction, as do their cohesion, their thermal conductivity, and their optical properties. Furthermore, the processes of regulation after fission and fusion, seen so strikingly in liquid crystals, is also interpreted in terms of molecular forces, for all that is required is that the molecules retain their pattern in space, and the properties of the crystal emerge from this directional alignment.

Such a molecular space-lattice would in every sense be

the basis of a micro-structure theory. It is unfortunate that we do not know whether this or whether some other physico-chemical mechanism is involved. But whichever it is, should any biologist establish such a micro-structure basis of development in living organisms as an irrefutable fact, the world will acclaim his discovery as a most satisfying explanation and a great advancement in science.

Bibliography

Abeloos, M. 1932. La Régénération et les Problèmes de la Morphogenèse. Gauthier-Villars, Paris.

Adolph, E. F. 1931. The Regulation of Size as Illustrated in Unicellular Organisms. C. C. Thomas, Baltimore.

Ankel, W. E. 1948. Über Fragen der Formbildung und der Zelldetermination bei Süsswasserschwämmen. Verhandl. Deutsch Zool. in Kiel. pp. 58-66.

Aristotle. De Generatione Animalium. Translated by A. Platt. 1912. Oxford University Press.

Arndt, A. 1937. Untersuchungen über *Dictyostelium mucoroides* Brefeld. Roux' Arch. Entwickl., *136*:681-744.

Astbury, W. T. 1945. The forms of biological molecules. From Essays on Growth and Form, pp. 309-354. Oxford University Press.

Avery, G. S., and P. R. Burkholder. 1936. Polarized growth and cell studies on the *Avena* coleoptile, phytohormone test object. Bull. Torrey Bot. Club, *63*:1-15.

Baker, J. R. 1948. The status of the protozoa. Nature, *161*:548-551, 587-589.

Barth, L. G. 1934. The effect of constant electric current on regeneration of certain hydroids. Physiol. Zool. 7:340-364.

Barth, L. G. 1940. The process of regeneration in hydroids. Biol. Rev., *15*:405-420.

Beadle, L. C., and F. A. Booth. 1938. The reorganization of tissue masses of *Cordylophora lacustris* and the effect of oral cone grafts, with supplementary observations on *Obelia gelatinosa*. J. Exp. Biol. *15*:303-326.

Beebe, J. M. 1941. Studies on the myxobacteria. Iowa State Col. J. Sci., *15*:307-337.

Bertalanffy, L. von, and J. H. Woodger. 1933. Modern Theories of Development. Oxford University Press.

Bidder, G. P. 1923. The relation of the form of a sponge to its currents. Quart. Jour. Micr. Sci., *67*:293-323.

Bidder, G. P. 1936-1937. The perfection of sponges. Proc. Linn. Soc. London, *149*:119-146.

Bliding, C. 1938. Studien über Entwicklung und Systematik in der Gattung Enteromorpha. I. Botaniska Notiser. Lund., pp. 83-90.

Bloch, H. 1950. Studies on the virulence of tubercule bacilli. Jour. Exp. Med., *91*:197-218.

Bloch, R. 1943. Polarity in plants. Bot. Rev., *9*:261-310.

Bonner, J. T. 1944. A descriptive study of the development of the slime mold *Dictyostelium discoideum*. Amer. J. Bot., *31*:175-182.

Bonner, J. T. 1947. Evidence for the formation of cell aggregates by chemotaxis in the development of the slime mold *Dictyostelium discoideum*. J. Exp. Zool., *106*:1-26.

Bonner, J. T. 1949. The demonstration of acrasin in the later stages of the development of the slime mold *Dictyostelium discoideum*. J. Exp. Zool. *110*:259-271.

Bonner, J. T. 1950. Observations on polarity in the slime mold *Dictyostelium discoideum*. Biol. Bull., *99*:143-151.

Bonner, J. T. 1951. The horn of the unicorn. Sci. Amer. *184*: (No. 3) 42-43.

Bonner, J. T. In press. The pattern of differentation in amoeboid slime molds. Amer. Nat.

Bonner, J. T., W. W. Clarke, Jr., C. L. Neely, Jr., and M. K. Slifkin. 1950. The orientation to light and the extremely sensitive orientation to temperature gradients in the slime mold *Dictyostelium discoideum*. J. Cell. Comp. Physiol., *36*:149-158.

Bonner, J. T., and D. Eldredge, Jr. 1945. A note on the rate of morphogenetic movement in the slime mold *Dictyostelium discoideum*. Growth, *9*:287-297.

Bonner, J. T., and M. K. Slifkin. 1949. A study of the control of differentiation: the proportions of stalk and spore cells in the slime mold *Dictyostelium discoideum*. Amer. J. Bot., *36*:727-734.

Bower, F. O. 1930. Size and Form in Plants. Macmillan, London.

Boycott, A. E., C. Diver, S. L. Garstang, and F. M. Turner. 1930. The inheritance of sinistrality in *Limnaea peregra*. Philos. Trans. Roy. Soc. B. (London), *219*:51-130.

Brachet, J. 1944. Embryologie Chimique. Masson, Paris.

Bragg, A. N. 1938. The organization of the early embryo of *Bufo cognatus* as revealed especially by the mitotic index. Zeitschr. f. Zellforsch. v. mik. Anat., *28*:154-178.

Bridgman, P. W. 1931. Dimensional Analysis (2nd ed.). Yale University Press, New Haven.

Brien, P. 1937. La réorganisation de l'Eponge après dissociation par filtration et phénomènes d'involution chez *Ephydatia fluviatilis*. Arch. Biol. *48*:185-268.

Brien, P., and M. Reniers-Decoen. 1949. La croissance, la blastogénèse, l'ovogénèse chez *Hydra fusca*. (Pallas.) Bull. Biol. France Belg. *83*:293-386.

Browne, E. (See E. B. Harvey.)

Butler, E. G. 1949. Reversal of polarity in limbs of urodele larvae. (Abstract) Biol. Bull., *97*:232.

Caspari, E. 1948. Cytoplasmic inheritance. Adv. in Gen., *2*:1-66.

Child, C. M. 1917. Experimental alteration of the axial gradient of the alga *Griffithsia Bornethiana*. Biol. Bull., *32*:213-233.

Child, C. M. 1941. Patterns and Problems of Development. Chicago University Press.

Clark, W. G. 1937. Electrical polarity and auxin transport. Plant Physiol., *12*:409-440.

Clark, W. G. 1938. Electrical polarity and auxin transport. Plant Physiol., *13*:529-552.

Conklin, E. G. 1905a. The organization and cell lineage of the ascidian egg. J. Acad. Nat. Sci., Phila., 2nd series, *8*:1-119.

Conklin, E. G. 1905b. Mosaic development in ascidian eggs. J. Exp. Zool., *2*:145-223.

Conklin, E. G. 1906. Does half of an ascidian egg give rise to a whole larva? Roux' Arch. Entwickl., *21*:727-753.

Conklin, E. G. 1931. The development of centrifuged eggs of ascidians. J. Exp. Zool., *60*:1-119.

Costello, D. P. 1948. Oöplasmic segregation in relation to differentiation. Ann. N. Y. Acad. Sci., *49*:663-683.

Dalcq, A. 1941. L'Oeuf et son Dynamisme Organisateur. Albin Michel, Paris.

Dalton, H. C. 1950. Inhibition of chromatoblast migration as a factor in the development of genetic differences in pigmentation in white and black axolotls. J. Exp. Zool., *115*:151-174.

Danielli, J. F. 1945. Some reflections on the forms of simpler cells. From Essays on Growth and Form, pp. 295-308. Oxford University Press.

Davenport, C. B. 1895. Studies in morphogenesis IV. A preliminary catalogue of the processes concerned in ontogeny. Bull. Mus. Comp. Zool. Harvard, 27:No. 6.

BIBLIOGRAPHY

de Beer, G. R. 1940. Embryos and Ancestors. Oxford Univ. Press.

de Laubenfels, M. W. 1932. Physiology and morphology of Porifera exemplified by *Iotrochota birotulata* Higgn. Paprs. Tort. Lab. Carn. Inst. Wash. Publ., *28*:37-66.

Dobell, C. C. 1911. The principles of protistology. Arch. Protist., *23*:269-310.

Dobell, C. C. 1932. Antony van Leeuwenhoek and his "Little Animals." Harcourt, Brace, N. Y.

Driesch, H. 1907. The Science and Philosophy of the Organism. Black, London.

Duboscq, O., and O. Tuzet. 1937. L'ovogénèse, la fécondation et les premiers stades du développement des éponges calcaires. Arch. Zool. Expér. et Gén., *79*:157-316.

Egli, P. H. 1949. Crystal research. Sci. Monthly, *68*:270-278.

Emerson, A. E. 1939. Social coordination and the superorganism. Amer. Midl. Nat., *21*:181-206.

Fankhauser, G. 1945a. The effects of changes in chromosome number of amphibian development. Quart. Rev. Biol., *20*:20-78.

Fankhauser, G. 1945b. Maintenance of normal structure in heteroploid salamander larvae, through compensation of changes in cell size by adjustment of cell number and cell shape. J. Exp. Zool., *100*:445-455.

Fauré-Fremiet, E. 1925. La Cinétique du Développement. Les Presses Universitaires de France. Paris.

Fauré-Fremiet, E. 1930. Growth and differentiation of the colonies of *Zoothamnium alternans*. (Clap. and Lachm). Biol. Bull., *58*:28-51.

Fauré-Fremiet, E. 1932. Morphogenèse expérimentale (Reconstitution) che *Ficulina ficus* L. Arch. d'Anat. microsc. *28*:1-80.

Fauré-Fremiet, E. 1945. Symétrie et polarité chez les ciliés bi-ou multicomposites. Bull. Biol. France Belg. *79*:106-150.

Fauré-Fremiet, E. 1948. Les méchanismes de la morphogenèse chez les ciliés. Folia Biotheor. Ser. B., *3*:25-58.

Fauré-Fremiet, E., and R. Wallich. 1925. Un facteur physique de mouvement cellulaire pendant la culture des tissus *in vitro*. Compts. Rendu. Acad. Sci., *181*:1096-1097.

Frey-Wyssling, A. 1948. Submicroscopic Morphology of Protoplasm and its Derivatives. Transl. by J. J. Hermans and M. Hollander. Elsevier Publ., N.Y.

Galilei, Galileo. Discourse on Two New Sciences. Translated by H. Crew and A. de Salvio. 1914. Macmillan, N.Y.

Galtsoff, P. S. 1923. The amoeboid movement of dissociated sponge cells. Biol. Bull., *45*:153-161.

Galtsoff. P. S. 1925. Regeneration after dissociation (an experimental study on sponges). I. Behavior of dissociated cells of *Microciona prolifera* under normal and altered conditions. J. Exp. Zool., *42*:183-221.

Gause, G. F. 1941. Optical Activity and Living Matter. Biodynamica Monographs, No. 2.

Goldacre, C. J., and I. L. Lorch. 1950. Folding and unfolding of protein molecules in relation to cytoplasmic streaming, amoeboid movement and osmotic work. Nature, *166*:497-500.

Goldschmidt, R. 1938. Physiological Genetics. McGraw-Hill, N.Y.

Gudger, E. W. 1949. Fishes that rank themselves like soldiers on parade. Zoologica, *34*:99-102.

Haberlandt, G. 1914. Physiological Plant Anatomy. Trans. from 4th Ed. by M. Drummond, Macmillan, London.

Hämmerling, J. 1946. Neue Untersuchungen über die physiologischen und genetischen Grundlagen der Formbildung. Naturwiss. *33*:337-342, 361-365.

Harper, R. A. 1908. The organization of certain coenobic plants. Bull. Univ. Wisconsin. No. 207.

Harper, R. A. 1916. On the nature of types in *Pediastrum*. Mem. N. Y. Bot. Garden, *6*:91-104.

Harper, R. A. 1918a. The evolution of cell types and contact and pressure responses in *Pediastrum*. Mem. Torrey Bot. Club, *17*:210-240.

Harper, R. A. 1918b. Organization, reproduction and inheritance in Pediastrum. Proc. Amer. Phil. Soc., *57*:375-439.

Harrison, R. G. 1910. The outgrowth of the nerve fibers as a mode of protoplasmic movement. J. Exp. Zool., *9*:787-846.

Harrison, R. G. 1933. Some difficulties of the determination problem. Amer. Nat., *67*:306-321.

Harrison, R. G. 1945. Relations of symmetry in the developing embryo. Trans. Conn. Acad. Arts Sci., *36*:277-330.

Harrison, R. G., W. T. Astbury, and K. M. Rudall. 1940. An attempt at an x-ray analysis of embryonic processes. J. Exp. Zool., *85*:339-363.

Harvey, E. B. (E. Browne) 1909. The production of new hydranths in *Hydra* by the insertion of small grafts. J. Exp. Zool., *7*:1-23.

Havis, A. L. 1940. Developmental studies with Brassica seedlings. Amer. J. Bot., *27*:239-245.

Heilbrunn, L. V. 1943. An outline of General Physiology (2nd ed.). W. B. Saunders, Phila.

Hempel, C. G., and P. Oppenheim. 1948. Studies in the logic of explanation. Phil. of Sci., *15*:135-175.

Henderson, L. J. 1913. The Fitness of the Environment. Macmillan, N.Y.

Hendy, N. I. 1945. Extra-frustular diatoms. Jour. Roy. Micr. Soc. (Series III) *65*:34-39.

Hill, A. V. 1950. The dimensions of animals and their muscular dynamics. Science Progress, *38*:209-230.

Hollaender, A. 1936. The problem of mitogenetic rays. From B. M. Duggar's "Biological Effects on Radiation." Vol. II, pp. 919-959.

Holmes, S. J. 1948. Organic Form and Related Biological Problems. Univ. of Calif. Press. Berkeley.

Holtfreter, J. 1943a. Properties and functions of the surface coat in amphibian embryos. J. Exp. Zool., *93*:251-323.

Holtfreter, J. 1943b. A study of the mechanics of gastrulation: Part I. J. Exp. Zool., *94*:261-318.

Holtfreter, J. 1944. A study of the mechanics of gastrulation: Part II. J. Exp. Zool., *95*:171-212.

Holtfreter, J. 1948. Concepts on the mechanism of embryonic induction and its relation to parthenogenesis and malignancy. Symposia Soc. Exp. Biol., No. 2, pp. 17-49.

Howard, F. L. 1931. Life history of *Physarum polycephalum*. Amer. J. Bot., *18*:116-133.

Honert, T. H. van den. 1932. On the mechanism of the transport of organic materials in plants. Proc. Kon. Akad. Wetensch. Amsterdam, *35*:1104-1111.

Huskins, G. L. 1947. The subdivision of the chromosomes and their multiplication in non-dividing tissues: possible interpretations in terms of gene structure and gene action. Amer. Nat., *81*:401-434.

Hutchinson, G. E. 1948. In memoriam: D'Arcy Wentworth Thompson. (Marginalia) Amer. Sci., *36*:577-606.

Huxley, J. S. 1932. Problems in Relative Growth. Methuen, London.

Huxley, J. S., and G. R. de Beer. 1934. The Elements of Experimental Embryology. Cambridge Univ. Press.

Hyman, L. H. 1940. The Invertebrates: Protozoa through Ctenophora. McGraw-Hill, N.Y.

Hyman, L. H. 1942. The transition from the unicellular to the multicellular individual. Biol. Symposia. *8*:27-42.

Imms, A. D. 1934. A General Textbook of Entomology (3rd ed.). Dutton, N.Y.

Ingold, C. T. 1946. Size and form in agarics. Trans. Brit. Mycol. Soc., *29*:108-113.

Jacobs, W. P. 1950. Auxin-transport in the hypocotyl of *Phaseolus vulgaris* L. Amer. J. Bot., *37*:248-254.

Jacobs, W. P. 1951. Studies on cell-differentiation: the role of auxin in algae, with particular reference to rhizoid formation in *Bryopsis*. Biol. Bull. *101*:300-306.

Jahn, E. 1924. Beiträge zur botanischen Protistologie I. Die Polyangiden. Gebr. Borntraeger, Leipzig.

Köhler, W. 1929. Gestalt Psychology. Liveright, N.Y.

Komai, T. 1951. Phyllotaxis-like arrangement of organs and zooids in some medusae. Amer. Nat., *85*:75-76.

Kühn, A. 1909. Sprosswachstum und Polypenknospung bie den Thecaphoren. Zool. Jahr. Abt. Anat. Ont., *28*:387-476.

Light, S. T. 1942-1943. The determination of the castes of social insects. Quart. Rev. Biol., *17*:312-326; *18*:46-63.

Lillie, F. R. 1902. Differentiation without cleavage in the egg of the annelid *Chaetopterus pergamentaceus*. Roux' Arch. Entwickl., *14*:477-499.

Liu, C. K. 1948. X-radiation effects on the restitution of dissociated *Microciona*. (Abstract) Biol. Bull., *95*:259.

Loeb, J. 1894. On some facts and principles of physiological morphology. Biological Lectures Delivered at the M. B. L. of Wood's Holl in 1893, pp. 37-61.

Loewy, A. G. 1949. A theory of protoplasmic streaming. Proc. Amer. Phil. Soc., *93*:326-329.

Lowrance, E. W. 1937. Effect of temperature gradients upon

BIBLIOGRAPHY

polarity in eggs of *Fucus furcatus*. J. Cell. Comp. Physiol., *10*:321-337.

Lund, E. J. 1947. Bioelectric Fields and Growth. Univ. of Texas Press, Austin.

Lwoff, A. 1944. L'Evolution Physiologique. Étude des Pertes de Fonctions chez les Microorganismes. Hermann, Paris.

Lwoff, A. 1950. Problems of Morphogenesis in the Ciliates. Wiley, N.Y.

Marsland, D. A., and D. E. S. Brown. 1936. Amoeboid movement at high hydrostatic pressure. J. Cell. Comp. Physiol., *8*:167-178.

Marx, W., M. E. Simpson, and H. M. Evans. 1942. Bioassay of the growth hormone of the anterior pituitary. Endocrinology, *30*:1-10.

Mayer, A. G. 1906. Rhythmical pulsation in Scyphomedusae. Carn. Inst. of Wash., No. 47, pp. 1-62.

Moore, A. R. 1945. The Individual in Simpler Forms. Univ. of Oregon Mon. Studies in Psych., No. 2.

Morgan, T. H. 1901. Regeneration. Macmillan, N.Y.

Morgan, T. H. 1903. Some factors in the regeneration of *Tubularia*. Roux' Arch. Entwickl. *16*:125-154.

Morrow, J. E., Jr. 1948. Schooling behavior in fishes. Quart. Rev. Biol., *23*:27-38.

Murray, P. D. F. 1936. Bones. Cambridge Univ. Press.

Nauss, R. N. 1949. *Reticulomyxa filosa* gen. et sp. nov., a new primitive plasmodium. Torrey Bot. Club, *76*:161-173.

Needham, J. 1936. Order and Life. Yale Univ. Press, New Haven.

Needham, J. 1942. Biochemistry and Morphogenesis. Cambridge Univ. Press.

Noback, C. V., and W. Modell. 1930. Direct bone formation in the antler tines of two of the American Cervidae, Virginia deer (*Odocoileus virginianus*) and Wapati (*Cervus canadensis*). Zoologica, *11*:19-60.

Olive, E. W. 1902. Monograph of the Acrasieae. Proc. Boston Soc. Nat. Hist., *30*:451-513.

Overbeek, J. van. 1935. The growth hormone and the dwarf type of growth in corn. Proc. Nat. Acad. Sci., *21*:292-299.

Papenfuss, E. J. 1934. Reunion of pieces in *Hydra*, with special reference to the rôle of the three layers and to the fate of differentiated parts. Biol. Bull., *67*:223-243.

Parr, A. E. 1927. A contribution to the theoretical analysis of the schooling behavior of fishes. Occasional Papers, Bingham Oceanogr. Coll., No. 1, pp. 1-32.

Pasteels, J. 1940. Un aperçu comparatif de la gastrulation chez les chordés. Biol. Rev., *15*:59-106.

Peebles, F. 1900. Experiments in regeneration and in grafting of Hydrozoa. Roux' Arch. Entwickl., *10*:435-488.

Perkins, H. F. 1902. Degeneration phenomena in the larvae of *Gonionema*. Biol. Bull., *3*:172-180.

Picken, L. E. R. 1940. The fine structure of biological systems. Biol. Rev., *15*:133-167.

Pijper, A. 1948. Bacterial flagella and motility. Nature, *161*: 200-201.

Pocock, M. A. 1933. *Volvox* in South Africa. Ann. S. African Museum, *16*:523-646.

Pocock, M. A. 1937. *Hydrodictyon* in South Africa. With notes on the known species of *Hydrodictyon*. Tran. Roy. Soc. South Africa, *24*:263-280.

Potts, G. 1902. Zur Physiologie des *Dictyostelium mucoroides*. Flora (Jena), *91*:281-347.

Poulson, D. F. 1940. The effects of certain X-chromosome deficiencies on the embryonic development of *Drosophila melanogaster*. J. Exp. Pool., *83*:271-325.

Raper, J. R. 1951. Sexual hormones in *Achlya*. Amer. Sci., *39*:110-120.

Raper, K. B. 1935. *Dictyostelium discoideum*, a new species of slime mold from decaying forest leaves. J. Agric Res., *50*:135-147.

Raper, K. B. 1940a. The communal nature of the fruiting process in the Acrasieae. Amer. J. Bot., *27*:436-448.

Raper, K. B. 1940b. Pseudoplasmodium formation and organization in *Dictyostelium discoideum*. J. Eli Mitchell Sci. Soc., *56*:241-282.

Raper, K. B. 1941. Developmental patterns in simple slime molds. Growth, Symposium, *5*:41-76.

Rashevsky, N. 1938. Mathematical Biophysics. (rev. ed.). Univ. of Chicago Press.

Richards, O. W., and G. A. Riley. 1937. The growth of amphibian larvae illustrated by transformed coordinates. J. Exp. Zool., *77*:159-167.

Robb, R. C. 1929. On the nature of hereditary size limitation.

II. The growth of parts in relation to the whole. Brit. J. Exp. Biol., 6:311-324.

Rose, S. M. 1939. Embryonic induction in ascidia. Biol. Bull., 77:216-232.

Rose, S. M., and F. C. Rose. 1941. The role of a cut surface in *Tubularia* regeneration. Physiol. Zool., 14:328-343.

Roudabush, R. L. 1933. Phenomenon of regeneration in everted *Hydra*. Biol. Bull., 64:253-258.

Runyon, E. H. 1942. Aggregation of separate cells of *Dictyostelium* to form a multicellular body. Collecting Net, 17:88.

Russell, E. S. 1945. The Directiveness of Organic Activities. Cambridge Univ. Press.

Schachner, J. 1928. Die Bolzen- oder Zapfenform von Bakterien und Hefenkolonien. Centralblatt f. Bakt., Parisit., Infect., Series II. 76:328-383.

Schmalhausen, I. I. 1949. Factors of evolution. Blakiston, Phila.

Schneirla, T. C. 1933. Studies on army ants. J. Comp. Psych., 15:267-299.

Schneirla, T. C. 1940. Further studies on the army-ant behavior pattern. J. Comp. Psych., 29:401-460.

Sheng, T. C. 1951. A gene that causes natural death in *Neurospora crassa*. Genetics, 36:199-212.

Simpson, G. G. 1949. The Meaning of Evolution. Yale Univ. Press, New Haven.

Sinnott, E. W. 1922. Inheritance of fruit shape in *Cucurbita pepo*. I. Bot. Gaz., 74:95-103.

Sinnott, E. W. 1927. A factorial analysis of certain shape characters in squash fruits. Amer. Nat., 61:333-344.

Sinnott, E. W. 1931. The independence of genetic factors governing size and shape. J. Heredity, 22:381-387.

Sinnott, E. W. 1935. Evidence for the existence of genes controlling shape. Genetics, 20:12-21.

Sinnott, E. W. 1939. The cell-organ relationship in plant organization. Growth, Symposium, 3:77-86.

Sinnott, E. W. 1942. An analysis of the comparative rates of cell division in various parts of the developing cucurbit ovary. Amer. J. Bot., 29:317-323.

Sinnott, E. W. 1944. Cell polarity and the development of form in cucurbit fruits. Amer. J. Bot., 31:388-391.

Sinnott, E. W. 1945. The relation of growth to size in cucurbit fruits. Amer. J. Bot., *32*:439-446.

Smith, G. M. 1916. Cytological studies in the Protococcales. II. Cell structures and zoospore formation in *Pedistrum boryanum* (Turp.) Menegh. Ann. Bot., *30*:467-479.

Sonneborn, T. M. 1949. Beyond the gene. Amer. Scient., *37*:33-59.

Spemann, H. 1938. Embryonic Development and Induction. Yale Univ. Press, New Haven.

Spencer, H. 1898. The Principles of Biology. D. Appleton and Co. N.Y.

Stableford, L. T. 1949. The blastocoel fluid in amphibian gastrulation. J. Exp. Zool., *112*:529-546.

Steinecke, F. 1925. Über Polarität von *Bryopsis*. Bot. Arch., *12*:97-118.

Stanier, R. Y. 1942. A note on elasticotaxis in myxobacteria. J. Bact., *44*:405-412.

Summers, F. M. 1938a. Some aspects of normal development in the colonial ciliate *Zoothamnium alternans*. Biol. Bull., *74*:117-129.

Summers, F. M. 1938b. Form regulation in *Zoothamnium alternans*. Biol. Bull., *74*:130-154.

Sussman, M. In Press. The origin of cellular heterogeneity in the slime molds, *Dictyosteliaceae*. J. Exp. Zool.

Swett, F. H. 1937. Determination of limb axes. Quart. Rev. Biol., *12*:322-339.

Szent-Györgyi, A. 1947. Chemistry of Muscular Contraction. Academic Press, N.Y.

Szent-Györgyi, A. 1948. Nature of Life. Academic Press, N.Y.

Tartar, V. 1941. Intracellular patterns: facts and principles concerning patterns exhibited in the morphogenesis and regeneration of ciliate protozoa. Growth, Symposium, *5*:21-40.

Thaxter, R. 1892. On the Myxobacteriaceae, a new order of Schizomycetes. Bot. Gaz., *17*:389-406.

Thaxter, R. 1897. Further observations on the Myxobacteriaceae. Bot. Gaz., *23*:395-411.

Thaxter, R. 1904. Notes on the Myxobacteriaceae. Bot. Gaz., *37*:405-416.

Thimann, K. V. 1949. Plant hormones, growth and respiration. Biol. Bull., *96*:296-306.

Teissier, G. 1931. Étude expérimentale du développement de quelques hydraires. Ann. Sci. Nat. Zool., 10e Série. *14*:5-60.

Thompson, D'A. W. 1942. Growth and Form. Macmillan, N.Y.

Topley, W. W. C., J. Wilson, and J. T. Duncan. 1935. The mode of formation of aggregates in bacterial agglutination. Brit. J. Exp. Path., *16*:116-120.

Torrey, J. G. 1950. The induction of lateral roots by indolacetic acid and root decapitation. Amer. J. Bot., *37*:-257-264.

Trembley, A. 1744. Mémoires pour Servir à l'Histoire d'un Genre de Polypes d'Eau Douce, à Bras en Forme de Cornes. Leide.

Twitty, V. C. 1928. Experimental studies on the ciliary action of amphibian embryos. J. Exp. Zool., *50*:319-344.

Twitty, V. C. 1940. Size-controlling factors. Growth, Symposium, *4*:109-120.

Twitty, V. C. 1949. Developmental analysis of amphibian pigmentation. Growth, Symposium, *9*:133-161.

Tyler, A. 1942. Developmental processes and energetics. Quart. Rev. Biol., *17*:197-212, 339-353.

Waddington, C. H. 1940. The genetic control of wing shape in *Drosophila*. J. Genet., *41*:75-139.

Waddington, C. H. 1940. Organisers and Genes. Cambridge Univ. Press.

Wagner, J. 1934. Beiträge zur Kenntnis der *Nitschia putrida* Benecke, insbesondere ihrer Bewegung. Archiv. f. Protist. *82*:86-113.

Warmke, H. E., and G. L. Warmke. 1950. The role of auxin in the differentiation of root and shoot primordia from root cuttings of *Taraxacum*. Amer. J. Bot., *37*:272-280.

Weiss, P. 1929. Erzwingung elementarer Strukturver schiedenheiten am in vitro wachsenden gewebe. Die Wirkung mechanischer Spannung auf Richtung und Intensität des Gewebewachtums und ihre Analyse. Roux' Arch. Entwickl., *116*:438-554.

Weiss, P. 1934. In vitro experiments on the factors determining the course of the outgrowing nerve fiber. J. Exp. Zool., *68*:393-448.

Weiss, P. 1939. Principles of Development. Henry Holt, N.Y.

Weiss, P. 1945. Experiments on cell and axon orientation in vitro: the role of colloidal exudates in tissue organization. J. Exp. Zool., *100*:353-386.

Weisz, P. B. 1949. The role of specific macronuclear nodes in the differentiation and the maintenance of the oral area in *Stentor*. J. Exp. Zool., *111*:141-155.

Went, F. W. 1942. Some physiological factors in the aging of a tree. 9th Western Shade Tree Conference. pp. 330-333.

Went, F. W. 1943. The regulation of plant growth. Amer. Scien., *31*:189-210.

Went, F. W., and K. V. Thimann. 1937. Phytohormones. Macmillan, N.Y.

Wheeler, W. M. 1911. The ant-colony as an organism. J. Morph., 22:307-325.

Wheeler, W. M. 1928. Emergent Evolution. W. W. Norton, N.Y.

Whitaker, D. M. 1940. Physical factors of growth. Growth, Symposium, *4*:75-90.

Wildman, S. G., and James Bonner. 1947. The proteins of green leaves. I. Isolation, enzymatic properties and auxin content of spinach cytoplasmic proteins. Arch. Biochem., *14*:381-413.

Wilson, E. B. 1925. The Cell in Development and Heredity. Macmillan, N.Y.

Wilson, H. V. 1907. On some phenomena of coalescence and regeneration in sponges. J. Exp. Zool., *5*:245-258.

Wilson, H. V. 1911a. Development of sponges from dissociated tissue cells. Bull. Bureau Fish., *30*:1-30.

Wilson, H. V. 1911b. On the behavior of the dissociated cells in hydroids, *Alcyonaria* and *Asterias*. J. Exp. Zool., *11*:281-338.

Wilson, M., and E. J. Cadman. 1928. The life-history and cytology of *Reticularia Lycoperdon*. Bull. Trans. Roy. Soc., Edinburgh, *55*:555-608.

Wilson, O. T. 1929. The colonial development of *Navicula rhombica* Greg. Amer. J. Bot., *16*:825-831.

Wislocki, G. B. 1942. Studies on the growth of deer antlers. I. On the structure and histogenesis of the antlers of the Virginia deer (*Odocoileus virginianus borealis*). Amer. J. Anat., *71*:371-415.

Witschi, E. 1932. Sex deviations, inversions and parabiosis. From E. Allen, Sex and Internal Secretions, pp. 160-245. Williams and Wilkins, Baltimore.

Woodger, J. H. 1929. Biological Principles. Harcourt, Brace, N.Y.

Acknowledgments

The following individuals have been kind enough to allow me to use their illustrations and I wish to record my thanks: W. E. Ankel, P. Brien, Mrs. W. H. Brown, R. Buchsbaum, C. M. Child, E. Colahan, E. G. Conklin, P. H. Egli, E. Fauré-Fremiet, E. W. Gudger, J. Hämmerling, J. Holtfreter, F. L. Howard, J. Huxley, L. Hyman, A. Lwoff, H. Neurath, W. H. Pearsall, M. A. Pocock, K. B. Raper, T. C. Schneirla, G. M. Smith, R. Y. Stanier, W. R. Taylor, G. Teissier, O. Tuzet, V. C. Twitty, D. Whitaker, P. Weiss.

I should also like to express my appreciation to the following publishing houses, scientific journals and scientific organizations for permission to use the illustrations listed: Académie des Sciences of Paris, Fig. 71; American Journal of Botany, Figs. 55, 68, Plate VII; Annals of Botany, Figs. 51, 59; Biological Bulletin, Fig. 30; Cambridge Entomological Society, Fig. 86; Cambridge University Press, Figs. 15, 16, 50, 54, 85; E. P. Dutton and Co., Figs. 6, 7, 8, 9a; Field and Stream, Plate IX; Ginn and Co., Figs. 17, 19, 21, 25, 26, 27, 33, 34, 36, 42, 56, 57, 58, 59; John Wiley and Sons, Figs. 12, 87; Macmillan Co., Figs. 23, 77; McGraw-Hill Book Co., Figs. 10, 18, 20, 22, 29, 41, 48, 88, 89; Masson and Cie., Fig. 76; Oxford University Press, Fig. 9b; Royal Society of South Africa, Plate V; Scientific American, Fig. 82; Scientific Monthly, Plate I; South African Museum, Figs. 28, 70, Plate IV; University of Chicago Press, Figs. 44, 60, 78, 80, 83; University of Michigan Press, Figs. 23, 39, 40; Williams and Wilkins Co. and the Journal of Bacteriology, Fig. 61; The Wistar Institute of Anatomy and Biology and the Journal of Experimental Zoology, Fig. 73; Zoological Society of London, Fig. 52.

Also I should like to thank J. G. Moner for the preliminary sketches upon which Fig. 37 is based and Mrs. Evelyn Frascella for her invaluable assistance both in arranging the illustrations for the engraver as well as checking the bibliography.

Index

INDEX

carbon, 37
cartesian transformations, 134, 135
Caspari, E., 246
Cassiopea, 222
Caulerpa, 94, 96
cellulose, 44ff.
cell wall, plant, 44, 220, 221
Chaetopterus, 262, 263
Chatton, E., 263
chemotaxis, in *Dictyostelium*, 177ff.
Child, C. M., 132ff., 147, 209, 214, 220
Chlamydomonas, 72, 73
Chondromyces, 166ff., 183, Plate VI
ciliary rows, 262, 263
ciliates, colonial, 86ff., 119, 120, 264, 265, 268
Cladophora, 44, 75
Clark, W. G., 225, 226
Clarke, W. W., 174
cleavage planes, direction of, 72ff.
Cole, K. C., 29
Coleochete, 75, 76
compensatory hypertrophy, 64ff.
Conklin, E. G., 188, 235ff.
contact guidance, 66ff., 169ff., Plate III
coremium, 97, 98
Costello, D. P., 188
crystals, 26, 31ff., 164, 275; capping of, 34, Plate I; growth of, 31ff., 242; hemimorphic, 37; liquid, 31, 45ff., 242, 275; polymorphism in, 37, 38; twins of, 37
cucurbits, 106ff., 146
cyclosis, 52, 151; in *Bryopsis*, 211
Cymbella, 89, 91, 153
Cystosira, 207
cytoplasmic inheritance, 245, 246

Dalcq, A., 240
Dalton, H. C., 203
Danielli, J. F., 29
Davenport, C. B., 188
de Beer, G. R., 9, 142, 196
deer antlers, 117, 130, 139, 140
De Generatione Animalium, 25, 131
de Laubenfels, M. W., 248
"determination," 8, 218ff., 239ff., 246, 247, 253, 257
diamond, 38

diatoms, colonial, 86ff., 227ff.; mosaic development of, 239; movement of, 152, 153; shells of, 41ff.
Dictydium, 185
Dictyostelium, 173ff., 210, 228, 229, 250ff., Plate VII, VIII
Didymium, 184
"difference" theory, 246ff.
differentiation, 7, 8, 17, 232ff., 271, 272
diffusion, 48ff., 150, 151, 188; of auxin, 224, 226
dimensional analysis, 12
Dinobryon, 91, 92
direct adaptations, 63ff.
Dobell, C. C., 190, 233
dodecahedra (regular), 41
Driesch, H., 210, 241, 248, 250, 274
Drosophila, 144, 260; *expanded* mutant of, 144, *miniature* mutant of, 144
Duboscq, O., 192, 193
DuBuy, H. G., 208
Dürer, A., 134

echinoderm development, 55, 56, 195, 210, 241, 274
Egli, P., 33, 34
Eldredge, D., 195
electrical fields, 226
Elodea, 151
emergence, 241
Emerson, A. E., 269
enantiomorphy, 34ff.
energids, 17
Enteromorpha, 77ff., 97
Epistylis, 86, 87, 119
Equisetum, 41
"equivalence" theory, 246ff.
Eucapsis, 81, 82, 94
Evans, H. M., 116

false branching, 74
Fankhauser, G., 247
Fauré-Fremiet, E., 86, 119, 120, 179, 215ff., 248, 262
field, biological, 100, 255
fish, schooling of, 231, 270, Plate IX
Fitting, H., 208
flatworms, 14, 214, 215
Foraminifera, shells of, 30, 41, 42

INDEX